ADVANCES IN

DRUG RESEARCH

VOLUME 14

ADVANCES IN
DRUG RESEARCH

Edited by

BERNARD TESTA

School of Pharmacy, University of Lausanne, Lausanne, Switzerland

VOLUME 14

1985

ACADEMIC PRESS

(Harcourt Brace Jovanovich, Publishers)

LONDON   ORLANDO   SAN DIEGO   NEW YORK
TORONTO   MONTREAL   SYDNEY   TOKYO

ACADEMIC PRESS INC. (LONDON) LTD.
24–28 Oval Road
LONDON NW1 7DX

United States Edition published by
ACADEMIC PRESS, INC.
Orlando, Florida 32887

LIBRARY OF CONGRESS CATALOG CARD NUMBER: 64-24672

ISBN: 0-12-013314-8

PRINTED IN THE UNITED STATES OF AMERICA

85 86 87 88   9 8 7 6 5 4 3 2 1

CONTENTS

Deuterium Isotope Effects in the Metabolism of Drugs and Xenobiotics: Implications for Drug Design

ALLAN B. FOSTER

Drug Design in Three Dimensions

N. CLAUDE COHEN

Mechanisms of Action of Antiinflammatory Drugs

WILLIAM E. M. LANDS

Recent Advances in the Molecular Pharmacology of Benzodiazepine Receptors and in the Structure–Activity Relationships of Their Agonists and Antagonists

WILLY HAEFELY, EMILIO KYBURZ, MAX GERECKE, AND HANNS MÖHLER

CONTRIBUTORS

N. CLAUDE COHEN, *Ciba-Geigy Ltd., Pharmaceutical Division, CH-4002 Basel, Switzerland*

ALLAN B. FOSTER, *Drug Metabolism Team, Cancer Research Campaign Laboratory, Institute of Cancer Research, Sutton, Surrey SM2 5PX, England*

MAX GERECKE, *Department of Pharmaceutical Research, F. Hoffmann-La Roche & Co. Ltd., CH-4002 Basel, Switzerland*

WILLY HAEFELY, *Department of Pharmaceutical Research, F. Hoffmann-La Roche & Co. Ltd., CH-4002 Basel, Switzerland*

EMILIO KYBURZ, *Department of Pharmaceutical Research, F. Hoffmann-La Roche & Co. Ltd., CH-4002 Basel, Switzerland*

WILLIAM E. M. LANDS, *Department of Biological Chemistry, University of Illinois at Chicago, College of Medicine, Chicago, Illinois 60612*

HANNS MÖHLER, *Department of Pharmaceutical Research, F. Hoffmann-La Roche & Co. Ltd., CH-4002 Basel, Switzerland*

PREFACE: THE PEN AND THE ART OF MONOTONY AVOIDANCE[1]

The present volume of *Advances in Drug Research,* the second edited by the undersigned, contains four chapters featuring interesting differences and analogies.

The first two chapters cover general topics, namely deuterium isotope effects in xenobiotic metabolism and drug design, and drug design in three dimensions. Both are thus closely related to medicinal chemistry, but the stories they tell are quite different. While deuterium isotope effects have proven invaluable in studying enzymatic reaction mechanisms but have found only limited applications in drug design, the combination of structural studies coupled with assessment of structure–activity relationships and computer graphics (three-dimensional drug design) has generated considerable interest and hopes, to say the least.

The third and fourth chapters discuss specific therapeutic classes, namely antiinflammatory agents and benzodiazepines. The former is a short and densely written review providing an incentive for further study. In contrast, the latter offers a truly encyclopedic treatment of recent advances in benzodiazepine research.

The four chapters in this volume differ in their approach, construction and layout, and style, reflecting the personalities and backgrounds of their authors. They also differ considerably in length, but not in their depth of treatment and wealth of information. Writing a review is always a demanding and lengthy task, and we must be grateful to those colleagues who give so much time and effort that might otherwise be applied to other, perhaps better rewarded goals. However, reviews can be highly readable and enriching, as opposed to plain, dull compilations. Accepting to put pen to paper, or having a ready pen, does not imply being a stimulating writer, and a good scientific review requires that its author be both a knowledgeable scientist and a clear and imaginative writer. But since expertise, clarity of mind, and imagination are prerequisites of a good scientist, it is not surprising that so many reviews to be found in journals and books are in fact readable and enriching. The past, present, and future volumes of *Advances in Drug Research* are and shall be aimed at contributing to this common wealth, to this body of reviews, chapters and books which are the fertilizers of scientific research.

BERNARD TESTA

---

[1]With apologies to Robert M. Pirsig, inspired author of "Zen and the Art of Motorcycle Maintenance," William Morrow & Co., Inc., New York, 1974.

Deuterium Isotope Effects in the Metabolism of Drugs and Xenobiotics: Implications for Drug Design

ALLAN B. FOSTER

Drug Metabolism Team
Cancer Research Campaign Laboratory
Institute of Cancer Research
Sutton, Surrey, England

ADVANCES IN DRUG RESEARCH, VOL. 14
0-12-013314-8

1 Introduction

The majority of drugs, when administered to humans and animals, are metabolized, often rapidly and extensively (Testa and Jenner, 1976). Metabolism, which usually occurs mostly in the liver but which can also occur in numerous other organs (Fry and Bridges, 1977), e.g., kidney, lungs, skin, and small intestine, has been regarded as a defense mechanism whereby ingested xenobiotics are converted into more polar derivatives that are excreted more readily either directly or after conjugation. However, in the case of drugs, rapid metabolism may limit plasma levels and half-lives and, consequently, efficacy.

Although some drugs [e.g., cyclophosphamide (Connors *et al.,* 1974)] are activated by metabolism or may be deliberately designed as prodrugs (Bodor, 1981a, 1984), the usual consequence of metabolism is deactivation. Moreover, in addition to being more rapidly excreted, metabolites usually have an affinity for the target (receptor, enzyme, membrane, etc.) lower than that of the parent drug or may have properties which limit access to, and therefore interaction with, the target. Metabolism can also generate products which have a biological activity different from that of the parent drug or which may be toxic and, in some instances, carcinogenic (Jefcoate, 1983).

Thus, the metabolism of drugs is usually an adverse process and its importance is often indicated when candidate drugs which show high activity in *in vitro* assays are inactive *in vivo*. The metabolism-directed approach (Jarman and Foster, 1978; Bodor, 1981b, 1984) to drug design is concerned with the rational modification of molecular structure in order to control adverse metabolism and/or confer desirable characteristics. The ideal starting point for a metabolism-directed design study involves a drug in clinical or experimental use with a known target, metabolism profile, and origin of toxicity. Structure–activity studies can then be undertaken aimed at retarding or blocking adverse metabolism while retaining (preferably, increasing) affinity for the target and ensuring that a plasma level and half-life can be achieved practically which will optimize interaction with the target.

It is in this context that specific deuterium substitution in drugs and the magnitude and consequences of the resulting deuterium isotope effects are now considered.

A wide variety of pathways of drug metabolism have been identified and categorized as phase I and II reactions (Fry and Bridges, 1977), also designated as functionalization and conjugation reactions (Testa and Jenner, 1978). The former category includes reactions whereby functional groups are introduced (e.g., hydroxylation), modified (e.g., aldehyde oxidation and reduction), or exposed (e.g., O-dealkylation) whereas the latter category includes reactions such as glucuronidation and sulfation. It is within the phase I category that metabolism pathways are found which are susceptible to deuterium isotope effects, namely, those in which a C—H bond is broken, for example, hydroxylation (C—H → C—OH) and dehydrogenation (CH—OH → C=O). Hydroxylation is a frequently encountered pathway of metabolism which is mediated by the cytochrome P-450 enzymes (mono-oxygenases, mixed function oxidases). Treatises on this category of enzyme are now available (e.g., Schenkman and Kupfer, 1982) so that only the salient relevant points need be noted here. The cytochrome P-450s are heme proteins commonly found as clusters of membrane-bound isoenzymes in the endoplasmic reticulum of many types of cell but they are particularly prevalent in liver cells. Some of these isoenzymes are inducible [e.g., by phenobarbital (PB) and methylcholanthrene], each has a characteristic substrate specificity, and each can generate from molecular oxygen an electrophilic species which will react with, and deliver to, the substrate the formal equivalent of atomic oxygen. The structure of this reactive species remains to be defined precisely but it has been termed oxenoid because its reactions are formally analogous to those of carbenes in adding to double bonds and inserting into single bonds. The overall reactions are as follows:

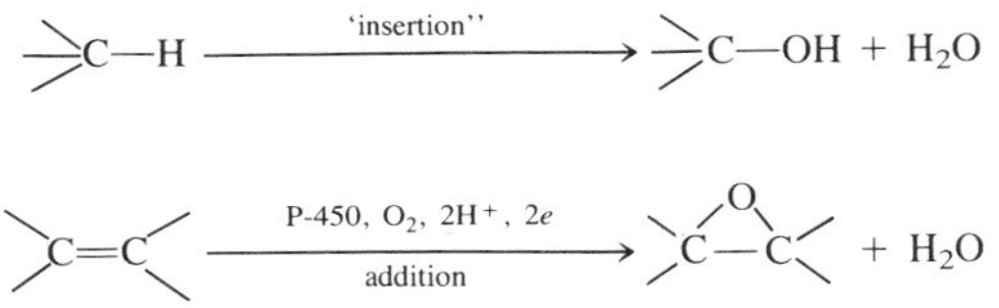

$$\begin{array}{c}\diagdown\\>C-H\diagdown\end{array} \xrightarrow{\text{``insertion''}} \begin{array}{c}\diagdown\\>C-OH\diagdown\end{array} + H_2O$$

$$\begin{array}{c}\diagdown\\>C=C<\\\diagdown\end{array} \xrightarrow[\text{addition}]{\text{P-450, }O_2\text{, }2H^+\text{, }2e} \begin{array}{c}O\\>C-C<\end{array} + H_2O$$

The so-called "oxygen insertion reaction" is by far the most important metabolism pathway considered in this article (see Section 3.4.2 for comments on mechanism).

2 Deuteration of Drugs and Xenobiotics

Deuterium labeling has found widespread application in studies of drug metabolism in such diverse aspects as identification and quantification (coupled with mass spectrometry) of drugs and metabolites in plasma, urine, and *in vitro* systems, determination of pharmacokinetics in general, and in chronic administration, bioavailability studies, mechanism of enzyme and drug action, elucidation of metabolic and biosynthetic pathways, differential metabolism of enantiomers, and isotope effects. Several reviews have appeared in the past decade dealing with deuterium labeling in the general context of applications of stable isotopes in biomedical research, pharmacology, and medicinal chemistry (Knapp and Gaffney, 1972; Knapp *et al.*, 1973; Gregg, 1974; Gaffney *et al.*, 1974; Nelson and Pohl, 1977; Halliday and Lockhart, 1978; Baillie, 1981; Baillie *et al.*, 1982; Haskins, 1982). Each review has a particular emphasis and viewpoint and all are well worth reading. The review by Blake *et al.* (1975) is devoted to deuterium and contains an excellent survey of the literature prior to 1975 on, *inter alia*, deuterium isotope effects associated with the metabolism and biological activity of drugs and related compounds. The present article is concerned mainly with deuterium isotope effects and is not intended to be comprehensive but illustrative. Apologies are tendered herewith to those authors whose relevant work is not mentioned.

2.1 DEUTERIUM ISOTOPE EFFECTS

In a reaction (chemical or enzymatic) in which cleavage of a C—H bond is rate determining the same reaction of the C—D analog will be retarded. The ratio (K_H/K_D) of the respective rate constants defines the *primary deuterium isotope effect* (DIE). The maximum theoretical DIE has been calculated (Bigeleisen, 1949) as 18 and although values up to 11–12 have been observed experimentally in metabolism studies (see below) most observed DIEs are relatively small (<5). The origin of DIEs relates to the difference in mass between hydrogen and deuterium which results in the zero-point energy (lowest ground state vibrational level) for C—D bonds being 1.2–1.5 kcal/mol lower than that of the C—H bond with a consequent increase in bond stability. Deuterium substitution near to a reaction center can give rise to *secondary isotope effects* which are usually small (1.05–1.25) and not likely to contribute significantly to the DIEs considered in this article.

DIEs in chemical reactions were reviewed by Wiberg (1955), and Wolfsberg (1982) has given a general theoretical analysis. Northrop (1982) has presented a detailed consideration of enzyme-catalyzed reactions in terms of a family of DIEs and emphasized the fact that the observed DIE (^Dv), which relates to the rates of disappearance of substrate and/or appearance of products, can be very much smaller than the intrinsic DIE (^Dk), which is associated with the conversion of the substrate into product(s) within the activated enzyme–substrate(product) complex. The mechanisms of action of various enzymes which can be involved in drug metabolism studies have been clarified on the basis of DIEs, e.g., aldehyde dehydrogenase (Feldman and Weiner, 1972), xanthine oxidase (Edmondson *et al.*, 1973), urocanase (Egan *et al.*, 1981), liver alcohol dehydrogenase (Cook and Cleland, 1981), and dopamine β-monooxygenase (Miller and Klinman, 1982). Deuterium labeling has also been used elegantly to probe the steric requirements of drug–receptor interaction of neuromuscular blocking agents in the norcoralydine series (Stenlake and Dhar, 1978). However, this article is concerned primarily with "observed" DIEs, frequently expressed as K_H/K_D or V^H_{max}/V^D_{max} [^Dv in Northrop's (1982) terminology], which reflect the gross effect of deuterium substitution on the rate and pathways of metabolism of drugs and xenobiotics and on their biological activity. Unless stated otherwise in the sections below, the term DIE connotes the observed deuterium isotope effect.

2.2 CONTROL OF METABOLISM BY DEUTERIUM SUBSTITUTION

For a DIE of 2 the rate of reaction of the C—D-containing compound will be 50% of that of the C—H analog and for DIEs of >5 the introduction of deuterium will suppress reactivity very substantially. Since DIEs in the range 6–12 associated with metabolic reactions have been reported (see below), interest has been stimulated in the use of this phenomenon to retard certain drug metabolism pathways and to explore the consequences *in vivo*. The attraction of specific deuterium substitution as a parameter in drug design is based on the facts that not only is the replacement of one or a few hydrogens in a drug molecule by deuterium the smallest structural change that can be made but also such a change will have negligible steric consequences or influence on physicochemical properties (providing that the deuterium is not α to nitrogen, see Section 5.1). This is in contrast to the use of groups such as alkyl or fluorine to block metabolism at a particular point in a drug molecule. The introduction of an alkyl group may create new possibilities for metabolism and significantly change lipophilicity and the introduction of fluorine may markedly modify the character of neighboring functional groups or remote ones if there is an intervening conjugated or aromatic system.

Cytochrome P-450-mediated aromatic hydroxylation usually involves initial oxene addition to give an epoxide (arene oxide) which, *inter alia*, can rearrange into a phenol. Although for deuterated aromatic compounds deuterium migration occurs (NIH shift; Daly *et al.*, 1968, 1969), the DIE is negligible for the overall hydroxylation process (e.g., Farmer *et al.*, 1975) when hydroxyl groups are introduced into the o- and p-positions in substituted aromatics. It was inferred that a different mechanism operates for m-hydroxylation *in vitro* and *in vivo* and for which DIEs of 1.3–1.75 have been observed (Tomaszewski *et al.*, 1975).

The biological activity of xenobiotics can sometimes be modified by polydeuteration (see review by Blake *et al.*, 1975) but a remarkable effect of monodeuteration has been reported by Dumont *et al.* (1981). The anticonvulsant potency of diphenylhydantoin (**1**) was enhanced by pentadeuteration of one phenyl group (→ **2**) and even more so by p-deuteration (→**3**). The mechanistic significance of these findings is not clear. p-Hydroxylation of one phenyl group is the main initial metabolism pathway for (**1**) and Hoskins and Farmer (1982) found no significant DIE for p- and m-hydroxylation of d_5-diphenylhydantoin (**2**) by liver microsomes (PB-induced rats) or in humans. Moreover, Moustafa *et al.* (1983) concluded that m- and p-hydroxylation of diphenylhydantoin (**1**) proceeded via the 3,4-epoxide. These findings contrast with those of Tomaszewski *et al.* (1975) noted above and suggest that m-hydroxylation could involve a duality of mechanisms.

Progressive replacement of hydrogen in a drug or another xenobiotic molecule with deuterium will progressively change the lipophilicity and the magnitude of this effect can be conveniently assessed by normal (Farmer *et al.*, 1978) and reversed-phase high-pressure liquid chromatography (HPLC) (Tanaka and Thornton, 1976). The shake-flask and HPLC methods were recently compared (El Tayar *et al.*, 1984). The results indicated deuterated compounds to be less lipophilic than the corresponding protium forms by ~0.006/D on the log P_{oct} scale. The effect of deuteration on binding, for example, to microsomal cytochrome P-450, is usually given by the ratio of the Michaelis constants K_m^D/K_m^H. When this ratio is <1 (see Section 5.1), stronger binding of the deuterated compound to the enzyme is indicated. Amines are an exception in that deuteration at the α-carbon will give a K_m^D/K_m^H ratio of >1. For example, deuteration of the NEt$_2$ moiety of lidocaine (**4**) results (Nelson *et al.*, 1975) in a K_m^D/K_m^H ratio of 1.23 (for rat liver microsomes) for the N(CD$_2$CH$_3$)$_2$ analog in contrast to a ratio of 0.92 for the N(CH$_2$CD$_3$)$_2$ analog.

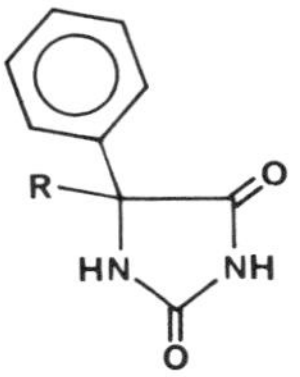

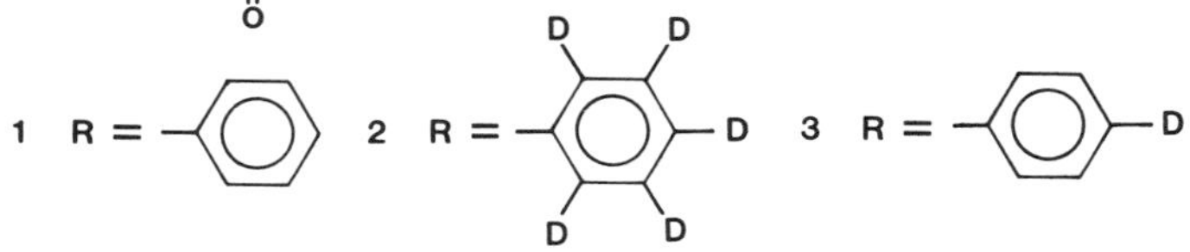

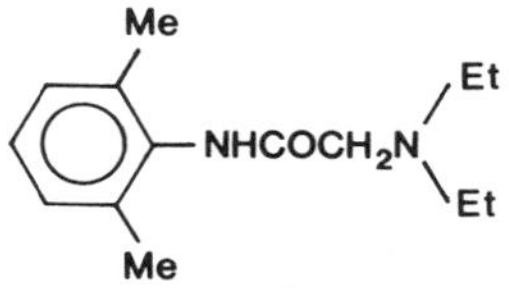

2.2.1 Metabolic Switching

When a drug is metabolized by two or more alternative pathways a possible consequence of deuteration is "metabolic switching." This term was introduced by Horning *et al.* (1976), who found that the metabolism of antipyrine (**5**), after intraperitoneal (ip) injection into rats and as reflected by the urinary metabolites, was switched from oxidation of the C-3-methyl group (normal major pathway) to N-demethylation (normal minor pathway) on trideuteration of the former group.

The effect was even more marked *in vitro*. Using the 10,000 *g* supernatant of homogenized rat liver, the ratio of 3-hydroxymethylantipyrine to 4-hydroxyantipyrine from antipyrine was 1.3 and 1.6 when the N-methyl group was trideute-rated. However, the ratio changed dramatically to <0.1 when the C-3-methyl group was trideuterated. This low ratio corresponded to a DIE of ~15.

A similar situation was encountered by Gorumaru *et al.* (1981) for the metabo-lism of aminopyrine (**6**) administered orally to rats. Analysis of the urinary metabolites revealed that trideuteration of the C-3-methyl group switched metab-olism to N-demethylation of the C-4-dimethylamino group. No metabolic switching occurred when the N-2-methyl group or the C-4-dimethylamino group was fully deuterated.

Horning *et al.* (1978) showed that for methsuximide (**7**), N-demethylation was suppressed and hydroxylation of the phenyl group was increased when the N-methyl group was trideuterated.

In studies with caffeine (**8**), Horning *et al.* (1976) found that trideuteration of the N-1-methyl group depressed N-demethylation at N-1 and, for the rat and ip administration, 1,3-dimethylxanthine (theophylline) became the major urinary metabolite. Likewise, trideuteration of the N-7-methyl group resulted in 1,7-dimethylxanthine being the major urinary metabolite. The same group (Horning *et al.*, 1979) also found that after ip injection into rats the plasma half-lives of caffeine (**8**) and its derivatives with the N-1-, N-7-, or N-9-methyl groups tri-deuterated were similar. However, the plasma half-life of the derivative with all these N-methyl groups trideuterated was twice that of caffeine (**8**). These results were taken to indicate that N-demethylation at positions 1, 7, and 9 occurred at the same rate *in vivo* and that replacement of CH_3 by CD_3 switches metabolism to de-N-methylation of an unlabeled methyl group.

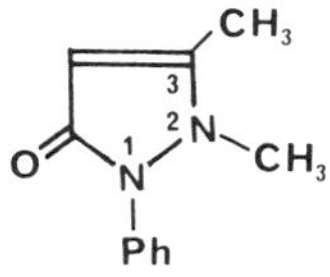

5 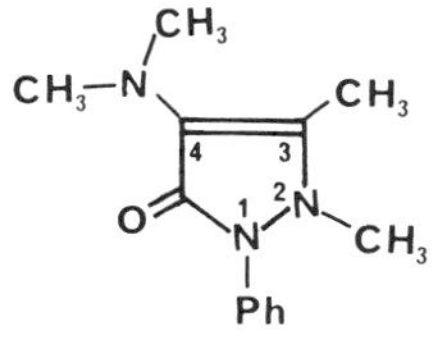   6

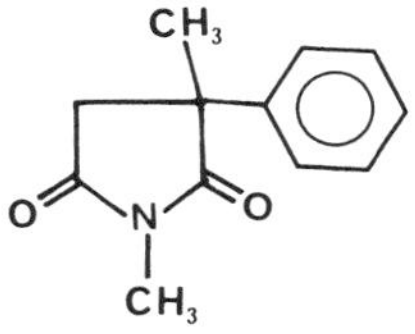

7 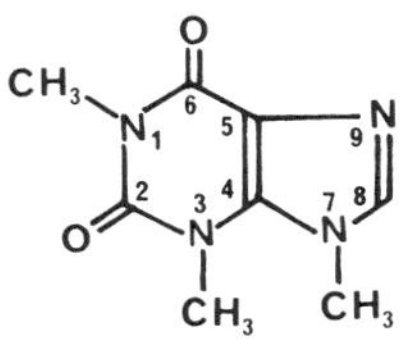   8

The foregoing results variously illustrate metabolic switching of three types, namely C→N, N→C, and N→N. An example of C→C switching associated with 7-ethylcoumarin is noted in Section 4.1.

The possibility exists, although apparently not yet realized, of using metabolic switching in drug design to deflect metabolism away from a pathway yielding a toxic metabolite to one (or more) leading to innocuous products or away from a pathway leading to inactive metabolites toward one yielding an active metabolite.

2.2.2 D/H Exchange

In *in vitro* and *in vivo* studies of the metabolism of deuterated drugs and other xenobiotics it is essential that the deuterium content of unchanged drug and its metabolites be monitored by mass spectrometry if other techniques are used for quantification. This precaution is essential in order to ensure that D/H exchange does not occur. Where enzymes, receptors, or other macromolecules are involved there is always the possibility of microenvironments in which D/H exchange can be promoted. Thus, following ip administration of α-d_2-chlorambucil (**9**) to rats, monitoring of the drug in the plasma by mass spectrometry revealed that D/H exchange was complete within 30 min even though chemically the deuterium was not intrinsically labile (Farmer *et al.*, 1979). Perel *et al.* (1967) found that, after administration of *p*-deuterophenobarbital (**10**) to dogs, the drug excreted in the urine had undergone 13–26% D/H exchange. Singer and Lijinsky (1979) have noted that, for nitrosamines deuterated α to nitrogen, pronounced biological isotope effects in feeding experiments (see Section 5.4) were observed only for those compounds which were not very susceptible to base-catalyzed D/H exchange. It was not practicable to monitor D/H exchange *in vivo* for these deuterated nitrosamines.

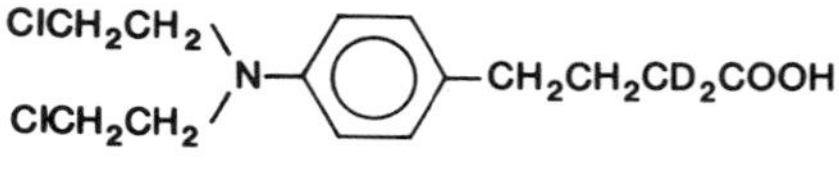

9

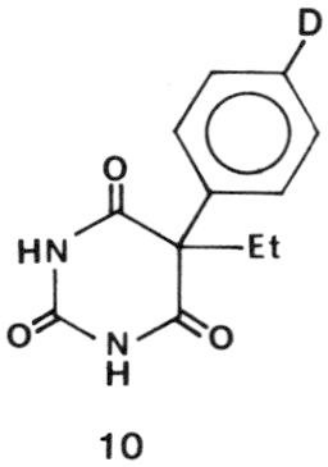

10

3 Hydroxylation of Hydrocarbons and Hydrocarbon Moieties

3.1 ALIPHATIC COMPOUNDS

3.1.1 Hydrocarbons

The outcome of microsomal hydroxylation of linear, saturated aliphatic hydrocarbons depends on the chain length and the inducer used. For the homologous series $CH_3(CH_2)_nCH_3$ when $n = 1$ or 2, two monohydroxy derivatives are possible, three when $n = 3$ or 4, four when $n = 5$ or 6, etc. Also, for hydroxylation at some secondary positions, the possibility of stereoselectivity exists and D- and/or L-alcohols can be formed. The regioselectivity associated with microsomal hydroxylation is illustrated by the results for n-hexane ($n = 4$) and n-heptane ($n = 5$).

Using liver microsomes (PB-treated rats) the ratio of 1- (ω), 2- ($\omega-1$), and 3-hexanols ($\omega-2$) from n-hexane was $\sim 1:11:2$ and diols were also formed (1,2, 1,3, and 2,3; ratio $\sim 1.6:0.3:0.7$) (Kramer $et\ al.$, 1974). The ratio of the three hexanols was not changed dramatically when noninduced microsomes were used. Under essentially similar conditions the ratio of 1- (ω), 2- ($\omega-1$), 3-($\omega-2$), and 4-heptanols ($\omega-3$) from n-heptane was $\sim 1:19.5:3.7:1.5$ (Frommer $et\ al.$, 1972). The relative proportions of the four heptanols was not greatly changed when noninduced microsomes were used but with benzpyrene-induced microsomes the ratio became $\sim 1:16.5:13.8:21.4$. Thus, for non- and PB-induced microsomes ($\omega-1$)-hydroxylation of linear, saturated aliphatic hydrocarbons preponderates.

Although the microsomal hydroxylation of cyclohexane and cyclohexane-d_{12} has been studied (see Section 3.4.1) apparently there has been no comparable investigation of linear aliphatic hydrocarbons.

3.1.2 Fatty Acids

The regioselectivity of microsomal hydroxylation of saturated linear fatty acids is dependent on chain length. Thus, for decanoic acid, $CH_3(CH_2)_8COOH$ (Hamberg and Björkhem, 1971), the ratio of 10- (ω) and 9-hydroxylation ($\omega-1$) was $>9:<1$. Metabolism of the 10-d_3 and 9-d_2 derivatives of decanoic acid revealed a DIE (1.5–2 based on yields of products) only for 9-hydroxylation. The ratio of the D- and L-forms of 9-hydroxydecanoic acid was $\sim 1:3$ and this was changed to $\sim 2:1$ when 9-d_2-decanoic acid was hydroxylated.

A somewhat different situation was encountered with lauric acid, $CH_3(CH_2)_{10}COOH$ (Björkhem and Hamberg, 1972). The ratio of microsomal 12-(ω) and 11-hydroxylation ($\omega-1$) was $\sim 3:2$ but for 11-d_2-lauric acid this ratio changed to $>9:<1$, reflecting a significant DIE (~ 2.5 based on yields of products). The ratio of D- and L-forms of the 11-hydroxy derivative was $\sim 3:2$, which, apparently, was not affected by deuteration at position 11.

The antitumor alkylating agent chlorambucil (**11**) is metabolized $in\ vivo$ to give, $inter\ alia$, phenylacetic mustard (**12**) presumably via β-oxidation. This metabolism pathway is probably adverse since the therapeutic index of the metabolite (**12**) is inferior to that of the parent drug (**11**) against, for example, the Walker 256 carcinoma in rats. Moreover, the neurotoxicity associated with high doses of chlorambucil (**11**) could be due to the formation of (**12**). Following ip administration of β-d_2-chlorambucil (**13**) to rats the plasma levels of phe-

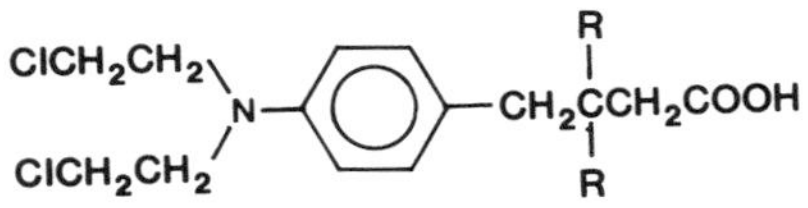

$ClCH_2CH_2$ \
$ClCH_2CH_2$ $\diagdown N$—⟨ring⟩—$CH_2\overset{R}{\underset{R}{C}}CH_2COOH$

11 R = H

13 R = D

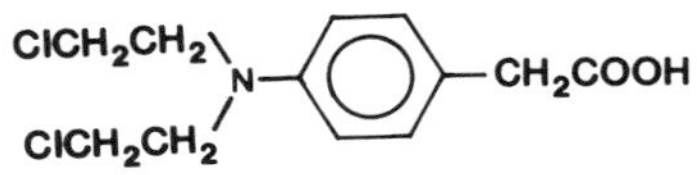

$ClCH_2CH_2$ \
$ClCH_2CH_2$ $\diagdown N$—⟨ring⟩—CH_2COOH

12

nylacetic mustard (12) were lower than those from the parent drug but the therapeutic index was not altered significantly (Farmer *et al.*, 1979).

Reinsch *et al.* (1980) have reported a remarkably high DIE for the reaction of perdeuterobutyryl-CoA with fatty acyl-CoA dehydrogenase:

$$RCH_2CH_2COSCoA \rightleftharpoons RCH_2\overline{C}HCOSCoA \rightleftharpoons RCH{=}CHCOSCoA$$

A DIE of 2 was found for the first step (H^+ abstraction) and a value of 30–50 was found for the second step.

3.1.3 Barbiturates

The effect of specific deuteration of the *n*-butyl group in 5-*n*-butyl-5-ethylbarbituric acid (14, butethal) has been explored. Soboren *et al.* (1965) observed that dideuteration at position 3 (→15) doubled the sleep time of mice whereas trideuteration at position 4 (→16) had no effect. That the modified behavior of 15 reflected a DIE was suggested by the identification of the 3-hydroxy derivative 17 as a microsomal metabolite of butethal. The same group (Tanabe *et al.*, 1969) showed later that dideuteration at position 3 in butethal (→15) increased the half-life from 100 to 270 min on incubation with the postmitochondrial supernatant of homogenized liver. They confirmed the 3-hydroxy derivative 17 to be the major metabolite and noted a DIE of ~1.6. Similar results were reported by Mark *et al.* (1971) for 5-ethyl-5-(1-methylbutyl)barbituric acid (18, pentobarbital). Thus, dideuteration at position 3 (→19) virtually doubled the plasma half-life on administration iv to dogs or ip to mice and delayed the time to peak sedation but prolonged the total sleep time.

The major metabolic route for 5-ethyl-5-phenylbarbituric acid (20, phenobarbital) is p-hydroxylation of the phenyl moiety. As would now be expected (Tomaszewski *et al.*, 1975), no DIE was found (Perel *et al.*, 1967) when the p-deutero derivative 21 was administered iv to dogs and rats.

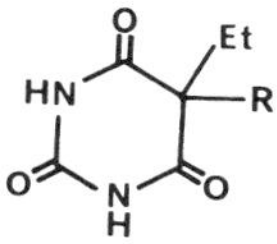

14 R = $CH_2CH_2CH_2CH_3$

15 R = $CH_2CH_2CD_2CH_3$

16 R = $CH_2CH_2CH_2CD_3$

17 R = $CH_2CH_2CH(OH)CH_3$

18 R = $CHMeCH_2CH_2CH_3$

19 R = $CHMeCH_2CD_2CH_3$

20 R =

21 R =

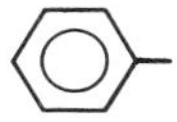

3.2 ARALKYL COMPOUNDS

Unlike O-methyl groups (Section 4.1) the metabolism of aryl methyl groups, presumably via initial hydroxylation, does not appear to be subject to a significant DIE. Thus, for the antidiabetic drug tolbutamide (**22**), the rate of urinary excretion of the acid **23** in humans was not affected by trideuteration of the methyl group (Lemieux *et al.*, 1961) nor was the hypoglycemic activity in male rats (Kimbrough, 1972). In the rat and the rabbit the hydroxymethyl derivative **24** was the major metabolite which was also formed on metabolism with liver microsomes (PB-treated rats) and a small DIE (1.14) was found for the *in vitro* metabolism (Tagg *et al.*, 1967).

McMahon *et al.* (1969) reported an elegant series of metabolism experiments with ethylbenzene (**25**). With liver microsomes (noninduced rats) **25** was hydroxylated to give both enantiomers of 1-phenylethanol (**26**) with an R(+)/S(−) ratio of ~4:1. When microsomes from PB-treated rats were used the stereoselectivity of the hydroxylation was substantially reduced. Using noninduced microsomes a DIE of 1.8 was found on dideuteration of the α-methylene group of **25** but there was no change in the R(+)/S(−) ratio for the metabolite **26**. Metabolism of S(+)-α-d_1-ethylbenzene gave ~92% of R(+)-1-phenylethanol with 86% retention of the deuterium.

In exploring the mode of action of chloramphenicol (**27**) Kutter and Machleidt (1971) prepared the deutero-α-D-threo derivative **28** and found it to have ~80% of the growth-inhibitory activity of the protium form **27** against *Escherichia coli*.

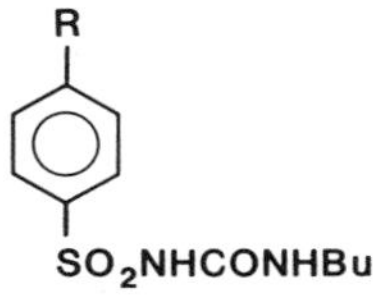

R

SO$_2$NHCONHBu

22 R = CH$_3$

23 R = COOH

24 R = CH$_2$OH

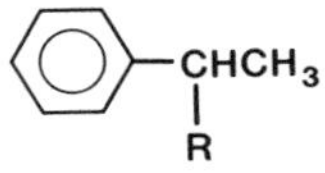

⟨⟩—CHCH$_3$
        |
        R

25 R = H

26 R = OH

                    R   NHCOCHCl$_2$
                    | /
O$_2$N—⟨⟩—CCH
                    | \
                   HO   CH$_2$OH

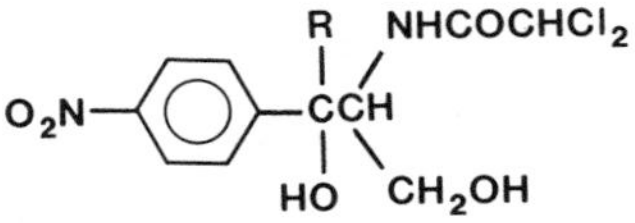

27 R = H

28 R = D

It was concluded that metabolism at the benzylic center in chloramphenicol (27) was involved in the expression of biological activity. A DIE of 1.4 for d_1-chloramphenicol (28) has been noted (Kutter and Garett, 1970).

Metabolism of 4-ethynylbiphenyl (29) and its 2′-fluoro derivative (30) with a 9000 g supernatant of rat liver homogenate gave the respective phenylacetic acid derivatives 31 and 32. Although deuteration of the ethynyl group (→33 and 34) resulted in DIEs of 1.42 and 1.95, respectively, with almost complete retention

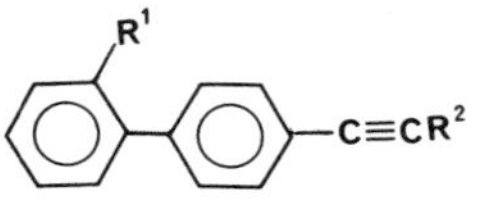

R^1

⟨⟩—⟨⟩—C≡CR^2

R

⟨⟩—⟨⟩—CH$_2$COOH

29 R^1 = R^2 = H

30 R^1 = F, R^2 = H

33 R^1 = H, R^2 = D

34 R^1 = F, R^2 = D

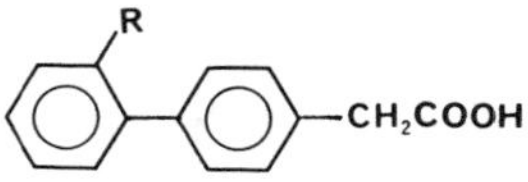

31 R = H

32 R = F

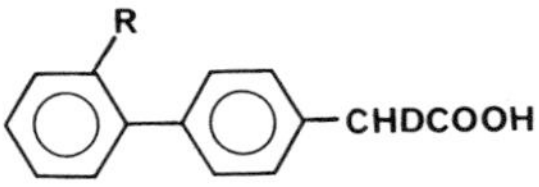

R

⟨⟩—⟨⟩—CHDCOOH

35 R = H

36 R = F

of deuterium in the products (**35** and **36**) it was not possible to distinguish between the two alternative mechanisms, namely, epoxidation of the triple bond or formation of an ethynyl alcohol (McMahon *et al.,* 1981). Each of these products could rearrange via a 1,2-deuterotropic migration with retention of deuterium to give a ketene (R—CD=C=O) which, on reaction with water, would yield a phenylacetic acid derivative. That prototropic and not biphenyl migration occurs was established by Ortiz de Montellano and Kunze (1981), who showed that $R^{13}CH_2COOH$ was the product formed on microsomal metabolism of $[^{13}C]$ethynylbiphenyl $(R^{13}C\equiv CH)$.

3.3 CONTROL OF DRUG LIPOPHILICITY

The variation of the lipophilicity of drugs by variation of the size and branching of alkyl groups attached thereto is a classic maneuver in structure–activity studies associated with drug design. However, as noted above, such groups may be hydroxylated *in vivo* and consequently the efficacy of the drug may be impaired. The DIEs encountered in aliphatic hydroxylation indicate that control of this metabolism pathway *in vivo* is not likely to be achieved effectively by selective or general deuteration.

An alternative approach worth considering is the use of polyfluorinated alkyl groups, e.g., $CF_3(CF_2)_nCH_2$-, where the point of attachment to the drug is not to nitrogen either directly or to a position which is conjugated to nitrogen. Alkyl halides and sulfonates of the type $CF_3(CF_2)_nCH_2X$ are alkylating agents which are readily available via reduction of the corresponding perfluorinated carboxylic acids and the methylene group in $CF_3(CF_2)_nCH_2$- substituents would be expected to be resistant to metabolic attack (see Section 4.1.1), as would perfluorinated alkyl groups. Thus, although perfluorohexane was found to bind to cytochrome P-450 it was not metabolized (Ullrich and Diehl, 1971). Perfluorooctanoic acid, when administered by gavage to rats, was rapidly absorbed but not metabolized (Ophang and Singer, 1980). Moreover, the contribution of such groups to the lipophilicity of a molecule can be calculated readily (Hansch and Leo, 1979). The influence of a CF_3CF_2 group is exemplified by the fact that metabolism of 1,1,1,2,2-pentafluorohexane with liver microsomes (PB-induced rats) gave only the 5-hydroxy derivative, hydroxylation at positions 3 and 4 being completely inhibited (Baker *et al.,* 1984) [cf. the behavior of hexane on hydroxylation (Section 3.4.1)]. Although $CF_3(CF_2)_nCH_2$- groups attached to amino-nitrogen will also be markedly resistant to metabolic N-dealkylation, the basicity of the amine will be greatly reduced (Reifenrath *et al.,* 1980).

3.4 ALICYCLIC COMPOUNDS

3.4.1 Cyclohexane and Its Derivatives

Cyclohexane is rapidly metabolized to a single product, cyclohexanol, by liver microsomes (PB-treated rats) but no DIE was observed for cyclohexane-d_{12}

(Ullrich, 1969). The cyclohexyl moiety of the antitumor drug CCNU [**37**, 1-(2-chloroethyl)-3-cyclohexyl-1-nitrosourea] is also rapidly hydroxylated by rat liver microsomes (May *et al.*, 1975) and a small DIE ($\sim$1.7) was observed (Farmer *et al.*, 1978) for CCNU-d_{10} (**40**). Metabolic switching of trans-2-hydroxylation of CCNU (a minor metabolism pathway accounting for $\sim$2.3% of the total hydroxylated metabolites) was found for partially deuterated derivatives, namely, away from position 2 in CCNU-d_4 (**38**, $\sim$0.2% of trans-2-hydroxy) and toward position 2 in CCNU-d_6 (**39**, $\sim$17% trans-2-hydroxy). However, there was no significant difference in the activities of CCNU and its d_4- (**38**), d_6- (**39**), and d_{10}- (**40**) derivatives against the TLX-5 lymphoma in mice.

A DIE of $\sim$6.8 was found (Tanaka *et al.*, 1976; see also Portig *et al.*, 1979) for the insecticide lindane (**41**, 14/2356-hexachlorocyclohexane, "γ-benzenehexachloride") and lindane-d_6 on metabolism by the 105,000 g supernatant of homogenized houseflies. The intrinsic activities of lindane and lindane-d_6 were similar but the *in vivo* toxicity of the latter compound was higher because of the slower rate of metabolism.

The metabolism of lindane involves dehydrogenation, dehydrochlorination, and dechlorination, and DIEs would be expected for the first two pathways. Kurihara *et al.* (1980) concluded that, on aerobic metabolism of a 1:1 mixture of lindane (**41**) and lindane-d_6 by rat liver microsomes, the dehydrogenation (**41**$\rightarrow$**42**) and dehydrochlorination (**41**$\rightarrow$**44**) pathways were associated with DIEs of 10 and $\sim$2.3, respectively. Also, for the microsomal metabolism of the dehydrochlorination product **43**-d_5 the DIEs associated with the disappearance of substrate and appearance of 2,4,6-trichlorophenol were $\sim$5.1 and $\sim$6.7, respectively.

Somewhat lower DIEs were observed *in vivo*. The rat urinary metabolites of lindane are mainly conjugates, namely, mercapturic acids formed by the reaction of glutathione with the first-formed metabolites. Thus, **42**, **43**, and **44** (formed by dechlorination of lindane) give rise to tri-, di-, and monochlorophenylmercapturic acids, respectively. Following ip injection of a 1:1 mixture of lindane and lindane-d_6 into rats 5- to 10-fold more of the latter was excreted unchanged and the DIEs associated with the excreted tri- (2,4,5 and 2,3,5), di- (2,4, 2,5, and 3,4), and monochlorophenylmercapturic acids were $\sim$2.7, 2.4–3.5, and $\sim$1.3, respectively.

The above results illustrate the well-known susceptibility to metabolic attack of hydrogen geminal to one or more chlorine substituents (Anders, 1982) and there are now several examples (Burke *et al.*, 1980; Teitelbaum *et al.*, 1981; Marcotte and Robinson, 1982) where fluorine is the geminal substituent although, apparently, no DIE studies have been reported for the latter category. However, it is becoming clear that fluorine substituents can markedly reduce the susceptibility of a vicinal C—H bond to metabolic attack. Thus, in the metabolism of 1,1-difluorocyclohexane with liver microsomes (PB-treated rats) (Baker

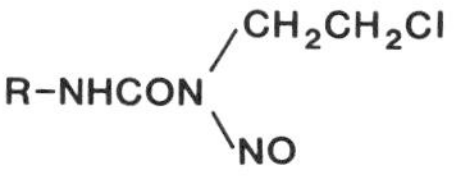

$$R-NHCON \begin{smallmatrix} \diagup CH_2CH_2Cl \\ \diagdown NO \end{smallmatrix}$$

37 R =

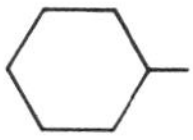

39 R =

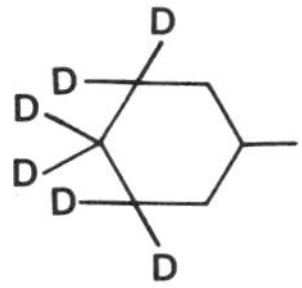

38 R =

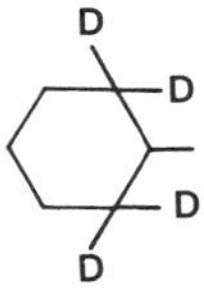

40 R =

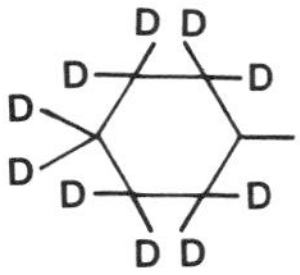

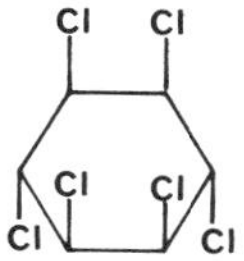

41

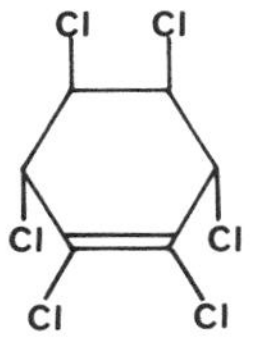

42

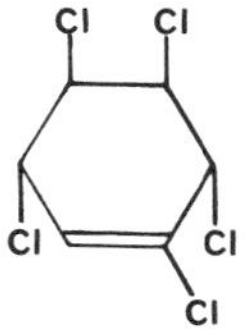

43

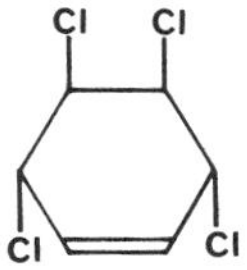

44

et al., 1984) virtually no hydroxylation occurred at position 2 and the rates of 3- and 4-hydroxylation were in the ratio 1:~5.5.

Cyclohexene (**45**) was metabolized by a fully reconstituted cytochrome P-450 system from rabbit liver by alternative pathways to give cyclohexene oxide (**46**) and cyclohex-1-en-3-ol (**47**) in the ratio 1:1.1 (Groves *et al.*, 1980). The ratio changed slightly ($\rightarrow$1.5:1) for the d_3-cyclohexene **48** but substantially ($\rightarrow$4.8:1) for the d_4-cyclohexene **49.** The relatively large DIE (4.9) calculated for cyclo-hexene hydroxylation probably reflects metabolic switching (Section 2.2.1). By analogy with aromatic compounds (Tomaszewski *et al.*, 1975) no DIE would be expected for epoxidation of the d_3-cyclohexene **48.**

45 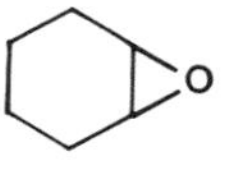   46 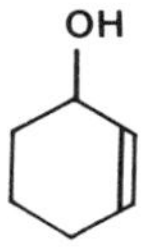   47

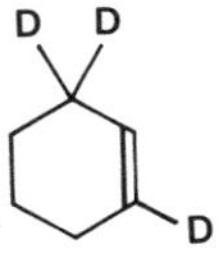

48    49

3.4.2 Norbornane and Camphor

Studies of the microsomal metabolism of these hydrocarbons and appropriate deuterated derivatives have helped to clarify the mechanism of hydroxylation mediated by cytochrome P-450.

Using purified rabbit liver microsomal P-450 (LM2, PB induction), Groves *et al.* (1978) showed that, whereas norbornane (**50**) gave a mixture of *exo*- (**52**) and *endo*-2-borneol (**53**) in the ratio 3.4:1, the ratio of alcohols from the exo-d_4-derivative **51** was 0.76:1. The overall yield of alcohols from **50** and **51** and the rates of hydroxylation were similar. Moreover, there was 25% retention of deuterium at the hydroxylated carbon in the exo-alcohol and 91% retention in the endo-alcohol, indicating a significant amount of epimerization during hydroxylation. The DIE for exo-hydrogen abstraction was 11.5 ±1. These findings are indicative of a hydrogen abstraction process giving a carbon radical intermediate. A much larger DIE would be expected in a reaction sequence where C—H bond cleavage is complete before hydroxylation occurs (Miwa *et al.*, 1980) than where an oxenoid species is inserted into a C—H bond and a three-center transition state is involved.

The norbornyl ring system is present in the antihypertensive drug tripamide (**54**) and among the urinary metabolites present after oral administration of the drug to the rat (Horie *et al.*, 1981) was the 8-hydroxy derivative subsequently (Horie *et al.*, 1983) assigned the exo-configuration **55**. However, the DIE (2) found for 8-exo-hydroxylation of the exo-d_2 derivative **56** by rat liver microsomes was much lower than that noted above for norbornane.

The hydrogen abstraction hypothesis received further support from the results of Gelb *et al.* (1982) for the hydroxylation of camphor (**57**) mediated by cytochrome P-450 from the soil bacterium, *Pseudomonas putida*. This cytochrome P-450 is similar to adrenal mitochondrial steroid 11β-hydroxylase.

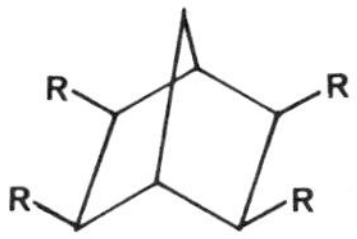

50 R = H

51 R = D

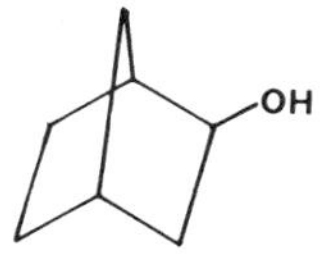

52 (exo)

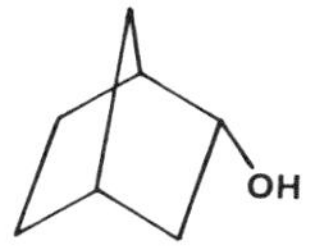

53 (endo)

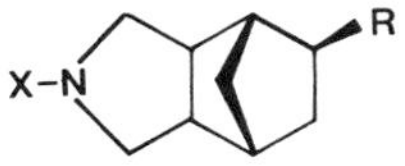

54 R = H

55 R = OH

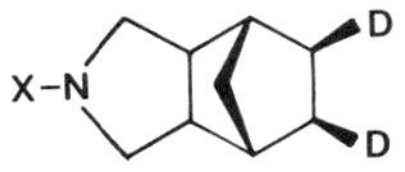

56

$$X = $$

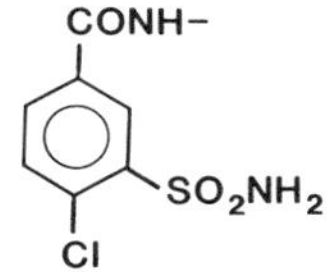

5-*exo*-Hydroxycamphor (**58**) was the sole product and only shall DIEs ($^D v$ <1.25) were observed for the hydroxylation of 5-*exo*-d_1- (**59**) and 5-*endo*-d_1-camphor (**60**). The D/H ratios for 5-*exo*-hydroxycamphor from these deuterated

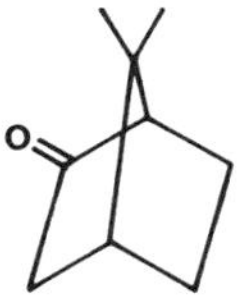

57

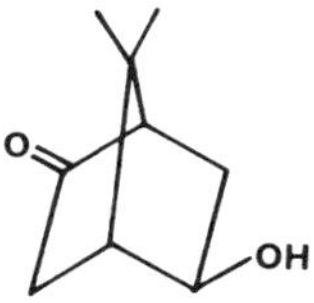

58

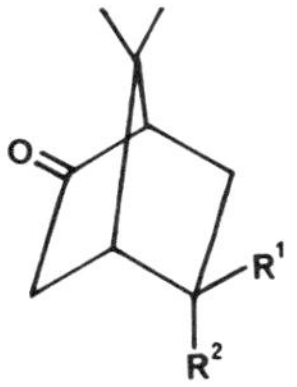

59 R^1 = D, R^2 = H

60 R^1 = H, R^2 = D

derivatives were 1.18 and 4.39, respectively, which reflected the preference of the enzyme for 5-exo-H(D) abstraction and also epimerization. It was concluded that, although 5-*exo*-hydroxycamphor was the sole product, both exo- and endo-H(D)-abstraction could occur and that the H(D)-abstracting and oxygen-donating species had different identities. A substantial but masked intramolecular (intrinsic) DIE ($^D k$) was found which was considered to be consistent with a reversible H(D)-abstraction step and/or a highly nonsymmetric transition state.

3.4.3 Steroids

The effect of deuteration on steroid hydroxylations has been widely investigated. In an early study Bollinger and Wendler (1959) found that 11α-deuteration of hydrocortisone (→**61**) reduced the potency in oral glycogen deposition tests in mice and enhanced the potency in the oral systemic granuloma assay in rats. It was concluded that oxidation–reduction at position 11 was involved in determining pharmacological properties. Likewise (Ringold *et al.*, 1961), oxidation to the 3-keto form was considered important for the expression of the androgenicity of 17α-methyl-5α-androstane-3β,17β-diol since 3α-deuteration (→**62**) reduced the androgenic potency in castrated rats.

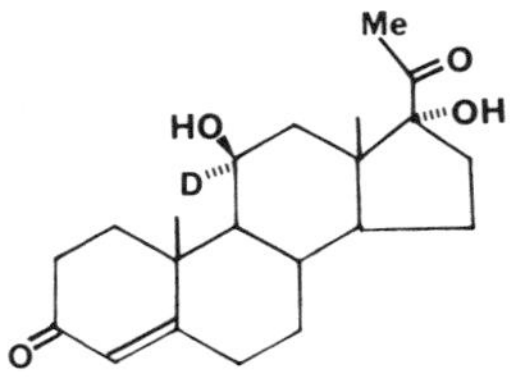

61 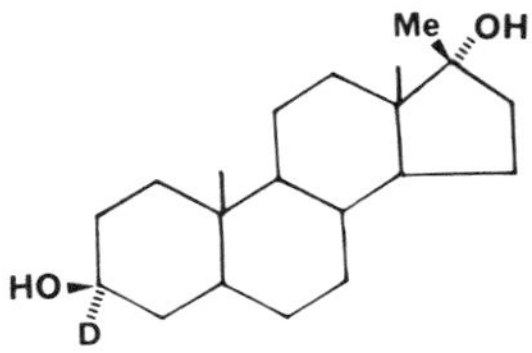   **62**

Björkhem (1971), using rat liver microsomes, found no DIE for 7α-hydroxylation of cholesterol and cholestanol and no tritium IE for 6β-hydroxylation of taurochenodeoxycholic acid but a tritium IE of 3.8 was found for 7α-hydroxylation of taurodeoxycholic acid. In further reports (Björkhem, 1972, 1975) no significant DIEs were found for microsomal 6β-hydroxylation of testosterone, 26-hydroxylation of 5β-cholestane-3α,7α,12α-triol, and 12α-hydroxylation of 7α-hydroxy-4-cholestene-3-one but DIEs of 3–4 were found for 16α-hydroxylation of pregnenolone and 24-hydroxylation of 5β-cholestane-3α,7α,12α-triol.

The variation in the magnitude of the DIEs associated with steroid C-hydroxylations is striking and although explicable in terms of current understanding of the mechanism of enzyme reactions (Northrop, 1982) they are certainly not as yet predictable (Björkhem, 1977).

3.4.4 Cotinine

Following iv administration of cotinine (**63**) to the rhesus monkey the metabolites which appear in the urine reflect pyridine N-oxidation, N-demethylation, and 5- and trans-3-hydroxylation (→**64**). When 3-d_2-cotinine (**65**) was administered a DIE of 6.2 was found for the trans-3-hydroxylation pathway (Dagne *et al.*, 1974).

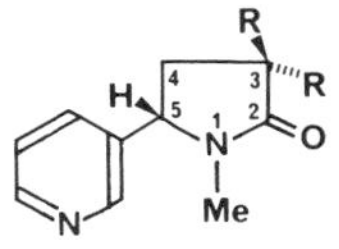

63 R = H

65 R = D

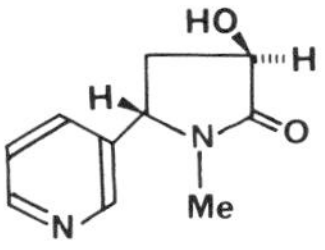

64

4 Hydroxylation of Carbon α to Oxygen

4.1 O-DEALKYLATION

Mitoma *et al.* (1967) were the first to describe a DIE associated with O-de-methylation. Using liver microsomes (PB-treated rabbits) they found a DIE of ~2 for *p*-nitroanisole (**66**). They also noted K_m^D/K_m^H to be 0.4, which indicated stronger binding of the deuterated compound to the microsomal protein. DIEs of ~2 were found (Foster *et al.*, 1974) and K_m^D/K_m^H values of <1 for the O-demethylation of *p*-methoxyacetanilide (**67**) and *p*-dimethoxybenzene (**68**) with liver microsomes (PB-treated rats).

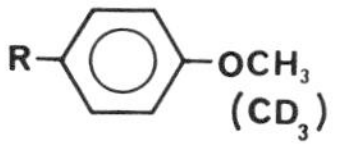

66 R = NO$_2$

67 R = AcNH

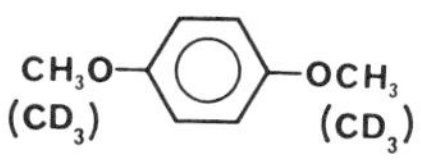

68

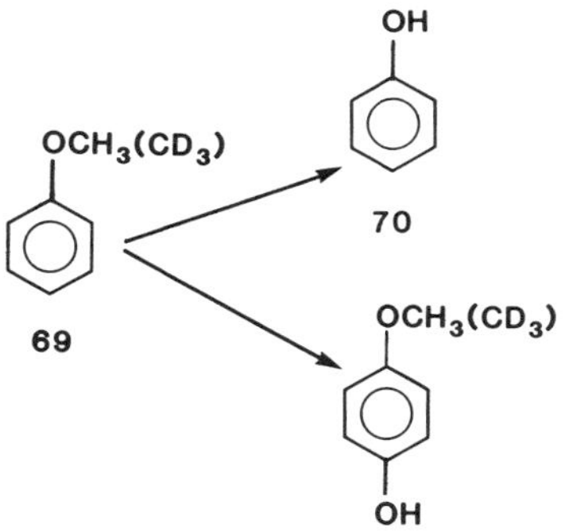

The metabolism of anisole (**69**) by rat liver microsomes involves the alternative pathways demethylation (→phenol, **70**) and p-hydroxylation (→4-methoxyphenol, **71**). By comparing the ratio of the yield of phenol to that of 4-methoxyphenol on metabolism of anisole and its CD_3O analog a DIE of ~7.5 was obtained (Lindsay Smith *et al.*, 1982). This relatively large DIE reflects metabolic switching since it was subsequently reported (Lindsay Smith and Sleath, 1983) that trideuteration of the methoxyl group depressed demethylation and enhanced p-hydroxylation although the combined yield of phenol (**70**) and 4-methoxyphenol (**71**) was not affected by the deuteration.

A DIE of 2.7–3.0 was reported by Al-Gailany *et al.* (1975) for the microsomal (PB-treated rats) O-deethylation of *p*-nitrophenetole (**72**). These workers also reported type I binding of **72** to cytochrome P-450.

Garland *et al.* (1976) metabolized phenacetin (**73**, *p*-ethoxyacetanilide) with noninduced rabbit liver microsomes and found a DIE of ~1.6 for the O-deethylation of **73**-α-d_2 but virtually none (~1.03) for **73**-β-d_3, reflecting a very weak secondary isotope effect. The K_m values for **73** and **73**-α-d_2 were closely similar and significantly higher than that for **73**-β-d_3. However, using a perfused rat liver system, Pang *et al.* (1982) found no marked difference in the rate of formation (by O-deethylation) of acetaminophen from phenacetin (**73**) and α-d_2,β-d_3-phenacetin injected simultaneously.

Using purified cytochromes P-450 and P-448 from liver microsomes of PB- and methylcholanthrene-induced rats, respectively, DIEs of ~3.8 and ~2 were obtained (Lu *et al.*, 1984) for the O-deethylation of α-d_2-7-ethylcoumarin (**74**) and the formation of some 6-hydroxy derivative **75** reflected metabolic switching. A DIE of ~6 was found for the O-deethylation of **74** with human liver microsomes. Apparently, this is the first example of the use of human liver microsomes in the study of DIEs and the finding of such a relatively high DIE is of potential importance. In evaluating the scope for using a DIE to influence the

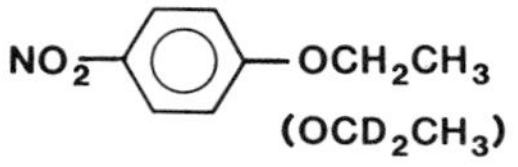

72

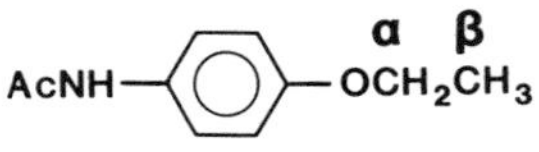

73

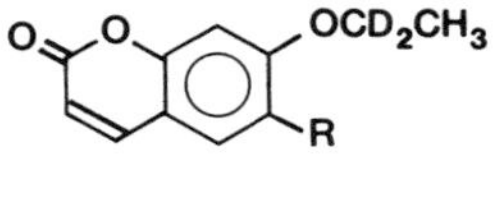

74 R = H

75 R = OH

metabolism of a drug in humans, liver microsomes from a human source should be used since DIEs associated with animal liver microsomes may be misleadingly low.

4.2 HYDROXYLATION OF O-ALKYL GROUPS

The effect of deuterium substitution on hydroxylation at β- and γ-positions in O-alkyl groups has been described by Mitoma *et al.* (1971). *p*-Nitrophenyl propyl ether (**76**) was metabolized by liver microsomes from (PB-treated) rats to give *p*-nitrophenol (**77**), 2-hydroxyl-1-propyl *p*-nitrophenyl ether (**78**) and 3-(*p*-nitrophenoxy)propionic acid (**79**), reflecting α-, β-, and γ-hydroxylation, respectively. The yields were always in the sequence **77**>**78**>**79** but the ratios varied quite markedly with each microsomal preparation. Deuteration severally at the α-, β-, and γ-positions in the propoxy group of **76** markedly suppressed metabolism at the deuterated site. DIEs were not reported but the effect of deuteration was expressed as the ratio of the yields of the appropriate metabolite from the protium and particular deuterium form. Thus, the ratio for the phenol **77** from **76** and **76**-α-d_2 was 0.06 (α-hydroxylation), that for the alcohol **78** from **76** and **76**-β-d_2 was 0.22 (β-hydroxylation), and that for the acid **79** from **76** and **76**-γ-d_3 was 0.24 (initial γ-hydroxylation followed by oxidation).

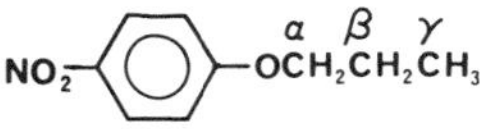

$$NO_2\text{—}\langle O \rangle\text{—}O\overset{\alpha}{C}H_2\overset{\beta}{C}H_2\overset{\gamma}{C}H_3$$

76

$$NO_2\text{—}\langle O \rangle\text{—}OH \qquad NO_2\text{—}\langle O \rangle\text{—}OCH_2\underset{HO}{C}HCH_3 \qquad NO_2\text{—}\langle O \rangle\text{—}CH_2CH_2COOH$$

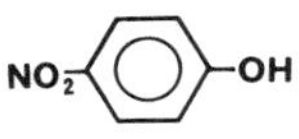

77 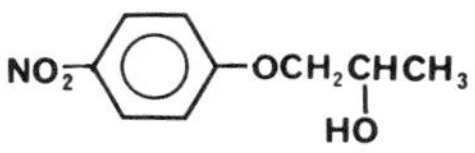   **78** 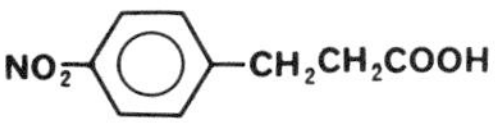   **79**

4.3 CONTROL OF METABOLIC O-DEALKYLATION

An approach alternative to α-deuteration for blocking metabolic O-dealkylation is β-fluorination. Thus, under conditions where *p*-nitroanisole (**66**) and *p*-nitrophenetole (**72**) underwent rapid microsomally mediated O-demethylation, *p*-(2,2,2-trifluoroethoxy)nitrobenzene (**80**) was virtually unaffected (Baker *et al.*, 1984). The relay of this type of deactivating effect of a trifluoromethyl group through a benzene ring is nicely illustrated by the observation (Hjelmeland *et al.*, 1977b) that microsomally mediated benzylic hydroxylation of 1-phenyl-3-(*p*-trifluoromethylphenyl)propane (**81**) occurs mainly (>95%) at position 1 (adjacent to phenyl).

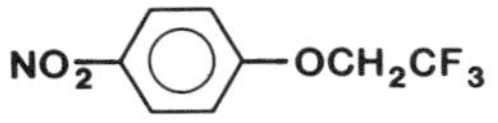

OH
|
NO_2—⟨O⟩—OCH_2CF_3 ⟨O⟩—$CH_2CH_2CH_2$—⟨O⟩—CF_3

80 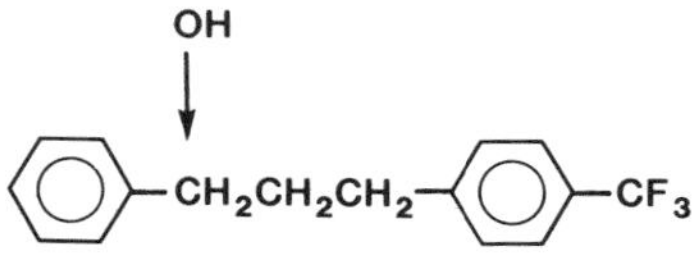   81

Further examples of the effect of vicinal fluorine substituents on the microsomally mediated hydroxylation of aliphatic and alicyclic hydrocarbons are
noted in Sections 3.3 and 3.4.1.

Although S-dealkylation is a known, albeit not widely exemplified, metabolism pathway (e.g., Sarcione and Stutzman, 1960; Mazel *et al.*, 1964; Taylor,
1973) apparently there has been no report of DIEs.

5 Hydroxylation of Carbon α to Nitrogen

5.1 N-DEALKYLATION

The first report on DIEs associated with N-demethylation was that of Elison *et
al.* (1961, 1963) on morphine (82). Using rat liver microsomes a DIE of 1.4 was
found for the trideutero derivative 83. It was also noted that 83 was the stronger
base (pK_a values: 82, 8.05; 83, 8.17) due to the greater inductive effect of the
CD_3 group and that the ratio of the Michaelis constants K_m^D/K_m^H was 1.43. A
value of this ratio of >1 signifies better binding of the protium form and the
situation for N-alkyl derivatives contrasts with that for O-alkyl compounds,
where the K_m^D/K_m^H ratio is <1, indicating better binding of the deuterium form
(see Section 4.1). As compared with morphine (82), the trideutero derivative 83
was a less potent analgesic in mice, and showed less toxicity (higher LD_{50})
toward this species.

A somewhat smaller DIE (1.21–1.28) was found by Thompson and Holtzman
(1974) for the N-demethylation of ethylmorphine (84) and trideutero-
methylnorethylmorphine (85) by liver microsomes (noninduced rats).

Arguing that, for O-demethylation, the lower K_m for the deuterium form
reinforces the DIE whereas, for N-demethylation, the higher K_m for the deuterium form opposes the DIE, Abdel-Monem (1975) studied the N-demethylation of *N*-methyl-*N*-trideuteromethyl-3-phenylpropylamine (86). Using liver
9000 *g* supernatant (noninduced and PB-induced rats), a DIE of 1.31 was found
(calculated from the ratio of the products). A somewhat higher DIE (1.45) was
found when mouse liver 9000 *g* supernatant was used. The metabolism of 86 has
been categorized (Hjelmeland *et al.*, 1977a) as reflecting an intramolecular DIE
(see Section 7).

This approach was developed further by Miwa *et al.* (1980) in studies with
N,N-dimethylphentermine (87). No DIE was found for the N,N-di-(trideutero-

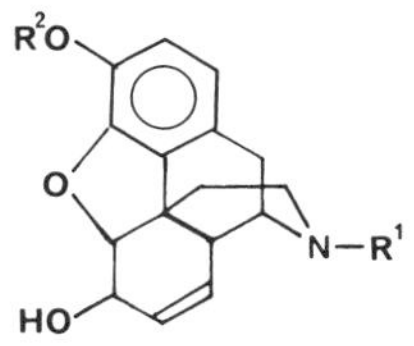

82 $R^1 = CH_3$, $R^2 = H$

83 $R^1 = CD_3$, $R^2 = H$

84 $R^1 = CH_3$, $R^2 = Et$

85 $R^1 = CD_3$, $R^2 = Et$

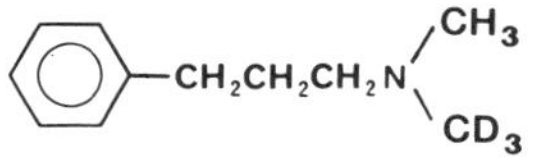

86

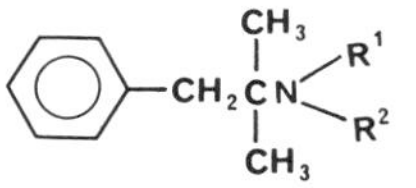

87 $R^1 = R^2 = CH_3$ 90 $R = N(CH_2CH_3)_2$

88 $R^1 = R^2 = CD_3$ 91 $R = N(CD_2CH_3)_2$

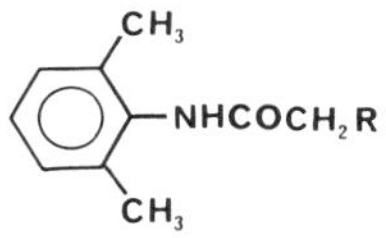

89 $R^1 = CH_3$, $R^2 = CD_3$ 92 $R = N(CH_2CD_3)_2$

methyl) derivative **88** on metabolism with liver microsomes (PB-treated rats). However, a DIE of 1.6–2.0 was found for the N-methyl-N-trideuteromethyl derivative **89**. No significant DIE in the K_m parameters was found and it was concluded that C—H bond cleavage did not contribute to V_{max} and that the NMe groups were free to exchange at the active site of the enzyme. It was also suggested that N-demethylation could involve a transition state different from that (probably free radical, see Section 3.4.2) associated with, for example, O-demethylation.

Nelson *et al.* (1975) investigated the N-deethylation of the anesthetic lidocaine (**90**) using liver microsomes (noninduced rats). For the d_4-derivative **91** (deuterium α to nitrogen) a primary DIE of 1.36 was found and, as expected, a K_m^D/K_m^H ratio of >1 (1.23). This finding accords with those noted above for N-demethylation. However, for the d_6-derivative **92** (deuterium β to nitrogen) a secondary DIE of 1.40 was obtained with, as expected, a K_m^D/K_m^H ratio of <1 (0.92). Secondary DIEs in metabolism studies are rare and a convincing explanation for the above observation remains to be found.

5.2 α-C-HYDROXYLATION

N-Desmethyldiazepam (**94**) is a major metabolite of diazepam (**93**) and is further metabolized by 3-hydroxylation to give oxazepam (**95**), which accumulates in

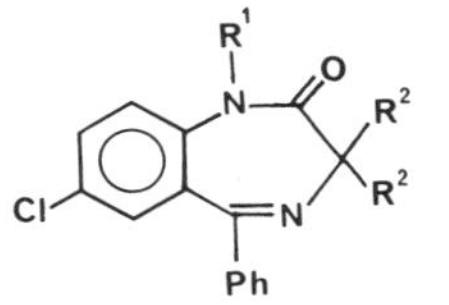

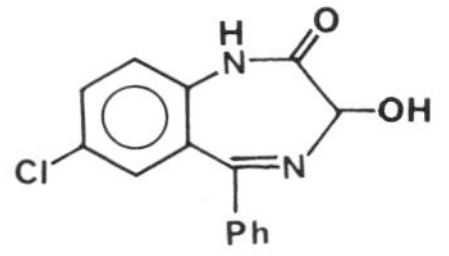

93 $R^1 = CH_3$, $R^2 = H$

94 $R^1 = R^2 = H$

96 $R^1 = H$, $R^2 = D$

95

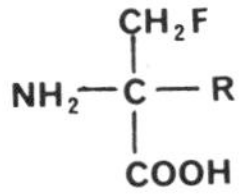

97 R = H

98 R = D

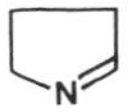

99

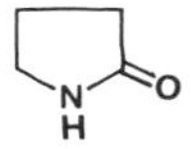

100

the brain of mice and is responsible for the prolonged anticonvulsant action of the administered drug. Dideuteration at position 3 ($\rightarrow$96) reduced the duration of the anticonvulsant activity from 20 to 5 hr and in *in vitro* experiments using liver microsomes (PB-induced mice) the extent of 3-hydroxylation was reduced $\sim$7.5-fold (Marcucci *et al.*, 1973).

3-Fluoro-L-alanine (97) was designed as a specific antibacterial metabolite and in refining the design (Kollonitsch and Barash, 1976) deuterium was introduced ($\rightarrow$98) in order to exploit the DIE to retard metabolism *in vivo*. The d_1-derivative 98 had enhanced metabolic stability in animals but the antibacterial activity was the same as that of the protium form.

Callery *et al.* (1980) reported a DIE of $\sim$1.7 for the conversion of Δ^1-pyrroline (99) into 2-pyrrolidinone (100) by a 10,000 g supernatant of rabbit liver homogenate. 2-Pyrrolidinone (100) is a metabolite of putrescine (1,4-diamino-butane).

Among the rat urinary metabolites of the antihypertensive drug tripamide (54) was the 3-hydroxy derivative (101). A DIE of 1.6 was found on metabolism of the d_4-derivative (102) by rat liver microsomes (Horie *et al.*, 1981).

A major metabolic detoxification pathway for the antitumor agent 6-mercap-topurine (103) is via 8-hydroxy-6-thiopurine (104) to thiouric acid (105) mediated by xanthine oxidase. Significant DIEs (3.5–3.8) were found (Jarman *et al.*, 1982) for the action of this enzyme *in vitro* on 8-d_1- (106) and 2,8-d_2-6-mercap-topurine (107) but not for the 2-d_1 derivative (108). Following ip administration of the 2,8-d_2 derivative (107) to rats 2.2–3.7 times as much unchanged drug was

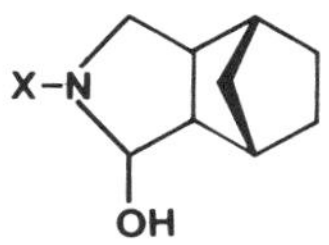

101

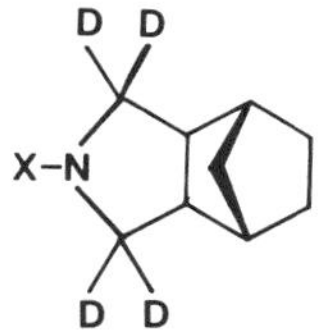

102

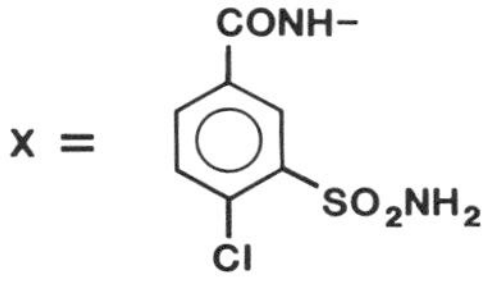

$$X = $$

CONH–

SO$_2$NH$_2$

Cl

excreted in the urine and 54–70% of thiouric acid in comparison with 6-mercaptopurine (**103**). Although the potency of the 2,8-d_2 derivative (**107**) against the adenocarcinoma Ca755 in mice was increased three- to fivefold the 8-d_1 derivative (**106**) had the same potency as 6-mercaptopurine. These results suggest that oxidation mechanisms other than or additional to that mediated by xanthine oxidase may occur *in vivo*.

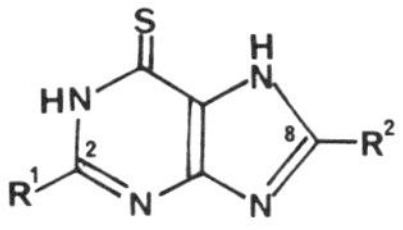

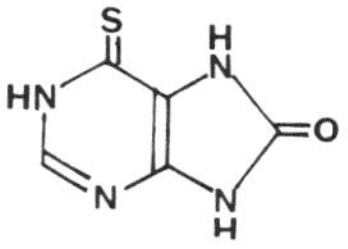

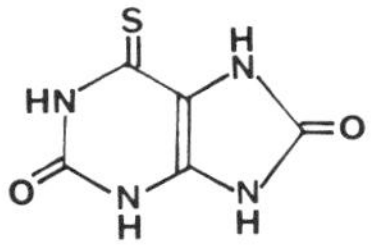

103 R^1 = R^2 = H **104** **105**

106 R^1 = H, R^2 = D

107 R^1 = R^2 = D

108 R^1 = D, R^2 = H

5.3 OXIDATIVE DEAMINATION

These reactions are mediated by enzymes such as monoamine oxidases and monooxygenases (Miller and Klinman, 1982).

5.3.1 *Phenylethylamine Derivatives*

Belleau *et al.* (1961), in an early attempt to modify biological properties of a drug by specific deuteration and thereby illuminate the mode of action, examined the effect of deuteration α to nitrogen in a series of biologically active amines which were substrates for monoamine oxidase.

Thus α-dideuteration ($\rightarrow$**110**) of the adrenergic p-tyramine (**109**) doubled the duration of the effect on arterial pressure and nictitating membrane contractions following iv administration to cats. A similar effect was found on α-dideuteration ($\rightarrow$**112**) of tryptamine (**111**) but there was no such effect on α-dideuteration ($\rightarrow$**114**) of ($-$)-norepinephrine (**113**). It was also found that for the enantiomeric monodeutero derivatives (**115**) of tyramine only one (not designated) showed a DIE.

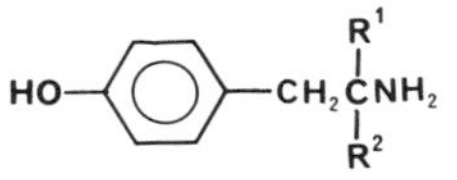

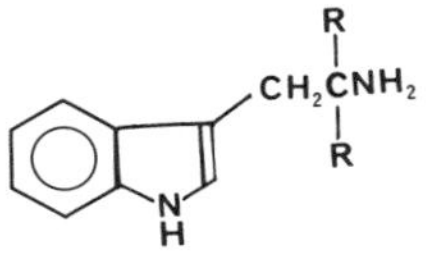

109 $R^1 = R^2 = H$

110 $R^1 = R^2 = D$

115 $R^1 = H(D)$, $R^2 = D(H)$

111 $R = H$

112 $R = D$

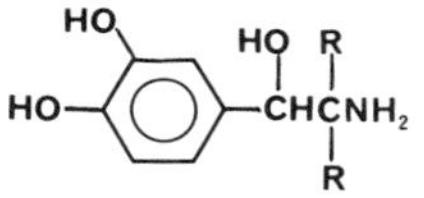

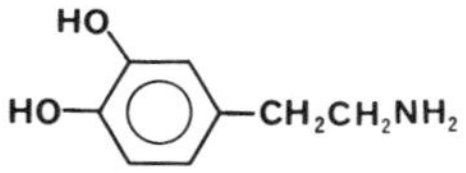

113 $R = H$

114 $R = D$

116

Perel *et al.* (1972) found that for dopamine (**116**, 3,4-dihydroxyphenyl-ethylamine), the side chain of which is oxidized by dopamine β-hydroxylase and monoamine oxidase, dideuteration α or β to nitrogen had no effect on the pharmacological activity. No *in vitro* studies were reported.

More recently Yu *et al.* (1981) have reported on the metabolism of p-tyramine (**109**) and related amines by monoamine oxidase isolated from rat liver mito-chondria. A DIE of ~2.4 was found for the α-dideutero derivative **110** (and also an increased K_m); there was no effect on β-dideuteration. Likewise, α-dideutera-tion of m-tyramine and β-phenylethylamine resulted in DIEs of ~2.2 and ~1.8, respectively, but β-dideuteration had no effect. It was noted without details that β-d_2-p-tyramine was less readily β-hydroxylated than the protium form.

The antidepressant phenelzine (PhCH$_2$CH$_2$NHNH$_2$) is a nonspecific inhibitor of monoamine oxidase and is metabolized *in vivo* to phenylacetic acid (PhCH$_2$COOH), presumably via hydroxylation α to nitrogen. Tetradeuteration

($\rightarrow PhCD_2CD_2NHNH_2$) did not change the enzyme inhibition potency *in vitro* (Dyck *et al.*, 1983) but profoundly potentiated the biphasic behavioral stimulation in the rat (Dourish *et al.*, 1983). It seems likely that the central potency was increased because of slowing of peripheral inactivation consequent on a DIE.

5.3.2 Amphetamines

Foreman *et al.* (1969) were the first to report a DIE for the oxidative deamination of amphetamine (**117**, 2-amino-1-phenylpropane) to phenylacetone (**118**). Using a rabbit liver homogenate and (−)-amphetamine a DIE of 1.9 was found for (−)-2-d_1-amphetamine (**119**).

Vree *et al.* (1971) subsequently reported on the fate of several N-substituted amphetamines and their deuterated derivatives in man. They found only a small DIE for (+)-amphetamine. After ingestion of a 1:1 mixture of (+)-amphetamine (**117**) and (+)-2-d_1-amphetamine (**119**) by patients the amphetamine in urine samples collected during the following 48 hr contained a 7–18% excess of deuterium. Similar studies with (+)-N-methylamphetamine (**120**) and its trideuteromethyl analog (**121**) and also (+)-N,N-dimethylamphetamine (**122**) and its N,N-di(trideuteromethyl) analog (**123**) revealed virtually no DIE. However, for a ~1:1 mixture of (+)-N-isopropylamphetamine (**124**) and its (+)-N-2'-d_1-isopropyl analog (**125**) a substantial DIE was observed since the deuterium content of the drug excreted in the urine increased from 48 to 80–90%. No such

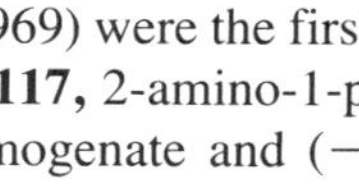

117 R = H

119 R = D

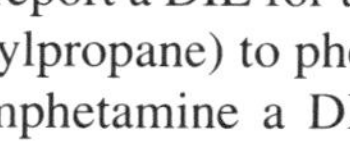

118

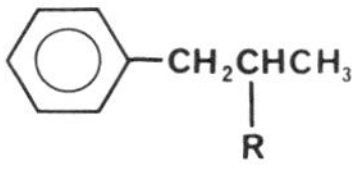

120 R = HNCH₃

121 R = HNCD₃

122 R = N(CH₃)₂

123 R = N(CD₃)₂

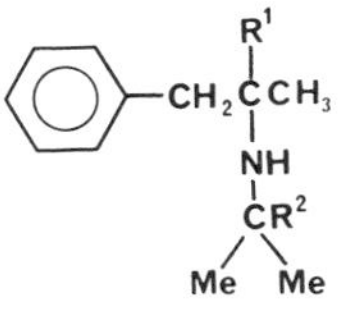

124 R¹ = R² = H

125 R¹ = H, R² = D

126 R¹ = R² = D

effect was observed for the $(-)$-analogs. Likewise, for a 1:1 mixture of **124** and $(+)$-N-2'-d_1-isopropyl-2-d_1-amphetamine (**126**) there was a substantial increase in the deuterium content of the excreted drug and there was no such effect for the $(-)$-analogs.

The members of the $(-)$-series of amphetamines are metabolized slowly via N-oxidation so that DIEs in the deuterated compounds noted above would not be expected whereas the corresponding $(+)$-compounds are metabolized by hydroxylation α to nitrogen. In an *in vitro* study, Henderson *et al.* (1974) found that, with liver microsomes (noninduced rats), $(+)$-N-isopropylamphetamine (**124**) was converted into $(+)$-amphetamine (**117**) and phenylacetone (**118**) and for $(+)$-N-2'-d_1-isopropyl-2-d_1-amphetamine (**126**) a DIE of 1.64 was found but the effect on the balance of the two metabolism pathways was not noted. In contrast to the findings of Foreman *et al.* (1969) for the *in vitro* metabolism of $(-)$-2-d_1-amphetamine (**119**) Henderson *et al.* (1974) found no DIE for $(-)$-N-2'-d_1-isopropyl-2-d_1-amphetamine (**126**).

5.4 NITROSAMINES

Dialkylnitrosamines and related cyclic compounds, e.g., nitrosomorpholine, are potent carcinogens which can cause the development of tumors in various organs when administered to animals via their drinking water. These compounds are activated by metabolism by membrane-bound (microsomal) and soluble enzymes to yield alkylating species which are believed to be responsible for carcinogenesis (Lai and Arcos, 1980). It is well established that dialkylnitrosamines undergo metabolic hydroxylation α to nitrogen and this process can yield an alkylating species (R—N≡N—OH, R—N≡N, or R^+) by the initial sequence shown in Scheme 1. The alkylating species would be susceptible to attack by cellular nucleophiles, including DNA.

Interest in dialkylnitrosamines has been stimulated not only because they are potent carcinogens which could be responsible for some human cancers, but also because variation in the structure of R^1 and R^2 varies the organotrophy. In seeking to define more precisely the mode of action of dialkylnitrosamines the effect of deuterium substitution α to nitrogen has been extensively explored.

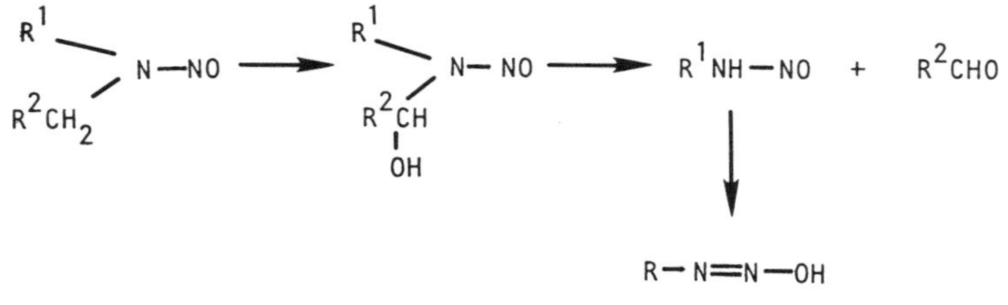

Scheme 1

Keefer *et al.* (1973) showed that the administration of di-(trideutero-methyl)nitrosamine [d_6-DMN, $(CD_3)_2$N-NO] at 5 ppm in the drinking water of rats for 30 weeks caused a ninefold lower incidence of liver tumors than did dimethylnitrosamine [DMN, $(CH_3)_2$N-NO]. Dagani and Archer (1976) subsequently reported a DIE of 3.8 for the demethylation of d_6-DMN by liver microsomes (PB-treated rats) and a K_m^D/K_m^H ratio of 0.62, indicating stronger binding of the deuterated compound to the hydroxylating enzyme [the opposite effect is found for amines (Section 5.1)].

There are at least two DMN demethylases in rat liver microsomes which operate at low (<4 mM) and high (50–200 mM) substrate concentrations (Arcos *et al.*, 1977). Using the S-9 fraction (9000 *g* supernatant) from the homogenized liver of PB-treated Long–Evans rats, Kroeger-Koepke and Michejda (1979) found a DIE (1.82) for the demethylation of d_6-DMN which was much lower than that (3.8) noted above. They also obtained evidence for a soluble demethylase and pointed out that the magnitude of the DIE depended on the cell fraction used (microsomal, postmicrosomal), rat species, inducer, and concentration of substrate and noted that variation in the levels of these enzymes might be partly responsible for the organotrophy of dialkylnitrosamines. A DIE of 5.38 was found for the demethylation of phenyltrideuteromethylnitrosamine [Ph(CD_3)N-NO].

Charnley and Archer (1977) reported that, after activation by a liver homogenate (PB-treated rats), nitrosomorpholine (**127**) was five times more mutagenic toward *Salmonella typhimurium* TA1535 than the tetradeuterated analog **128**. A similar finding was reported by Elespura (1978) using a different mutagenesis system (reversion of a nonsense mutation in *E. coli*). It was also noted that d_6-DMN and the octadeuterated derivative of dinitrosopiperazine (**129**) were less mutagenic than the corresponding protium forms.

This apparently clear-cut picture of DIEs in dialkylnitrosamine carcinogenesis subsequently became somewhat blurred mainly as a result of the findings of Lijinsky and co-workers. As noted in Section 2.2.2, it is important in determining the magnitude and biological consequences of DIEs to verify that no D/H exchange occurs *in vitro* or *in vivo*. This precaution cannot be taken in animal feeding experiments with dialkylnitrosamines and Singer and Lijinsky (1979) have suggested that biological DIEs are only likely to occur when compounds with deuterium α to nitrogen have a relatively low susceptibility to base-catalyzed D/H exchange.

Lijinsky *et al.* (1980a) found that the d_4-derivative (**131**, D α to nitrogen) of 2,6-dimethylnitrosomorpholine (**130**) was less carcinogenic and the d_2-derivative (**132**, D α to oxygen) was more carcinogenic than the parent compound in causing esophageal cancer in the rat. This result is suggestive of metabolic switching in the d_2-derivative **132** away from hydroxylation α to oxygen, a process known (Section 4) to have a DIE of ~ 2 and which would not be expected to yield alkylating species.

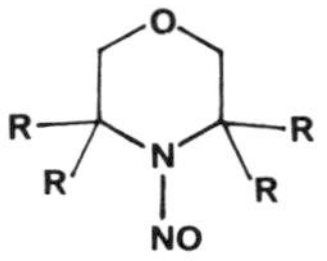

127 R = H   129 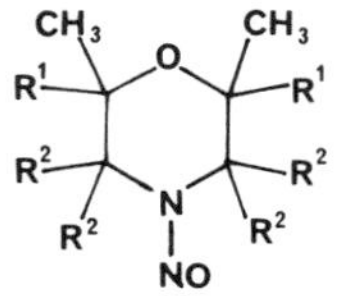   130 R^1 = R^2 = H

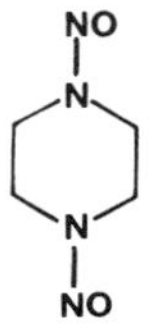

128 R = D   131 R^1 = H, R^2 = D

                                 132 R^1 = D, R^2 = H

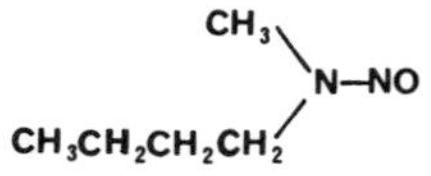

133 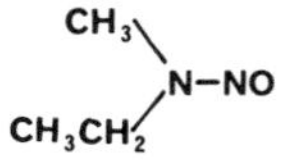   134 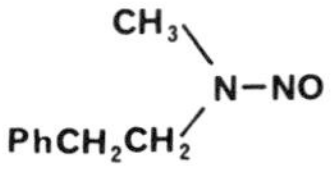   135

For n-butylmethylnitrosamine (133), replacement of the methyl group by CD_3 increased the carcinogenic potency whereas replacement of the n-butyl group by $CH_3CH_2CH_2CD_2$ decreased the potency (Lijinsky et al., 1980b). These findings contrast with those (Lijinsky and Reuber, 1980) for ethylmethylnitrosamine (134), which causes esophageal and liver cancer in rats. Replacement of the ethyl group by CH_3CD_2 or CD_3CD_2 enhanced the carcinogenicity in feeding experiments whereas replacement of the methyl group by CD_3 or perdeuteration of the molecule did not significantly change the potency. When the modified ethyl group contained CD_3 there was an increased incidence of esophageal tumors.

Farrelly et al. (1982) reported on the metabolism of deuterated n-butylmethylnitrosamine (133, BMN) and ethylmethylnitrosamine (134, EMN) in vitro using liver microsomes (noninduced rats). DIEs of 1.9 and ~5, respectively, were found for the debutylation of d_2-BMN ($CH_3CH_2CH_2CD_2$ group) and demethylation of d_3-BMN (CD_3 group). Using the same procedure a DIE of 2.2 was found for both deethylation of d_2-EMN (CH_3CD_2 group) and demethylation of d_3-EMN (CD_3 group). Yet another trend was found for methylphenylethylnitrosamine (135, MPN). DIEs of 3.2 and 1.35, respectively, were found for dephenylethylation of d_2-MPN ($PhCH_2CD_2$ group) and demethylation of d_3-MPN (CD_3 group). Marked metabolic switching to demethylation was found for d_2-BMN, d_2-EMN, and d_2-MPN.

The foregoing DIEs for BMN (133), EMN (134), and MPN (135) relate to the low-affinity enzyme (Arcos et al., 1977), which probably contributes little to the overall metabolism at the concentrations of dialkylnitrosamines used in feeding experiments. The carcinogenic potencies of d_2-EMN and d_2-MPN (Lijinsky et *al.*, 1982) were higher than those of the corresponding protium forms but this was not so for d_2-BMN.

As would be expected since the mode of action does not involve metabolic activation, no biological DIEs were observed in rat feeding experiments with nitroso-*N*-methylurethane and its CD_3 analog and nitroso-*N*-ethylurethane and its CD_3CD_2 analog (Lijinsky and Reuber, 1982).

6 Miscellaneous Compounds

6.1 ANESTHETICS

6.1.1 Chloroform

An early study (Krantz *et al.*, 1967) showed that, for dogs and mice, exhaled $CDCl_3$ had undergone no D/H exchange and that $CDCl_3$ was somewhat more potent than $CHCl_3$.

Chloroform causes renal and hepatic damage in humans and animals. That the formation of phosgene from chloroform by the process

$$CHCl_3 \rightarrow [HOCCl_3] \rightarrow COCl_2$$

is probably responsible for this damage is indicated by the reduced hepato- and nephrotoxicity of $CDCl_3$ in rats (Pohl and Krishna, 1978; McCarty *et al.*, 1979; Ahmadizadeh *et al.*, 1981). Using liver microsomes (PB-treated rats), Pohl and Krishna (1978) found a DIE of ~1.9 for $CDCl_3$ (based on the yield of phosgene). Serum pyruvic transaminase levels are a reflection of hepatic damage and after administration of $CDCl_3$ to rats the serum level of this enzyme was 38.3 mU/ml compared to values of 56.3 and 24.8 for $CHCl_3$ and controls, respectively (McCarty *et al.*, 1979).

6.1.2 Methoxyflurane

The metabolism of methoxyflurane (MOF) proceeds by two pathways which reflect hydroxylation at the methyl and dichlorodifluoroethyl groups:

Fluoride ion is released only after hydroxylation of the methyl group. Using liver microsomes (PB-treated rats), Hitt *et al.* (1979) showed that the release of fluoride ion from MOF was reduced from 19.6 to 3.8 nmol F$^-$/15 min/mg of protein on tetradeuteration ($\rightarrow$CD$_3$OCF$_2$CDCl$_2$). This corresponds to a DIE of 5.24 (reduced to 1.19 when liver microsomes from noninduced rats were used). The K_m values of MOF and d_4-MOF were similar (13 and 19 μM, respectively).

McCarty *et al.* (1979) noted a 19% *increase* in urinary excretion of fluoride ion in rats after administration of d_1-MOF (CH$_3$OCF$_2$CDCl$_2$) and a 29% *decrease* for d_3-MOF [CD$_3$OCF$_2$CHCl$_2$; cf. 33% for d_4-MOF (CD$_3$OCF$_2$CDCl$_2$)]. These results are suggestive of metabolic switching. However, Baden *et al.* (1982) noted that for rats the serum fluoride levels and renal dysfunction after anesthesia for 2 hr with d_4-MOF were still unacceptable.

6.1.3 Enflurane and Related Compounds

Two metabolism pathways are possible for enflurane (HCF$_2$OCF$_2$CFClH) reflecting attack at the two CH centers. Each pathway could lead to the release of fluoride ion but that leading to HCF$_2$OCF$_2$COOH has been suggested to be the major route (Cousins and Mazze, 1974). For d_1-enflurane (HCF$_2$OCFClD) there was a 65% decrease in excretion of urinary fluoride (McCarty *et al.*, 1979). An even higher reduction (76%) was found for d_1-difluoroflurane (HCF$_2$OCF$_2$CFBrD) and there was a twofold increase in serum bromide. These results accord with expectations if HCF$_2$OCF$_2$COOH is the major metabolite. However, a decrease of 29% was found for d_1-difluoromethoxyflurane (HCF$_2$OCF$_2$CCl$_2$D) and this finding is not readily explained.

6.1.4 Halothane

The metabolism of halothane (CF$_3$CBrClH) can involve dehydrobromination (via hydroxylation $\rightarrow$CF$_3$COCl) and dehydrofluorination ($\rightarrow$CF$_2$=CBrCl) to give products that can undergo further reactions. Each of these routes should be subject to a DIE and after administration of d_1-halothane (CF$_3$CBrClD) to rats there was a 15–26% reduction in serum bromide (McCarty *et al.*, 1979).

6.2 ANTIOXIDANTS

Butylated hydroxytoluene (**136**, BHT, 2,6-di-*tert*-butyl-4-methylphenol) is a widely used antioxidant. It causes lung damage in mice and the covalent binding to lung tissue is probably mediated by the reactive quinone methide metabolite (**137**, BHT-QM, 2,6-di-*tert*-butyl-4-methylene-2,5-cyclohexadienone). Metabolism of BHT (**136**) with 9000 g supernatant of homogenized mouse liver (Mizutani *et al.*, 1983) gave BHT-QM (**137**) and BHT-OH (**138**, 2,6-di-*tert*-butyl-4-hydroxy-4-methyl-2,5-cyclohexadienone). Metabolism of a 1:1 mixture of BHT and d_3-BHT (**139**, CD$_3$ group) resulted in ratios of 0.59 for d_2-BHT-QM/BHT-QM and 1.68 for d_3-BHT-OH/BHT-OH, reflecting metabolic switching.

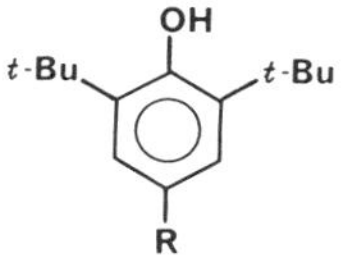

136 R = CH_3

139 R = CD_3

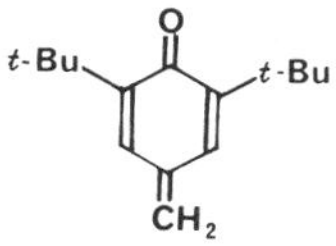

137

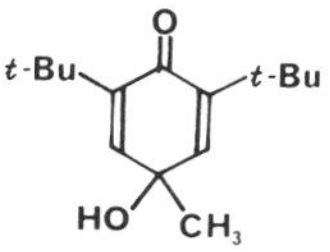

138

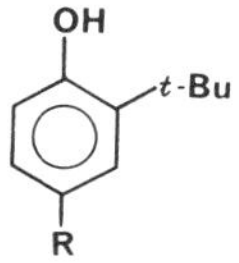

140 R = CH_2CH_3

141 R = CD_2CH_3

142 R = CH_2CD_3

In *in vivo* experiments, it was shown that trideuteration of the methyl group in BHT (→**139**) reduced the pulmonary toxicity. In contrast to the usual practice of studying urinary metabolites, Mizutani *et al.* (1983) investigated the metabolites in lung and liver tissue. Thus, after ip administration of a 1:1 mixture of BHT and d_3-BHT to mice the ratios of d_2-BHT-QM/BHT-QM in lung and liver tissue were 0.66 and 0.85, respectively. The ratios of d_3-BHT-OH/BHT-OH, which had to be obtained by separate administration of d_3-BHT and BHT, were 1.39 and 1.26 for lung and liver tissue, respectively. Hence, the DIE and metabolic switching observed *in vitro* were paralleled *in vivo* and BHT-QM (**137**) is further indicated to be the reactive metabolite of BHT (**136**).

The pulmonary toxicity of 2-*tert*-butyl-4-ethylphenol (**140**) was reduced on replacing the ethyl group with CH_3CD_2 (→**141**) but there was no effect on replacement by CD_3CH_2 (→**142**).

7 Intrinsic and Intramolecular Deuterium Isotope Effects

In contrast to chemical reactions, enzyme-catalyzed reactions display a broad range of DIEs, depending on the reaction conditions. Northrop (1982) has described a family of DIEs associated with the following sequence of events:

$$E + A \rightleftharpoons EA + B \rightleftharpoons EAB \rightleftharpoons {}^*EAB \rightleftharpoons {}^*EPQ \rightleftharpoons EPQ \rightarrow P + EQ \rightarrow Q + E$$

where E is the enzyme, A and B are substrates or substrate and cofactor, P and Q are the products, and * connotes as activated complex. Only two of this family of

DIEs need be considered here, namely, (1) the observed DIE (^Dv), which is dependent on the entire steady-state distribution of enzyme forms and which is usually determined from the ratio of the rates (k_H/k_D) of the disappearance of the protium and deuterium forms under particular conditions of metabolism, and (2) the intrinsic DIE (^Dk), which refers only to the *EAB $\rightleftharpoons$ *EPQ component of the above sequence and, in reflecting the full effect of hydride transfer, is analogous to the DIEs in chemical reactions.

The maximal velocity of most enzyme reactions is dependent on several rate-contributing or partially rate-limiting steps (Northrop, 1982). It is therefore not surprising that, for an enzyme such as cytochrome P-450, which operates by a multistep process (Schenkman and Kupfer, 1982), most of the ^Dv values reported in the literature are lower (range 1–5) than the expected ^Dk values. The variation in ^Dv values is also explicable if not predictable.

Lu et al. (1984) have shown that, for the metabolism (O-deethylation) of 7-ethoxycoumarin (74) and its d_2-derivative 75 with purified cytochrome P-450 from liver microsomes (PB-treated rats), the values of ^Dv and ^Dk were ~3.8 and ~12, respectively. Such a high ^Dk value is consistent with a hydrogen abstraction process (see Section 3.4.2). Although the determination of ^Dk values is important in studies of the mechanism of enzyme action it is the magnitude of the ^Dv values which determines the scope of specific deuterium substitution for controlling drug metabolism.

The ^Dv values reported in this article so far may also be classified as intermolecular in that they have usually been determined by monitoring the relative rates of metabolism of, or the appearance of products from, the protium and deuterium forms either separately in parallel reactions or as a mixture (usually 1:1) in a single reaction. Hjelmeland et al. (1977a) suggested that, for two alternative sites for metabolic attack in the same molecule which differ only in isotopic substitution, the intramolecular DIE associated with the relative rates of reaction at the protonated and deuterated sites should approximate to the ^Dk values. They found an intramolecular DIE of 11 ±1 for the benzylic hydroxylation of 1,3-diphenylpropane (143) and its 1-d_2-derivative 144 with liver microsomes from noninduced rats which contrasts with, for example, the intermolecular DIE of 1.14 for the benzylic hydroxylation of tolbutamide (22) with liver microsomes from PB-treated rats (Tagg et al., 1967).

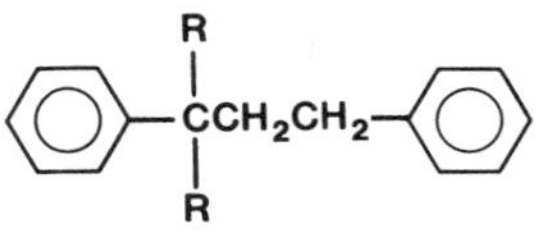

143 R = H

144 R = D

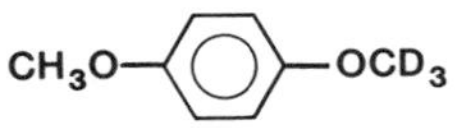

145

Foster *et al.* (1974) reported an intramolecular DIE of ~10 for the O-de-methylation of *p*-(trideuteromethoxy)anisole (**145**) by liver microsomes (PB-treated rats) and an intermolecular DIE of ~2 for *p*-dimethoxybenzene (**68**) and its *p*-di-(trideuteromethoxy) analog. These findings conflict with those of Watanabe *et al.* (1982) using liver microsomes from PB-treated rabbits, who reported inter- and intramolecular DIEs of 5.1 and 3.4, respectively. Hitherto, the highest reported intermolecular DIE for microsomally mediated O-de-methylation was 2.7 for *p*-nitroanisole (Al-Gailany *et al.*, 1975) (see Section 4.1) and it is not easy to explain why the intermolecular DIE has the higher value in the work reported by Wanatabe *et al.* (1982).

Although no DIE was found for the hydroxylation of perdeutercyclohexane (C_6D_{12}) using liver microsomes (PB-treated rats) (Ullrich, 1969), a large k_H/k_D value (8.6) was found for $C_6D_{11}H$ (Castle and Ullrich, 1980). Presumably, most of the hydroxylation occurred at the carbon carrying the single protium substit-uent.

Other examples which could reflect an intramolecular DIE involve α-hydrox-ylation of $S(+)$-α-d_1-ethylbenzene (McMahon *et al.*, 1969) (see Section 3.2) and the N-demethylation of *N*-methyl-*N*-trideuteromethyl-3-phenylpropylamine (**86**) (Abdel-Monem, 1975) and *N*-methyl-*N*-trideuteromethylphentermine (**89**) (Miwa *et al.*, 1980) (Section 5.1).

Although the use of intramolecular competition reactions are of value in determin-ing intrinsic DIEs (^Dk values), there is little scope for their deployment in drug design because of the symmetry requirements. The one type of intramolecular DIE of those so far described which could easily be deployed in drug design, namely, that associated with the replacement of —$N(CH_3)_2$ by —$N(CH_3)CD_3$, has a relatively low magnitude (<2) and would not be expected to cause a marked change in metabolism profile.

8 Conclusions

It is now becoming clear that the scope for using DIEs effectively in drug design to block adverse metabolism or to deflect metabolism away from toxic products (metabolic switching) is very limited although there is little doubt that DIEs will continue to be of value in studies of the mechanism of enzyme action and that specifically deuterated compounds will continue to be used to probe metabolism pathways.

In their excellent review, Blake *et al.* (1975) commented ''At the present time, there are no drugs on the market that contain deuterium in the mole-cule. . . .'' A decade later the situation has not changed and some of the reasons are not difficult to identify. For drugs not intended for use in humans or for products such as insecticides the advantage to be gained by specific or general deuteration in modifying biological activity and/or duration of action must significantly outweigh the additional cost of chemical synthesis. For drugs intended for use in humans there will be a substantial additional cost, namely, that associated with preclinical toxicology and clinical trials. It seems very unlikely that the regulatory authorities associated with the drug industry would regard a deuterated drug designed to have biological activity significantly different from that of the parent protium form as other than a new drug.

References

Abdel-Monem, M. M. (1975). *J. Med. Chem.* **18,** 427–430.

Ahmadizadeh, M., Kuo, C. H., and Hook, J. B. (1981). *J. Toxicol. Environ. Health* **8,** 105–111.

Al-Gailany, K. A. S., Bridges, J. W., and Netter, K. J. (1975). *Biochem. Pharmacol.* **24,** 867–870.

Anders, M. W. (1982). *In* "Metabolic Basis of Detoxification: Metabolism of Functional Groups" (W. B. Jakoby, J. R. Bend, and J. Caldwell, eds.), pp. 29–49. Academic Press, New York.

Arcos, J. C., Davies, D. L., Brown, C. E. L., and Argus, M. F. (1977). *Z. Krebsforsch.* **89,** 181–199.

Baden, J. M., Rice, S. A., and Mazze, R. I. (1982). *Anesthesiology* **56,** 203–206.

Baillie, T. A. (1981). *Pharmacol. Rev.* **33,** 81–132.

Baillie, T. A., Hughes, H., and Davies, D. S. (1982). *In* "Stable Isotopes" (H. L. Schmidt, H. Forstel, and K. Heinzinger, eds.), pp. 187–201. Elsevier, Amsterdam.

Baker, M. H., Foster, A. B., Hegedüs, L., Jarman, M., Rowlands, M. G., Coe, P. L., and Troth, J. (1984). *Biomed. Mass Spectrom.* **10,** 512–521.

Belleau, B., Burba, J., Pindell, M., and Reiffenstein, J. (1961). *Science* **133,** 102–104.

Bigeleisen, J. (1949). *Science* **110,** 14–16.

Björkhem, I. (1971). *Eur. J. Biochem.* **18,** 299–304.

Björkhem, I. (1972). *Eur. J. Biochem.* **27,** 354–363.

Björkhem, I. (1975). *Eur. J. Biochem.* **51,** 137–143.

Björkhem, I. (1977). *Pharmacol. Ther. Part A* **1,** 327–348.

Björkhem, I., and Hamberg, M. (1972). *Biochem. Biophys. Res. Commun.* **47,** 333–340.

Blake, M. I., Crespi, H. L., and Katz, J. J. (1975). *J. Pharm. Sci.* **64,** 367–391.

Bodor, N. (1981a). *Drugs Future* **6,** 165–181.

Bodor, N. (1981b). *In* "Drug Metabolism and Drug Design: Quo Vadis?" (M. Briot, W. Cautreels, and W. Roncucci, eds.), pp. 222–251. Centre de Recherches CLIN MIDY, Montpellier.

Bodor, N. (1984). *Adv. Drug Res.* **13,** 255–331.

Bollinger, F. W., and Wendler, N. L. (1959). *J. Org. Chem.* **24,** 1139.

Burke, T. R., Martin, J. L., George, J. W., and Pohl, L. R. (1980). *Biochem. Pharmacol.* **29,** 1623–1626.

Callery, P. S., Nayar, M. S. B., Geelhaar, L. A., Stogniewm, M., and Jakubowski, E. M. (1980). *Biomed. Mass Spectrom.* **7,** 525–528.

Castle, L., and Ullrich, V. (1980). Data presented at the Priestley Conference, University of Birmingham (U.K.) and quoted by Lindsay Smith, J. R., and Sleath, P. R. (1983).

Charnley, G., and Archer, M. G. (1977). *Mutat. Res.* **46,** 265–268.

Connors, T. A., Cox, P. J., Farmer, P. B., Foster, A. B., and Jarman, M. (1974). *Biochem. Pharmacol.* **23,** 115–129.

Cook, P. F., and Cleland, W. W. (1981). *Biochemistry* **20,** 1805–1816.

Cousins, M. J., and Mazze, R. I. (1974). *Int. Anesthesiol. Clin.* **12,** 111–119.

Dagani, D., and Archer, M. C. (1976). *J. Natl. Cancer Inst.* **57,** 955–957.

Dagne, E., Gruenke, L., and Castagnoli, N. (1974). *J. Med. Chem.* **17**, 1330–1333.

Daly, J., Jerina, D., and Witkop, B. (1968). *Arch. Biochem. Biophys.* **128**, 517–527.

Daly, J., Jerina, D., Farnsworth, J., and Guroff, G. (1969). *Arch. Biochem. Biophys.* **131**, 238–244.

Dourisch, C. T., Dewar, K. M., Dyck, L. E., and Boulton, A. A. (1983). *Psychopharmacology* **81**, 122–125.

Dumont, P., Poupaert, J. H., de Laey, P., and Claesen, M. (1981). *J. Pharmacol. Belg.* **36**, 21–26.

Dyck, L. E., Durden, D. A., Yu, P. H., Davies, B. A., and Boulton, A. A. (1983). *Biochem. Pharmacol.* **32**, 1519–1522.

Edmondson, D., Ballou, D., van Heuvelen, A., Palmer, G., and Massey, V. (1973). *J. Biol. Chem.* **248**, 6135–6144.

Egan, R. M., Matherly, L. H., and Phillips, A. T. (1981). *Biochemistry* **20**, 132–137.

Elespura, R. K. (1978). *Mutat. Res.* **54**, 265–270.

Elison, C., Rapoport, H., Laursen, R., and Elliot, W. H. (1961). *Science* **134**, 1078–1079.

Elison, C., Elliot, H. W., Look, M., and Rapoport, H. (1963). *J. Med. Chem.* **6**, 237–246.

El Tayar, N., van de Waterbeemd, H., Gryllaki, M., Testa, B. and Trager, W. F. (1984). *Int. J. Pharm.* **19**, 271–281.

Farelly, J. G., Stewart, M. L., Saavedra, J. E., and Lijinsky, W. (1982). *Cancer Res.* **42**, 2105–2109.

Farmer, P. B., Foster, A. B., and Jarman, M. (1975). *Biomed. Mass Spectrom.* **2**, 107–111.

Farmer, P. B., Foster, A. B., Jarman, M., Oddy, M. R., and Reed, D. J. (1978). *J. Med. Chem.* **21**, 514–520.

Farmer, P. B., Foster, A. B., Jarman, M., Newell, D. R., Oddy, M. R., and Kiburis, J. H. (1979). *Chem. Biol. Interact.* **28**, 211–224.

Feldman, R. I., and Weiner, H. (1972). *J. Biol. Chem.* **247**, 267–272.

Foreman, R. L., Siegel, F. P., and Mrtek, R. G. (1969). *J. Pharm. Sci.* **58**, 189–191.

Foster, A. B., Jarman, M., Stevens, J. D., Thomas, P., and Westwood, J. H. (1974). *Chem. Biol. Interact.* **9**, 327–340.

Frommer, U., Ullrich, V., Staudinger, H., and Orrenius, S. (1972). *Biochim. Biophys. Acta* **280**, 487–494.

Fry, J. R., and Bridges, J. W. (1977). *Prog. Drug Metab.* **2**, 71–118.

Gaffney, T. E., Knapp, D., Walle, T., Privitera, P., and Saelens, D. (1974). *South. Med. J.* **67**, 990–1002.

Garland, W. A., Nelson, S. D., and Sasame, H. A. (1976). *Biochem. Biophys. Res. Commun.* **72**, 539–544.

Gelb, M. H., Heimbrook, D. C., Malkonen, P., and Sliger, S. G. (1982). *Biochemistry* **21**, 370–377.

Gorumaru, T., Furuta, T., Baba, S., Noda, A., and Iguchi, S. (1981). *Yakugaku Zasshi* **101**, 544–547.

Gregg, C. T. (1974). *Eur. J. Clin. Pharmacol.* **7**, 315–319.

Groves, J. T., McClusky, G. A., White, R. E., and Coon, M. J. (1978). *Biochem. Biophys. Res. Commun.* **81**, 154–160.

Groves, J. T., Krishnan, S., Avaria, G. E., and Nemo, T. E. (1980). *Adv. Chem. Ser.* **191**, 277–289.

Halliday, D., and Lockhart, I. M. (1978). *Prog. Med. Chem.* **15**, 1–73.

Hamberg, M., and Björkhem, I. (1971). *J. Biol. Chem.* **24**, 7411–7416.

Hansch, C., and Leo, A. (1979). "Substituent Constants for Correlation Analysis in Chemistry and Biology," pp. 18–43. Wiley, New York.

Haskins, N. J. (1982). *Biomed. Mass Spectrom.* **9**, 269–277.

Henderson, P. T., Vree, T. B., van Ginneken, C. A. M., and van Rossum, J. M. (1974). *Xenobiotica* **4**, 121–130.

Hitt, B. A., Mazze, R. I., and Denson, D. D. (1979). *Drug Metab. Dispos.* **7**, 446–447.

Hjelmeland, L. M., Aronow, L., and Trudell, J. R. (1977a). *Biochem. Biophys. Res. Commun.* **76**, 541–549.

Hjelmeland, L. M., Aronow, L., and Trudell, J. R. (1977b). *Mol. Pharmacol.* **13**, 634–639.

Horie, T., Ohno, T., and Kinoshita, K. (1981). *Xenobiotica* **11**, 197–206.

Horie, T., Kinoshita, K., Kitada, M., and Kitagawa, H. (1983). *Abstr. Int. Symp. Foreign Compound Metab. 1st, West Palm Beach Oct. 30–Nov. 4* p. 35.

Horning, M. G., Haegele, K. D., Sommer, K. R., Nowlin, J., Stafford, M., and Thenot, J. P. (1976). *Proc. Int. Conf. Stable Isotopes, 2nd* NTIS, *Springfield,* Va. CON-751027, pp. 41–54.

Horning, M. G., Lertratanangkoon, K., Haegele, K. D., and Brendel, K. (1978). *In* "Stable Isotopes. Applications in Pharmacology, Toxicology, and Clinical Research" (E. R. Klein and P. D. Klein, eds.), pp. 55–64. Macmillan, New York.

Horning, M. G., Nowlin, J., Thenot, J. P., and Bousma, O. J. (1979). *In* "Stable Isotopes" (E. R. Klein and P. D. Klein, eds.), pp. 379–384. Academic Press, New York.

Hoskins, J. A., and Farmer, P. B. (1982). *In* "Stable Isotopes" (H. L. Schmidt, H. Förstel, and K. Heinzinger, eds.), pp. 223–228. Elsevier, Amsterdam.

Jarman, M., and Foster, A. B. (1978). *Adv. Pharmacol. Ther.* **7**, 225–233.

Jarman, M., Kiburis, J. H., Elion, G. B., Knick, V. C., Lambe, G., Nelson, D. J., and Tuttle, R. L. (1982). *In* "Stable Isotopes" (H. L. Schmidt, H. Förstel, and K. Heinzinger, eds.), pp. 217–222. Elsevier, Amsterdam.

Jefcoate, C. R. (1983). *In* "Biological Basis of Detoxification" (J. Caldwell and W. B. Jakoby, eds.), pp. 31–76. Academic Press, New York.

Keefer, L. K., Lijinsky, W., and Garcia, H. (1973). *J. Natl. Cancer Inst.* **51**, 299–302.

Kimbrough, R. D. (1972). *J. Med. Chem.* **15**, 409–410.

Knapp, D. R., and Gaffney, T. E. (1972). *Clin. Pharmacol. Ther.* **13**, 307–316.

Knapp, D. R., Gaffney, T. E., and Compson, K. R. (1973). *Adv. Biochem. Psychopharmacol.* **7**, 83–91.

Kollonitsch, J., and Barasch, L. (1976). *J. Am. Chem. Soc.* **98**, 5591–5593.

Kramer, A., Staudinger, H., and Ullrich, V. (1974). *Chem. Biol. Interact.* **8**, 11–18.

Krantz, J. C., Koski, W. S., and Loecher, C. K. (1967). *Biochem. Pharmacol.* **16**, 603–604.

Kroeger-Koepke, M. B., and Michejda, C. J. (1979). *Cancer Res.* **39**, 1587–1591.

Kurihara, N., Suzuki, T., and Nakajima, M. (1980). *Pestic. Biochem. Physiol.* **14**, 41–49.

Kutter, E., and Garett, E. R. (1970). Unpublished results cited by Hansch, C., and Kerley, R. (1970). *J. Med. Chem.* **13**, 957–964.

Kutter, E., and Machleidt, H. (1971). *J. Med. Chem.* **14**, 931–934.

Lai, D. Y., and Arcos, J. C. (1980). *Life Sci.* **27**, 2149–2165.

Lemieux, R. U., Sporek, K. F., O'Reilly, I., and Nelson, E. (1961). *Biochem. Pharmacol.* **7**, 31–34.

Lijinsky, W., and Reuber, M. D. (1980). *Cancer Res.* **40**, 19–21.

Lijinsky, W., and Reuber, M. D. (1982). *Cancer Lett.* **16**, 273–279.

Lijinsky, W., Reuber, M. D., Saavedra, J. E., and Blackwell, B. N. (1980a). *Carcinogenesis* **1**, 157–160.

Lijinsky, W., Saavedra, J. E., Reuber, M. D., and Blackwell, B. N. (1980b). *Cancer Lett.* **10**, 325–331.

Lijinsky, W., Reuber, M. D., Davies, T. S., Saavedra, J. E., and Riggs, C. W. (1982). *Food Chem. Toxicol.* **20**, 393–399.

Lindsay Smith, J. R., and Sleath, P. R. (1983). *J. Chem. Soc. Perkin Trans.* **11**, 621–628.

Lindsay Smith, J. R., Piggott, R. E., and Sleath, P. R. (1982). *J. Chem. Soc. Chem. Commun.* 55–56.

Lu, A. Y. H., Harada, N., and Miwa, G. T. (1984). *Xenobiotica* **14**, 19–26.

McCarty, L. P., Malek, R. S., and Larsen, E. R. (1979). *Anesthesiology* **51**, 106–110.

McMahon, R. E., Sullivan, H. R., Craig, J. C., and Pereira, W. E. (1969). *Arch. Biochem. Biophys.* **132**, 575–577.

McMahon, R. E., Turner, J. C., Whitaker, G. W., and Sullivan, H. R. (1981). *Biochem. Biophys. Res. Commun.* **99**, 662–667.

Marcotte, P. A., and Robinson, C. H. (1982). *Biochemistry* **21**, 2773–2778.

Marcucci, F., Mussini, E., Martelli, P., Guaitani, A., and Garratini, S. (1973). *J. Pharm. Sci.* **62**, 1900–1902.

Mark, L. C., Brand, L., Heiver, S., and Perel, J. M. (1971). *Fed. Proc. Fed. Am. Soc. Exp. Biol.* **30**, 442.

May, H. E., Boose, R., and Reed, D. J. (1975). *Biochemistry* **14**, 4723–4730.

Mazel, P., Henderson, J. F., and Axelrod, J. (1964). *J. Pharmacol. Exp. Ther.* **143**, 1–6.

Miller, S. M., and Klinman, J. P. (1982). *In* "Methods in Enzymology" (D. L. Purich, ed.), vol. 87, pp. 711–732. Academic Press, New York.

Mitoma, C., Yasuda, D. M., Tagg, J., and Tanabe, M. (1967). *Biochim. Biophys. Acta* **136**, 566–567.

Mitoma, C., Dehn, R. L., and Tanabe, M. (1971). *Biochim. Biophys. Acta* **237**, 21–27.

Miwa, G. T., Garland, W. A., Hodshon, B. J., Lu, A. Y. H., and Northrop, D. B. (1980). *J. Biol. Chem.* **255**, 6049–6054.

Mizutani, T., Yamamoto, K., and Tajima, K. (1983). *Toxicol. Appl. Pharmacol.* **69**, 283–290.

Moustafa, M. A. A., Claesen, M., Adline, J., Vandervorst, D., and Poupaert, J. H. (1983). *Drug Metab. Dispos.* **11**, 574–580.

Nelson, S. D., and Pohl, L. R. (1977). *Annu. Rep. Med. Chem.* **12**, 319–330.

Nelson, S. D., Pohl, L. R., and Trager, W. F. (1975). *J. Med. Chem.* **18**, 1062–1065.

Northrop, D. B. (1982). *In* "Methods in Enzymology" (D. L. Purich, ed.), Vol. 87, pp. 607–641. Academic Press, New York.

Ophang, R. H., and Singer, L. (1980). *Proc. Soc. Exp. Biol. Med.* **163**, 19–23.

Ortiz de Montellano, P. R., and Kunze, K. L. (1981). *Arch. Biochem. Biophys.* **209**, 710–712.

Pang, K. S., Waller, L. S., Horning, M. G., and Chan, K. K. (1982). *J. Pharmacol. Exp. Ther.* **222**, 14–19.

Perel, J. M., Dayton, P. G., Tauriello, C. L., Brand, L., and Mark, L. C. (1967). *J. Med. Chem.* **10**, 371–374.

Perel, J. M., Dawson, D. K., Dayton, P. G., and Goldberg, L. J. (1972). *J. Med. Chem.* **15**, 714–716.

Pohl, L. R., and Krishna, G. (1978). *Life Sci.* **23**, 1067–1072.

Portig, J., Kraus, P., Stein, K., Koransky, W., Noack, G., Gross, B., and Sodoman, S. (1979). *Xenobiotica* **9**, 353–378.

Reifenrath, W. G., Roche, E. B., Al-Turk, W. A., and Johnson, H. L. (1980). *J. Med. Chem.* **23**, 985–990.

Reinsch, J., Katz, A., Wean, J., Aprahamian, G., and McFarland, J. J. (1980). *J. Biol. Chem.* **255**, 9093–9097.

Ringold, H. J., Burstein, S., and Dorfman, R. I. (1961). *Nature (London)*. **191**, 1294–1295.

Sarcione, E. J., and Stutzman, L. A. (1960). *Cancer Res.* **20**, 387–392.

Schenkman, J. B., and Kupfer, D., eds. (1982). "Hepatic Cytochrome P450 Mono-oxygenase System." Pergamon, Oxford.

Singer, G. M., and Lijinsky, W. (1979). *Cancer Lett.* **8**, 29–34.

Soboren, J., Yasuda, D. M., Tanabe, M., and Mitoma, C. (1965). *Fed. Proc. Fed. Am. Soc. Exp. Biol.* **24**, 427.

Stenlake, J. B., and Dhar, N. C. (1978). *Eur. J. Med. Chem.* **13**, 343–346.

Tagg, J., Yasuda, D. M., Tanabe, M., and Mitoma, C. (1967). *Biochem. Pharmacol.* **16**, 143–153.

Tanabe, M., Yasuda, D. M., LeValley, S., and Mitoma, C. (1969). *Life Sci.* **8,** 1123–1128.

Tanaka, K., Kurihara, N., and Nakajima, M. (1976). *Pestic. Biochem. Physiol.* **6,** 386–391.

Tanaka, N., and Thornton, E. R. (1976). *J. Am. Chem. Soc.* **98,** 1617–1619.

Taylor, J. A. (1973). *Xenobiotica* **3,** 151–164.

Teitelbaum, P. J., Chu, N. I., Cho, D., Tokes, L., Patterson, J. W., Wagner, P. J., and Chaplin, M. D. (1981). *J. Pharmacol. Exp. Ther.* **218,** 16–22.

Testa, B., and Jenner, P. (1976). "Drug Metabolism: Chemical and Biochemical Aspects." Dekker, New York.

Testa, B., and Jenner, P. (1978). *Drug Metab. Rev.* **7,** 325–369.

Thompson, J. A., and Holtzman, J. L. (1974). *Drug Metab. Dispos.* **2,** 577–582.

Tomaszewski, J. E., Jerina, D. M., and Daly, J. W. (1975). *Biochemistry* **14,** 2024–2031.

Ullrich, V. (1969). *Hoppe-Seyler's Z. Physiol. Chem.* **350,** 357–365.

Ullrich, V., and Diehl, H. (1971). *Eur. J. Biochem.* **20,** 509–512.

Vree, T. B., Gorgels, J. P. M. C., Muskens, A. T. J. M., and van Rossum, J. M. (1971). *Clin. Chim. Acta* **34,** 333–344.

Watanabe, Y., Oae, S., and Iyanagi, T. (1982). *Bull. Chem. Soc. Jpn.* **55,** 188–195.

Wiberg, K. B. (1955). *Chem. Rev.* **55,** 713–743.

Wolfsberg, M. (1982). *In* "Stable Isotopes" (H. L. Schmidt, H. Förstel, and K. Heinzinger, eds.), pp. 3–14. Elsevier, Amsterdam.

Yu, P. H., Barclay, S., Davis, B., and Boulton, A. A. (1981). *Biochem. Pharmacol.* **30,** 3089–3094.

Drug Design in Three Dimensions

N. CLAUDE COHEN

Ciba-Geigy Ltd., Pharmaceutical Division, Basel, Switzerland

ADVANCES IN DRUG RESEARCH, VOL. 14
0-12-013314-8

1 Introduction

Ever since the beginning of time practitioners of the healing art have been interested in the therapeutic properties of substances found in our environment. This interest has induced them to seek a deeper understanding of the structure of matter and that of vital processes. Although not entirely aware of the subtle organization of Nature, man aims to relate it to his own intelligent rationale and aspires to have some control over it. The possibilities now available in drug research permit us to envisage feasible new ways of working because molecular biology reveals how biological function is embedded in molecular structure. Moreover it helps us to explain diseases in molecular terms.

These discoveries have widened the horizons of drug research in allowing us to understand how the key to the efficacy of some drugs is to be found in their stereochemical and structural three-dimensional features. In this perspective the availability of computerized simulators of molecules will provide in the next decade a useful way of advancing in medicinal chemistry.

The aim of this article is to show in which direction the rational design of drugs is now developing in medicinal chemistry and how ongoing efforts of "molecular modelists" toward the design of new lead structures are going to influence traditional research methods in this area. A new generation of rationally developed drugs is already in preparation. Computerized drug design in three dimensions participates in the conception of new molecules with high information content as the fruit of intensive multidisciplinary scientific effort. Multiple structural, biological, and clinical parameters are taken into account. These, along with the efficacy of the human effort involved, offer good chances of success.

2 Scope and Limitations

2.1 HOW NEW MOLECULES ARE CONCEIVED

A layman is generally surprised to learn that medicinal chemists would often be unable to conceive a new molecule if they were not aware of the chemical structures of compounds already known to be active in the therapeutic area concerned. This is, in fact, a strong constraint. Medicinal chemists need reference molecules and generally prefer to remain close to the known chemical formulas of these substances rather than to create entirely new chemical entities. In fact, it is also possible to envisage drug design in a way where the new molecules are conceived on the basis of steric and electronic complementarity with the receptor sites. The rapid progress in molecular biology and in the X-ray crystallography of proteins provides deep insight into the macromolecular processes involved and appears to be of great potential interest in drug research in the sense that these approaches may facilitate the rational design of new, original lead structures in a different way than that prevailing in previous decades.

2.2 CLASSICAL DESIGN

Until now, practical efforts have been concentrated on the design of analogs of known structures. An example of this very common way of proceeding is illustrated by the following molecules, where the knowledge of the chemical structure of propranolol (**1**), for example, permitted the design of pindolol (**2**). An-

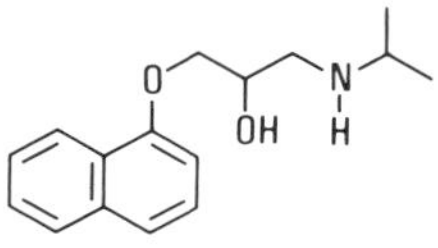

(1)   propranolol 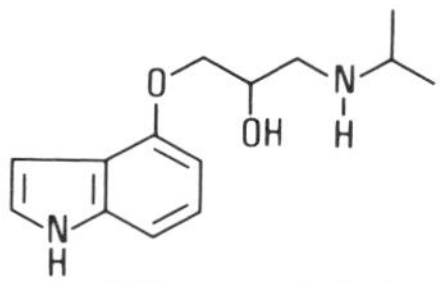   (2)   pindolol

other, but very similar working method in medicinal chemistry is to introduce, replace or suppress chemical fragments such as rings, side chains, etc., in the chemical structures of a known active compound.

For example, the knowledge of the chemical structure of bromocriptine (**3**) may inspire the design of simplified topological analogs such as **4**.

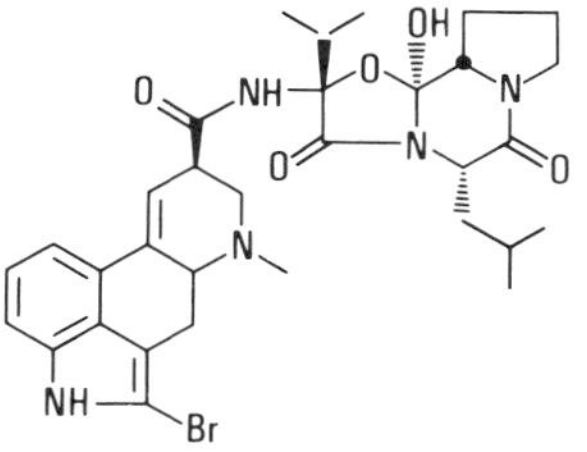

(3)   bromocriptin 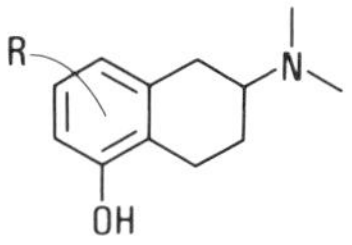   (4)

Originality is a constant preoccupation for both chemists and pharmacologists involved in pharmaceutical research, and the results obtained have to be continuously compared with those of the best known reference compounds. The more the field is explored, the more difficult it is to achieve originality in both chemical structures and biological activities.

Particularly in the approach outlined above, the criterion of originality of the chemical formulas cannot easily be satisfied, as the designed compounds always remain topological analogs of known molecules. When molecules are considered in three dimensions, it becomes possible to avoid falling into this trap or at least to reduce the effects of a strong attraction toward known structures.

With this approach, medicinal chemistry may find a new working method

permitting the discovery of new therapeutic agents and a more rigorous design of
molecular structures.

2.3 BEYOND THE TWO-DIMENSIONAL CHEMICAL STRUCTURE

Molecular biology reveals to us how biological function is embedded in molecular structure. The ''lock and key'' considerations provide attractive practical
concepts capable of widening the medicinal chemist's horizons. These ideas
enable one to understand how, in biological systems, the 3-D specificity of
molecular interactions can define the principles of molecular recognition and
molecular discrimination. Such fundamental keys to the understanding of life
processes stress the crucial importance of 3-D stereochemical features and offer
an operational way of working in medicinal chemistry.

Such considerations have been widely used to rationalize results already observed, yet the number of research groups which use 3-D drug design systematically to discover new lead structures is very limited. The approach may merely
be used as a guide through a classical stepwise modification of the structure of a
known active compound. When applied in this way, the methodology is conceptually not very different from the classical one; the only difference is that the
similarity principle is not applied only to analogies between chemical formulas,
but mainly to analogies in three dimensions. For example, molecule **6** could have
been designed in this perspective from the knowledge of the 3-D structure of
cimetidine (**5**). Both compounds have anti-H_2 activities and potent antiulcer

(5) cimetidine   (6)

properties. Their chemical formulas are very different and it is not possible to
design compound **6** merely on the basis of the chemical formula of molecule **5.**
In contrast, when the 3-D aspects are considered, the design appears as perfectly
conceivable and it is shown in Fig. 1 how both compounds may conform in terms
of similar 3-D features (Lipinski, 1983).

This example illustrates one important possibility of 3-D drug design, namely
that it permits the creation of original chemical entities whose 2-D chemical
structures differ very much from that of the parent molecule but which exhibit 3-
D structural similarity to the reference molecules.

Another and more ambitious way of using the 3-D drug design approach
consists of envisaging an *ab initio* drug design perspective when the stereochemical features of the receptor sites involved are known in great detail.
Controlled 3-D chemical entities can therefore be designed for direct and optimal
interaction with the receptor site. This new approach of great potential interest is

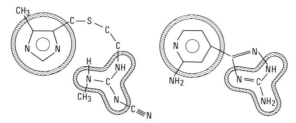

FIG. 1. Possible 3-D similarities between molecules **5** (cimetidine) and **6**. (Adapted from Lipinski, 1983.)

going to be of practical utility in the next decade since our knowledge of the 3-D structure of macromolecules and proteins is rapidly growing. Although such information is generally not yet available in most current research projects, it remains possible to design drugs in a conceptually similar perspective where a surrogate of the receptor site is envisaged and materialized through a ''model'' either representing a working hypothesis of an active site, or constructed from stereochemical features of known active compounds. Examples of successfully designed molecules based on each of these approaches will be discussed in due place in this article.

2.4 COMPUTERIZED MOLECULAR DESIGN

Preliminary successes have prompted pharmaceutical companies to develop extensive computerized molecular design projects. This new way of working enables the structural possibilities of hypothetical (unsynthesized) compounds to be fully examined and therefore allows one to evaluate whether they conform to the desired requirements (working hypotheses or precise complementarity with a receptor site as previously outlined).

This way of working was already possible with the use of computerized quantitative structure–activity relationship (QSAR) approaches which enabled one to predict the activities of analogs prior to their synthesis. However, these methods only permit the optimization of a known family of compounds; they do not allow one to go beyond the common chemical frame of the particular family analyzed.

In the last decades, great efforts have been made to escape from classical drug manipulation and optimization. Together with rapid progress in theoretical calculations and in X-ray crystallography, an increasing number of computerized systems of great utility in drug design were developed, as reviewed in Section 3.4.

Existing systems, together with those now in development, show that the next decade will witness some modifications of the pharmaceutical chemist's ideal profile. It is probable that a new generation of ''molecular modelists,'' consisting of medicinal chemists with great aptitude to consider and design new 3-D entities, will appear. The new molecules will carry higher "information content."

2.5 LIMITATIONS

However sophisticated drug design will be in medicinal chemistry, it will always remain an experimental science obeying the unavoidable process of successive trials and errors. The aim of the so-called rational approaches is to reduce the part of empiricism in drug research to the very minimum. Several years ago, considerable effort was necessary to overcome the reluctance of medicinal chemists concerning the utility of computerized approaches in drug design. Today there are no longer false expectations from these approaches, and enthusiasm becomes more common. Although the initial psychological difficulties have been swept away, the inherent limitations in drug research still remain. In addition to methodological approximations in the activities themselves (animal species, selected organs, metabolism, passage of barriers, etc.), the way of evaluating molecular properties also induces some limitations. For example, X-ray data or any model concerning the active site of an enzyme or a given molecule unavoidably introduce approximations. Molecules exist very often in multiple conformations; the predominant form, even in solution, may not be the one which is actually bound, and bound forms may quite well be of high energy. Also connected to 3-D drug design is the fact that two molecules can be compared only if they both act at the same level and with the same mechanism of action. In the same perspective the way the biological activities are measured should be as far as possible directly connected to the relevant mechanism of action and, in particular, *in vitro* studies are highly preferable in the early stage of the design. Those who have not yet seen the humorous drawing presented by Mautner several years ago are invited to look at it and to remember that it can be dangerous in a multicomponent system to extrapolate "from the shape of a drop of water, the shape of the keyhole of a door" (Mautner, 1974).

Computerized approaches are not a panacea. They are just an instrument permitting an increase in the molecular modelist's creativity, allowing him to conceive "intelligent" molecules with which he may have more control in terms of their molecular features.

3 The Molecular Modelist's Panoply

3.1 GENERAL CONSIDERATIONS

One of the masterpieces of the molecular modelist's panoply is the availability of practical ways permitting the rapid geometrical analysis of isolated, superimposed, or interacting molecules. The simplicity of use and the availability of commercial kits such as Dreiding or Corey–Pauling–Koltun (CPK) models explain their wide use by chemists all over the world. They have the great advantage of being very easy to manipulate, but they suffer from serious disadvantages in the quality of the information they provide, and they cannot be used beyond precise limits which may be detrimental to the user or even be ignored by him. They may be excellent stimulators of the chemist's creativity but may lead down a blind alley those who are not aware of their limitations and of their directions for use. When associated with good experimental or theoretical analysis, molecular models become an excellent accessory for the understanding of 3-D features. Computerized molecular modeling systems can considerably widen the possibilities of molecular models, particularly when they are associated with efficient molecular graphics systems.

3.2 EXPERIMENTAL DATA AND THEORETICAL CALCULATIONS

Experimentally, X-ray crystallography is the most direct way of studying molecular geometries. The Cambridge crystallographic data base (Kennard *et al.*, 1975) constitutes a useful data bank for search and retrieval purposes. Systematic analysis of 3-D substructure features (Allen *et al.*, 1979, 1983; Murray-Rust and Motherwell, 1978; Wilson and Huffman, 1980) now becomes possible. However, one should never forget that a molecule in the solid state may not correctly represent its real possibilities when it participates in complex biological processes. This drawback has often been compensated with additional studies of the molecule either in solution or by using theoretical simulations. There is actually no unique technique capable of providing a complete knowledge of a molecule's conformational possibilities in different aggregate states and different environments.

3.3 CRYSTALLOGRAPHIC DATA BANKS

Associated with the current molecular modeling systems outlined in the next paragraph, a number of computerized data banks are now of common utility in providing 3-D data for a great variety of molecules and macromolecules. These data banks are generally X-ray crystallography based, the more widely used sources being the Cambridge Crystallography Data (Kennard *et al.*, 1975) for small molecules and the protein data bank (Bernstein *et al.*, 1977) for biological macromolecules. The former contains more than 30,000 structures whereas only 50 can be found in the latter. Both data banks are continuously fed, therefore strengthening the quality of the information they provide. A number of additional proteins, not available from the protein data bank, have now been solved and the corresponding coordinates may be generally obtained directly from the scientists concerned. In practice, the molecular modelist must select those which seem most appropriate for his analysis and must find the good combination of different techniques which may help him to reveal the relevant 3-D entities of possible biological significance.

Concerning theoretical calculations, great progress has been made in the last few years for analyzing the conformational possibilities of molecules. There are two sets of methods: those using molecular orbital (MO) calculations (*ab initio* and semiempirical MO), and those using molecular mechanics simulation procedures. The scope and the limitations of these methods have been repeatedly reviewed, as summarized by Osawa and Musso (1982). The major source of programs of this type remains the quantum chemistry program exchange (QCPE, Indiana University, Bloomington, Indiana) where most programs can be easily obtained. Since *ab initio* methods require a large computer memory and also great amounts of computing time, this explains why the semiempirical MO calculations are more popular nowadays. Among these one should mention the CNDO/2 (Pople and Segal, 1966), PCILO (Diner *et al.*, 1969a,b), MNDO (Dewar, 1969; Dewar and Ford, 1979), PRDDO (Halgren *et al.*, 1978), and EHT methods (Hoffmann, 1963).

As regards the very cheap molecular mechanics calculations, they have a number of additional advantages, including simplicity, accuracy, and speed, and are now the "best sellers" for 3-D calculations (Osawa and Musso, 1982). These methods consider a molecule as consisting of an assembly of balls and springs submitted to intramolecular forces as expressed through appropriate potential energy functions. Initial rough geometries of the molecule are submitted to relaxation treatments in order to obtain the geometries' minimum energies on the conformational potential surface. Among the most used programs are MM2 (Allinger, 1977; Allinger and Yuh, 1980a), MMI/MMPI (Wertz and Allinger, 1974; Allinger and Sprague, 1973; Allinger and Yuh, 1980b), BIGSTRN (Andose *et al.*, 1980), and CAMSEQ (Weintraub, 1975, 1979; Weintraub and Hopfinger, 1975). Some efforts are also made to include the solvent effect in such calculations (Hopfinger, 1971; Weintraub, 1979).

3.4 MOLECULAR MODELING BASED ON COMPUTER GRAPHICS

3.4.1 Current Molecular Modeling Systems

In addition to these now classical theoretical calculations, extensive computerized molecular modeling systems have been developed in pharmaceutical companies, universities, and research institutes. Beyond the use of particular programs, these systems were conceived in combination with molecular graphic terminals facilitating the manipulation and the visualization of isolated or interacting 3-D dynamic structures. These systems also permit the molecular features of various active molecules to be compared in order to reveal common stereochemical features ("indirect drug design"). Some new techniques are now opening up the way to the study of enzyme specificity and enzyme regulation in terms of the fundamental intermolecular forces governing these processes. In this perspective it will become possible to design specific effector ligands for known receptors (*ab initio*, Cushman and Ondetti, 1982, or "direct drug design") by simulating the ligand's 3-D dynamic properties and energetics of interaction with the putative receptor (Dauber *et al.*, 1982).

One of the great advantages of molecular modeling systems is that the study of as yet unknown molecules becomes possible: the molecular possibilities of hypothetical compounds can be studied and their synthesis envisaged only if they conform to the desired requirements.

Most of the molecular modeling systems used in drug design have the same philosophy, being generally conceived either for allowing the comparison of rather small molecules (i.e., less than 200 atoms) or for permitting the docking of a ligand with a macromolecule. Their aim is to provide efficient ways for studying the conformational possibilities of the molecules analyzed and they permit not only the manipulation and the visualization of 3-D entities but also the calculation of additional structural properties associated with the molecular structure (energies, charge densities, surfaces, volumes, molecular potential electrostatic contours, etc.). The following systems have been developed recently:

MMMS: Merck Sharp & Dohme (Gund *et al.*, 1980)
MMSX: Washington University (Marshall *et al.*, 1979)
PROPHET/CAMSEQ: NIH (Rindone and Kush, 1980; Weintraub and Hopfinger, 1975)
MOLOCH-3: Searle (Nordby and Hodges, 1975)
TRIBBLE: du Pont (Pensak, 1979)
SCRIPT: Roussel Uclaf (Cohen *et al.*, 1981)
AMBER: University of California, San Francisco (Weiner and Kollman, 1981)

Some of the systems currently used by other groups have also been outlined in various meetings, e.g., those existing at Lederle (Carhart *et al.*, 1981), Eli Lilly (Boyd and Marsh, 1982), SKF (Cramer, 1982), and Abbott (O'Donnel *et al.*, 1982). Others are becoming commercially available, such as MACCS and associated CHEMLAB II software (Molecular Design, Limited), PROPHET (Rindone and Kush, 1980), TRIPOS (Tripos Assoc., St. Louis, Missouri), etc. The reader should refer to specialized articles where some of these systems are described (Humblet and Marshall, 1981; Gund *et al.*, 1980; Marshall *et al.*, 1974). A comprehensive bibliography for molecular graphics can be found in the article by Morffew (1983).

Molecular modeling systems oriented toward the manipulation of macromolecular entities and allowing the understanding of ligand–receptor stereochemical complementarities, and electronic or energetic implications, are now in continuous progress (Langridge, 1980; Langridge *et al.*, 1981; Cole *et al.*, 1979; Meyer, 1980; Jones, 1978, 1982).

With a view to visualize the utility of current molecular modeling systems, the author would like to illustrate with a practical example the possibilities now available for the treatment of small molecules. Molecular modeling concerned with docking experiments will be reviewed in Sections 5 and 6.

3.4.2 Examples of Molecular Modeling

a. Single Molecular Modeling Study: Analysis of Pleurotin. Pleurotin (**7**) is an antibiotic substance produced by the fungus *Pleurotus griseus,* and the knowledge of its conformational possibilities could be of some interest for the design of new antibiotics in this area. The molecule is used here to illustrate the possibilities of existing molecular modeling systems. The systematic enumeration and generation of the various conformational possibilities of complicated chiral moieties having fused, polycyclic, spiro, or bridged ring fragments can now be automatically treated by the system SCRIPT (Cohen *et al.*, 1981). This operation is not possible in most existing molecular modeling systems, which require a geometrical input and lead to only one conformation of the molecule.

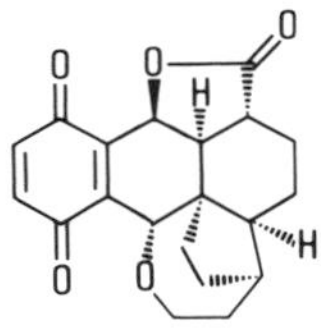

(7)   pleurotin

The study starts with the drawing of the chemical formula on the first panel board shown in Fig. 2. It is drawn with the aid of a joystick which is equivalent to an electronic light pen. Figure 3 shows what the screen looks like when the chemical formula is complete. Then by striking the "conformer" control one asks for the construction of the various possible conformations. In the SCRIPT system two levels have been defined, and there is a hierarchy as far as the stability of the elementary ring conformations are considered: the more stable forms of the rings are stored in level 1 (e.g., the chair form for saturated six-membered rings); and in level 2, the less stable ones (e.g., twist or boat). For rings endowed with possible pseudorotating movements only one form is defined in level 1 and the other pseudorotamers are in level 2. In the SCRIPT molecular modeling system, level 2 is activated only upon request; otherwise the standard option corresponds to level 1.

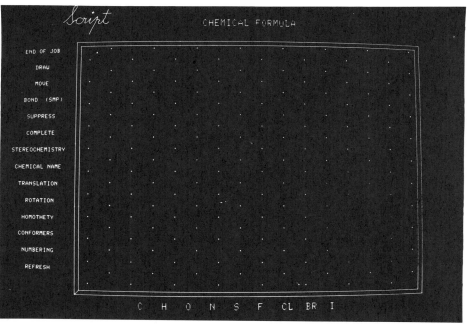

Fig. 2. SCRIPT molecular modeling system: the first panel board.

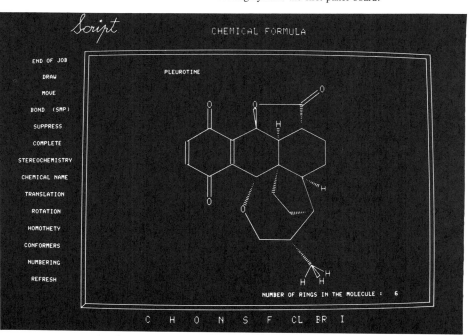

Fig. 3. The drawing of the chemical formula is complete.

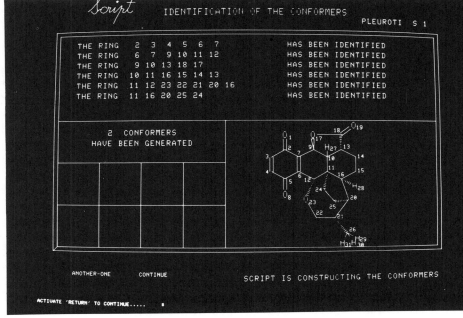

FIG. 4. Identification of two conformers in level 1 (Section 1).

In the case of pleurotin two conformers are generated on level 1 analysis (Figs. 4 and 5). This evaluation and construction requires only 2 CPU seconds using an IBM 3032 computer. These generated forms actually represent rough 3-D geometries constructed as representative points of the two valleys identified on the conformational potential surface. These theoretical geometries are subsequently submitted to force field minimization procedures (Fig. 6) in order to reach the minimum on the conformational potential surface. The molecular geometry of the molecule studied is a function of 87 independent parameters and approximately 1 min CPU time is necessary to complete the 1000 energy calculations outlined in Fig. 5. Less than six more minutes would be necessary if one wants to analyze in detail (geometrically and energetically) the actual minimum on the conformational potential surface (convergence criterion satisfied at the 0.01 kcal/mol threshold).

The two generated conformers of pleurotin differ in the precise conformations of their seven-membered ring. The difference of energy between the two forms is 0.7 kcal/mol, the most stable being conformer 1 (Fig. 7). The 3-D entities can be analyzed in stereoscopic view (Figs. 8 and 9) while the geometrical differences between the two forms can be analyzed in terms of the signs of the torsional angles of the rings (Fig. 10). The manipulation of any of the 3-D entities is

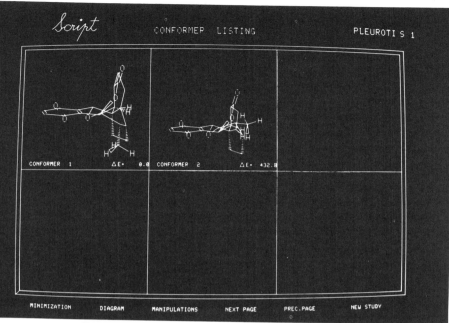

FIG. 5. Perspective views of the two generated conformers.

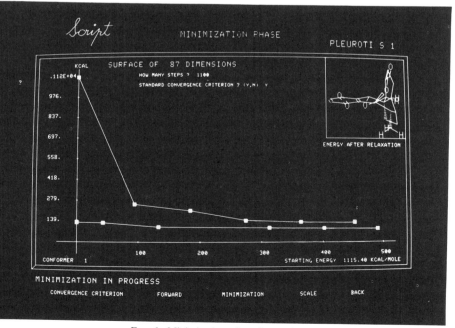

FIG. 6. Minimization of conformer 1.

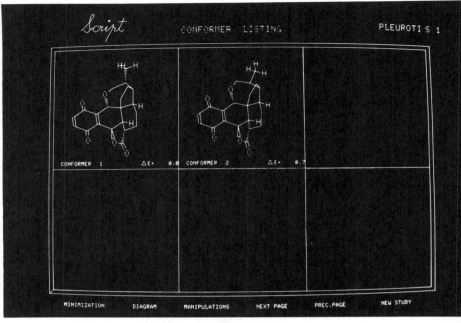

FIG. 7. Perspective views and relative stability of the two conformers.

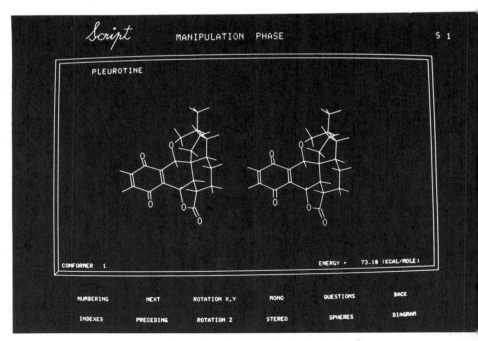

FIG. 8. Stereoscopic view of conformer I (Section 1).

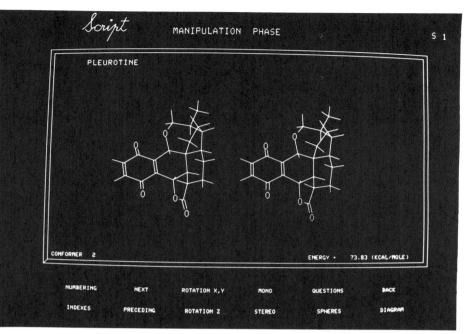

Fig. 9. Stereoscopic view of conformer 2 (Section 1).

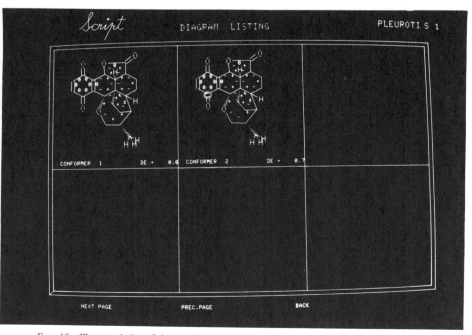

Fig. 10. Characteristics of the two forms in terms of the signs of their torsion angles.

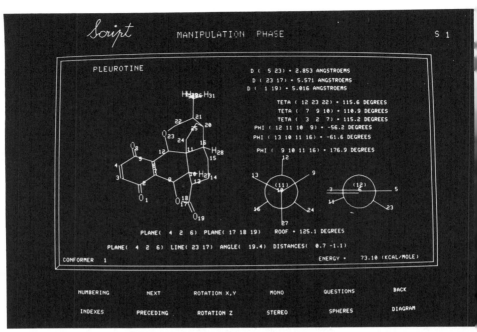

FIG. 11. Example of some questions: distances, angles, Newman projections, etc.

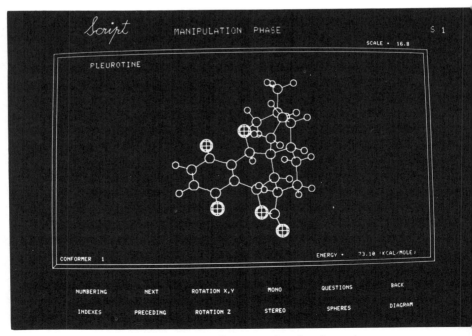

FIG. 12. Stick-and-ball representation of conformer 1.

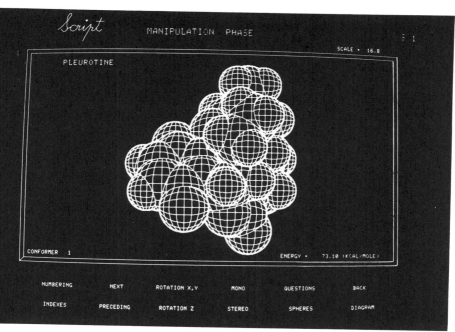

FIG. 13. Space-filling representation of conformer 1.

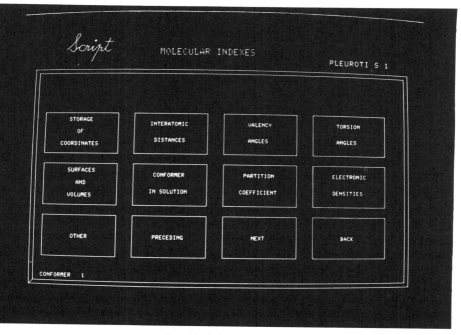

FIG. 14. Other controls.

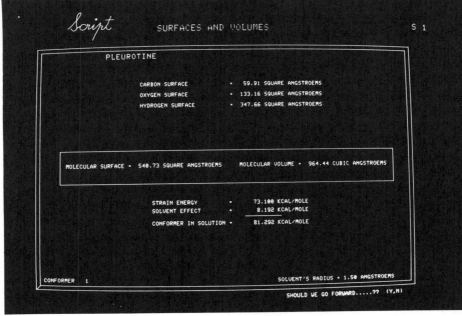

FIG. 15. Analysis of the molecule in solution (water).

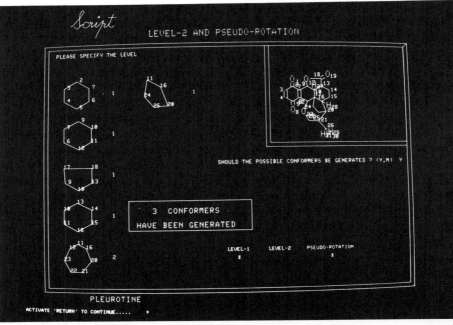

FIG. 16. Three new conformers are generated when level 2 is activated for the seven-membered ring (Section 2).

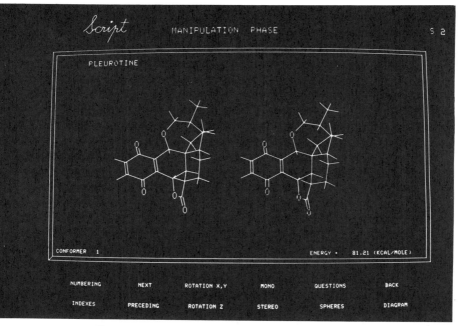

FIG. 17. Stereoscopic view of conformer 1 of Section 2.

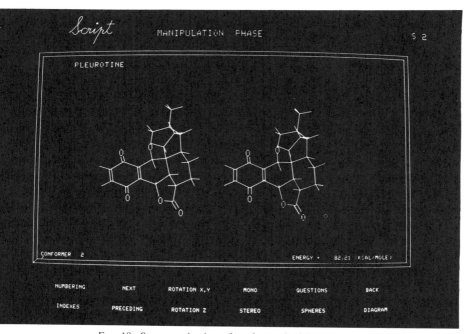

FIG. 18. Stereoscopic view of conformer 2 of Section 2.

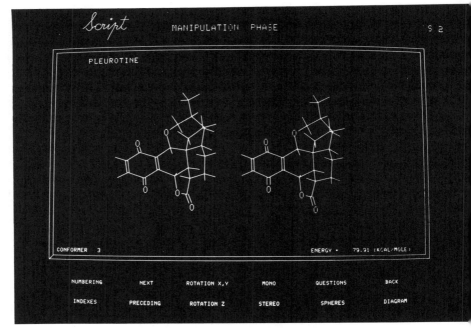

Fig. 19. Stereoscopic view of conformer 3 of Section 2.

possible when asking for specific geometrical calculations (distances, angles, Newman projections, etc., see Fig. 11). Other controls allow the rotation or different visualizations of the molecule such as stick-and-ball (Fig. 12) or space-filling representations (Fig. 13). Quantitative data are also available from the "molecular indexes" panel board which enables one to carry on with other molecular treatments (Fig. 14). The results for the molecule in water appear in Fig. 15, the solvent effect being calculated from the atomic exposed areas contributions in the interaction of the conformer with solvent molecules (Cohen and Régnier, 1976). When level 2 is activated for the seven-membered ring (Fig. 16), less than one CPU second is necessary to identify the existence and to generate in 3-D three new conformers. After minimization these conformations appear to be of greater energies. The stereo views of each of these forms are shown in Figs. 17–19, whereas a global summary of the whole study is indicated in Fig. 20.

b. Logical Basis of the Treatment. The theoretical formalism, allowing the automatic identification and construction of the various conformers presented in this example, is based on conformational assembly rules established for ring and chain fragments (Cohen *et al.*, 1981). This logical treatment requires the auto-

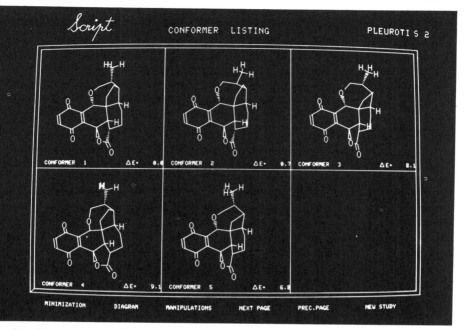

FIG. 20. Summary: the five minimized conformers analyzed: their perspective views and calculated stabilities.

matic constitution of a diagram of torsional constraints represented in Fig. 21. The systematic generation of all the possible conformers is based on this key diagram: any assembly of fragments which conforms to these requirements will lead to the various forms of the molecule; any of these forms being perfectly defined can therefore be perfectly generated. In particular the "+ − +" se-

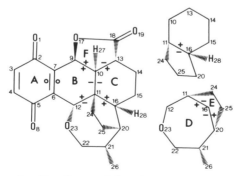

FIG. 21. The conformational key diagram of pleurotin (automatically constructed by the molecular modeling system).

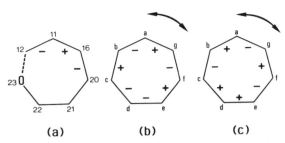

FIG. 22. Torsional constraints of the seven-membered ring moiety of (a) pleurotin and (b and c) stable forms of a saturated seven-membered ring stored in the program.

quence appearing either in ring B or in ring C indicates that only chair forms are possible for these two rings. The five generated conformers actually differ only in the conformation of the seven-membered ring. Figure 21 shows that the torsional constraints of this ring, established on the basis of the stereochemistry of the fusion with the other rings, have negative, positive, and negative signs around bonds 12–11, 11–16, and 16–20, respectively (see Fig. 22a). In Figure 22b and c is indicated the stable forms (two mirror images) of this elementary ring as stored in the program. Upon examination of the different possibilities of fitting these two forms into the actual constraints as indicated in Fig. 22a, the following five alternatives were found (Fig. 23). They all conform to the torsional constraints revealed for this ring and they actually represent exactly the five conformations generated in the study of this molecule.

   c. Docking Experiments.   One of the most promising tools for the direct design of new drugs can be found in the so-called docking experiments. Starting from the X-ray structure of a key macromolecule (enzyme, receptor, etc.), an area which is growing very rapidly these days, it becomes possible to imagine hypothetical ligands presenting appropriate stereochemical features and to analyze by direct simulations their binding to the known active site of the macromolecule. Some typical examples are discussed in Sections 5 and 6. This approach was recently reviewed by Goodford (1984), Beddell (1984), and Cohen (1985).

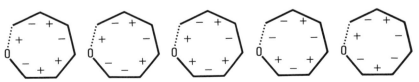

FIG. 23. Fitting the stored forms into the actual constraints leads to the identification of five alternative possibilities.

3.5 FUTURE PERSPECTIVES

As already mentioned, "direct" and "indirect" drug design perspectives address two ways of working now used in the conception of drugs. In both approaches the conceptual framework is based on detailed analyses of the structural properties of the molecules concerned and interpreted in terms of complementary steric and electronic features with the known/hypothetical 3-D recognition site. When combined with good molecular modeling systems both approaches are expected to rationally lead to the creation of new drugs. Up to now computerized systems have shown little capacity for recognizing patterns in 3-D when compared to the human ability to perceive complex objects much as molecules.

"Artificial intelligence" techniques are now experimented with to identify and computerize the fundamental key operations able to provide some control of important treatments such as the 3-D substructure search (Lesk, 1979; Crandell and Smith, 1982). In practical applications the computerized tools existing for "pharmacophoric pattern searching" (reviewed by Gund, 1979; Humblet and Marshall, 1980; Esaki, 1982) provide inert models in the hands of creative molecular modelists. Great progress is needed in this area where the power of computerized perspective lies in its ability to consider molecules not only in terms of 3-D, but also in terms of dynamic deformability and flexibility.

There is no doubt that advances in this field will result from new progress in computer capabilities, pattern recognition, and artificial intelligence. These advances will lead to more appropriate systems providing enough "expertise" and considerable practical interest in drug research.

4 The Conformational Parameter in Drug Design

4.1 QSAR AND STERIC PARAMETERS

QSAR methodologies have been widely used in the last few decades but appear to lack enough generality for modeling new chemical entities. Initially constructed on a family of compounds with an implicit common invariable topological frame, these methods have been used and developed mainly toward the optimization of biological properties of known series of analogs.

Even if the introduction of geometrical parameters or related molecular parameters is quite feasible in these analyses, 3-D features are poorly represented. In general, they are introduced through appropriate parameters believed to directly or indirectly account for steric effects, e.g., steric substituent constants E_s, the molar refractivity MR, and the molecular weight, MW. However, in view of the 3-D complementarity of ligands to the binding sites of biomolecules much more precise information is required to enable subtle stereochemical effects to be analyzed.

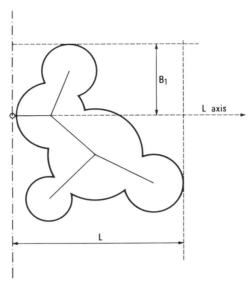

FIG. 24. Projection of a substituent along the L axis showing Verloop L and B_1 parameters. (From Verloop *et al.*, 1976, with permission. Copyright 1976 by Academic Press.)

Recent attempts were undertaken to include more precise 3-D features in the QSAR formalism. For example, Verloop *et al.* (1976) proposed the use of a set of five parameters, B_1, B_2, B_3, B_4, and L, to characterize molecular sizes and shapes. Substituent parameters can be calculated by a program, STERIMOL, which includes consideration of bond lengths, bond angles, van der Waals radii and a user-inputed "reasonable" conformation of the fragment concerned. Figures 24 and 25 show a schematic view of these parameters for hypothetical substituents. Tables for typical substituents are also proposed (Verloop *et al.*, 1976). Another means of accounting for molecular geometry is found in the use of difference parameters. Initially based on 2-D representation, the minimal steric difference parameter (MSD) has been enlarged to code for conformation 3-D distances.

Pattern recognition techniques can also account for 3-D aspects. In a typical analysis (Jurs *et al.*, 1979) where, for example, 28 descriptors are used to characterize each molecule, 10 are essentially geometrical parameters (the molecular volume and a combination of the various X, Y, and Z principal radii).

Of great potential interest are some recent efforts meant to reconcile QSAR with the "lock and key" picture. Exposed surface areas and molecular shape descriptors were quantitatively evaluated (Hopfinger, 1981), but when simply introduced in a classical Hansch equation they do not enable one to go too far beyond the internal limits of the QSAR formalism. It is certain that satisfactory QSAR equations provide a quantitative basis to perceive chemical structures in

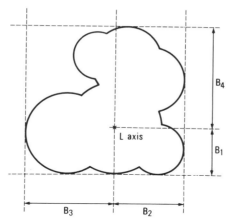

FIG. 25. Projection of a substituent perpendicular to the L axis showing the four B parameters. (From Verloop *et al.*, 1976, with permission. Copyright 1976 by Academic Press.)

terms of bioisosterism (Martin, 1981), but precise stereochemical features remain excluded from this analysis. To compare the actual potential possibilities and the limits of QSAR with those of the molecular modeling approach the last decade's continuous research on dihydrofolate reductase (DHFR) inhibitors provides an example of illuminating signification.

Extensive work has been undertaken in this area using a wide variety of approaches, such as QSAR studies and molecular modeling analyses. These two approaches were used in such a manner that it was possible to combine (Li *et al.*, 1982) but not to unify them, as reviewed later.

An effort aimed at unifying different approaches can be found in the work of Crippen where hypothetical L binding sites of a receptor are deduced from a set of known ligands. The computerized treatment consists of a heuristic approach (Crippen, 1979, 1983) which combines information concerning the conformational possibilities of the ligands (a matrix containing the upper and lower boundaries of selected atom distances) with the corresponding measured binding affinities. This so-called "distance geometry analysis" has the advantage of being independent of the coordinate referential describing the molecule's geometry (mathematically the distances matrices are invariant under translations and rotations). However, a great limitation lies in the length of combinatorial searches, thus reducing the practical interest of the method. This led the author to envisage simplifications such as nonexhaustive interactive search procedure and reduction of the number of points to the very minimum. This approach has the merit of trying to avoid a purely empirical correlation with given ligand properties by proposing some possible geometrical features of the receptor site. The method was applied to various examples, such as chymotrypsin inhibitors (Crippen, 1979), dihydrofolate reductase (DHFR) inhibitors (Crippen, 1980), thyroxine

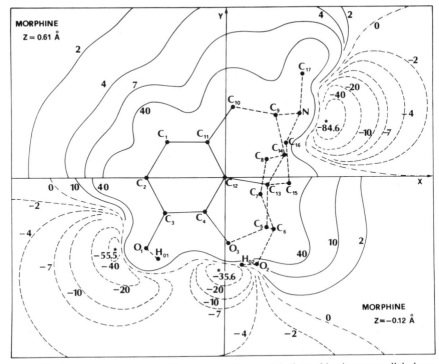

FIG. 26. Isoenergy contour map of the electrostatic potential of morphine in two parallel planes. (From Agresti *et al.*, 1980, with permission. Copyright 1980 by the *American Society for Pharmacology and Experimental Therapeutics.*)

(Crippen, 1981), and benzodiazepine receptor agonists and/or antagonists (Crippen, 1982). The methodology may not always lead to acceptable results. The study of the benzodiazepine binding site eventually leads, for example, to the overlap of only three points between two competitive agonists, diazepam and zopiclone, a poor result indeed. On the other hand, the study on DHFR inhibitors shows that the method may enable the detection of homologs that do not bind with the same orientation to the binding site.

4.2 MOLECULAR GEOMETRY VERSUS STEREOCHEMISTRY

Three-dimensional chemical entities are not only constituted as an assembly of 3-D spheres representing different atoms but also consist of sets of chemical

FIG. 27. Molecules in four dimensions: (a) stick and ball; (b) space filling; (c) 3-D molecular envelope; and (d) drawing of contour lines of the electrostatic potential on the molecular envelope of diazepam.

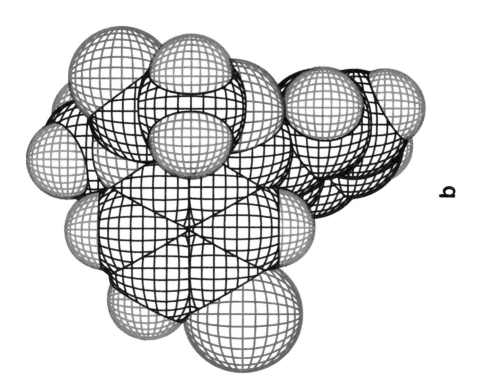

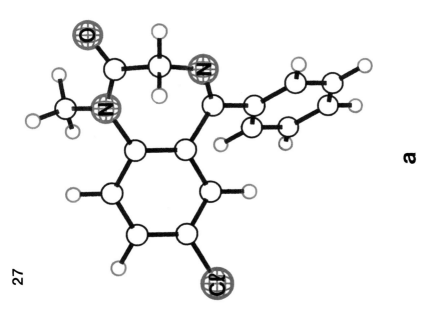

a

b

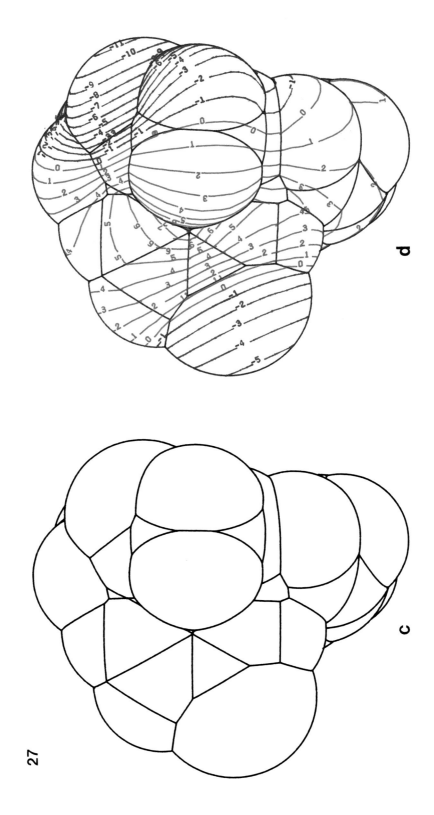

27

c

d

fragments possessing subtle electronic features. The term stereochemistry when considered broadly includes both geometric and electronic aspects, and is often used to recall that when a drug interacts with a biological receptor, both aspects should be taken into consideration. The examples reviewed in this article demonstrate that geometrical and electronic aspects cannot be dissociated when studying the molecular basis of a drug's action.

4.3 BEYOND THE THIRD DIMENSION: MOLECULES IN FOUR DIMENSIONS

In addition to the 3-D molecular features, electronic aspects also play a very important role in the biological activity of a drug. As already mentioned, a molecule must not be considered as a mere 3-D geometrical entity, it also constitutes a complex three-dimensional organization of atomic nuclei and electrons controlling intrinsic and "relational" properties. The fundamental electronic nature of molecular structure has led to a great number of operational concepts associated with it, e.g., chemical functionalities, atomic polarizabilities, electronic densities, atomic and molecular orbitals, hydrophobicity, and hydrogen bonding. Quantum mechanical calculations provide a deep insight into such properties. In applied research the net atomic charges were widely used to rationalize chemical and physicochemical properties of compounds as well as structure–activity relationships. The electrostatic molecular potential is a closely related electronic feature of great utility in understanding molecular properties of drugs. Being a function computed in the overall surrounding space of a molecule, it therefore carries more compact information on the 3-D implications of electronic charge distribution. It can be calculated directly from molecular wave functions (Bonaccorsi et al., 1970; Giessner-Prettre and Pullman, 1972; Srebrenik et al., 1973; Scrocco and Tomasi, 1973) or by simple electrostatic calculations (Baldwin et al., 1980) involving the atomic charge distribution. It has the dimension of an energy and is generally expressed in kcal/mol. Since a unitary positive charge is used as a probe, positive values correspond to repulsive regions whereas negative potentials correspond to attractive regions. In practice the electrostatic molecular potential is represented by contour maps from which useful information can be drawn, particularly with regard to chemical reactivity (Scrocco and Tomasi, 1978; Tomasi, 1980) and structure–activity relationships (Weinstein and Osman, 1977; Rein et al., 1972; Kier and Aldrich, 1974; Bonaccorsi et al., 1972; Politzer and Daiker, 1977; Breon et al., 1978; Baldwin et al., 1980; Weinstein et al., 1981). A typical map is shown in Fig. 26 where the isoenergy contours of morphine are drawn in two parallel planes (Z values are indicated, the benzene defining the plane $Z = 0$) as taken from the data published by Agresti et al. (1980).

Such contour maps are particularly convenient for handling planar molecules.

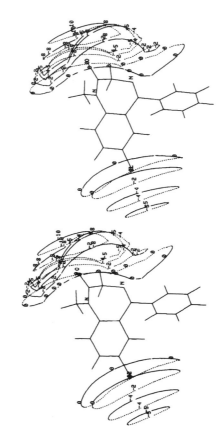

FIG. 28. Molecules in four dimensions: contour lines of the negative electrostatic potential around the 3-D structure of diazepam (stereoview).

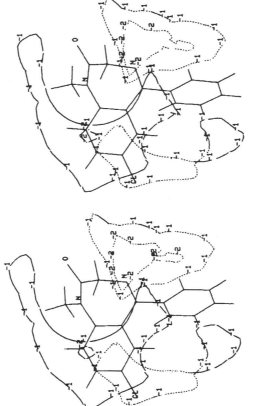

FIG. 29. Van der Waals contours around the 3-D structure of diazepam (stereoview).

69

When nonplanar molecules are concerned, as is generally the case in drug research, several analyses are performed using various referential planes. This requires, on the one hand, the use of 3-D models to perceive geometrical features and, on the other hand, the manipulation of various sections representing potential energy contours. It sometimes becomes cumbersome to analyze the precise 3-D implications of the electronic charge distribution as the information is not available from a unique model. In order to unify the two aspects we have proposed a representation of molecules "in four dimensions" (Cohen, 1979), providing in the same frame information for both the 3-D aspects and electronic features. Such a representation is illustrated for diazepam in Fig. 27. The molecule's geometrical features appear in Fig. 27a,b using the classical stick-and-ball and space-filling representations, respectively. Figure 27c represents the envelope of this molecule as constructed at contact distance with a possible biomacromolecule. It is defined by calculating for each atom a radius R_a such as

$$R_a = R_{vdW} + R_0$$

where R_{vdW} is the Van der Waals radius and R_0 a value which can be considered either constant or variable (in Fig. 27 it was fixed at 1.5 Å).

The "fourth dimension" is revealed on this 3-D surface when the electrostatic contour lines are drawn as shown in 27d. This treatment operates like a photographic developer, revealing the electronic features associated with molecular geometry. Positive lines are revealed in red and negative lines in blue. The zero potential line appears between the attractive and the repulsive regions. For this drawing the classical coulombic expression was used for calculating the electrostatic potential contours and less than 15 sec CPU time on an IBM 3032 was necessary for the complete drawing in Fig. 27d. In general, the contour lines are drawn in a plane; here they are drawn on a 3-D surface which is directly related to the molecular geometry. Another way of visualizing the same features is shown in Fig. 28, where the molecular envelope is simply not drawn. Other properties can also be visualized in the same way. Surcouf and Mornon have stressed the importance of the Van der Waals potentials (*signatures de Van der Waals*) all around active sites and ligands (Surcouf, 1982; Surcouf and Mornon, 1983). Figure 29 illustrates a representation of the most stable Van der Waals contour lines around the diazepam molecule using spherical molecular shells (N. C. Cohen and P. Colin, unpublished). Taking advantage of the new possibilities of advanced color graphics sytems, Weiner *et al.* (1982) have developed the so-called "electrostatic potential molecular surfaces." The potential energies are calculated on the surface envelope of a molecule or a part of a macromolecule,

---

Fig. 30. Molecules in four dimensions: Color-coded representation of the electrostatic potential surface of fragments of double-helical DNA. Contour levels: red, $V < -10$ kcal/mol; green, $-10 < V < 10$ kcal/mol; blue $V > 10$ kcal/mol. (From Weiner *et al.*, 1982, with permission.)

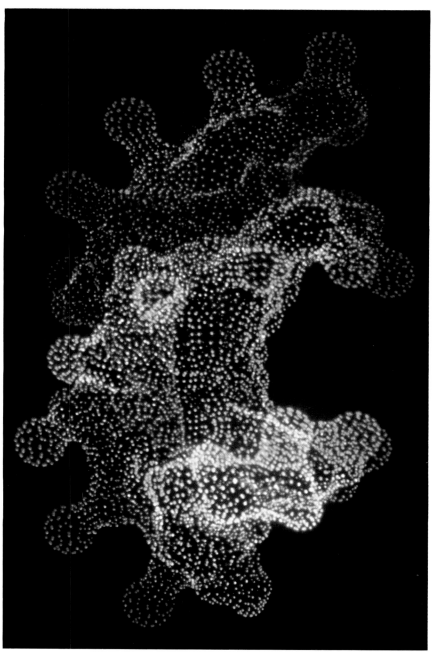

30

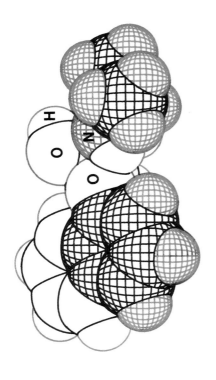
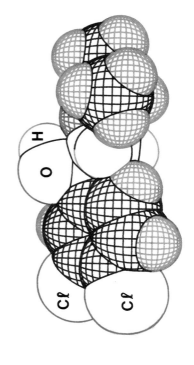

35

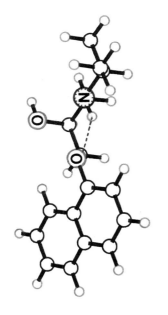
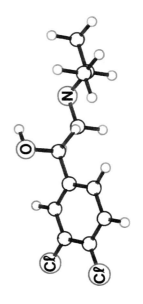

36

the numerical values of which are color coded. The resulting picture obtained on the screen is generally of good scientific value and also endowed with some artistic quality. In Fig. 30, for example, the electrostatic potential surface of fragments of double-helical DNA is shown with Na^+ counterions on each phosphate. Three colors are used for coding the potential energies V as follows (values in kcal/mol): red ($V < -10$), green ($-10 < V < 10$), and blue ($V > 10$).

Recently it has been shown that the molecular electrostatic field (MEF) may introduce additional insights in understanding the biochemical reactivity of nucleic acids (Pullman *et al.*, 1983), and in a certain sense could be better than the molecular electrostatic potential.

5 Understanding SAR: Stereochemical Considerations

5.1 β-ADRENERGIC AGENTS

Pharmacological actions of adrenergic drugs have been shown to be linked to relatively strict structural requirements. Synthetic adrenergic agents are related,

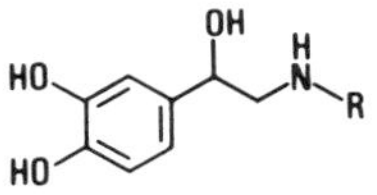

(8) 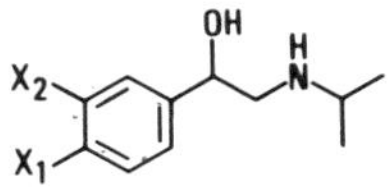　　　　(9)

(a) R= CH_3 (adrenaline)　　(a) X_1 = X_2 = OH　(isoproterenol)
(b) R= H　(noradrenaline)　　(b) X_1 = X_2 = Cl　(dichloroisoproterenol)
　　　　　　　　　　　　　　　(c) X_1 = NH-SO_2-CH_3; X_2 = H　(sotalol)
　　　　　　　　　　　　　　　(d) X_1 = NH-SO_2-CH_3; X_2 = OH　(soterenol)
　　　　　　　　　　　　　　　(e) X_1 = OH; X_2 = NH-SO_2-CH_3

FIG. 31. Some β-adrenergic agents with the phenethanolamine (PEA) fragment.

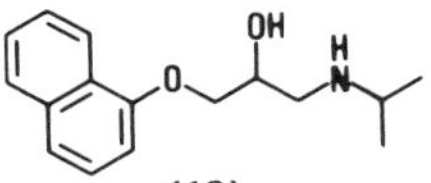

(10)　　　　　(11)　　　　(12)
(propranolol)　　(alprenolol)　　(pindolol)

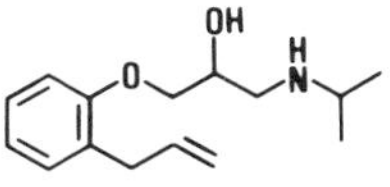

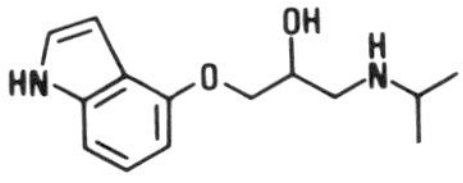

FIG. 32. Some β-blocking agents with the aryloxypropanolamine (AOPA) fragment.

FIG. 35. Folded conformation of AOPA [propranolol (**10**)] and pharmacophore that could fit the receptor site according to Jen and Kaiser (1977).

FIG. 36. Conformation of PEA [dichloroisoproterenol (**9b**)] and pharmacophore that could fit the receptor site according to Jen and Kaiser (1977).

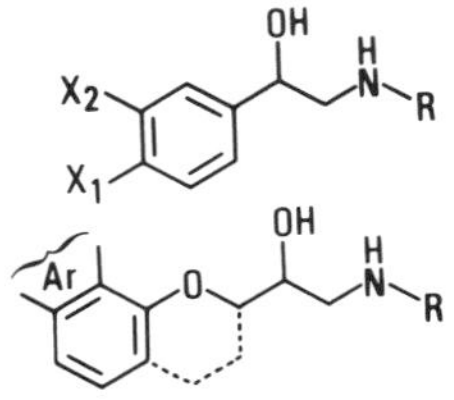

FIG. 33. How AOPA can mimic PEA molecules according to Ammon *et al.* (1975).

either to the natural hormones adrenaline (**8a**) and noradrenaline (**8b**) having a phenethanolamine (PEA) moiety, or to the aryloxypropanolamine (AOPA) analogs such as propranolol (**10**). Typical structures of the two classes are given in Figs. 31 and 32. In both series it was observed that small structural changes such as modification of the substitution of the aromatic ring can transform an agonist into an antagonist and vice versa. For example, dichloroisoproterenol (**9b**) is a β-blocker, whereas isoproterenol (**9a**) is a β-adrenergic agonist.

It was suggested that the different biological actions may be explained in terms of electrostatic molecular potentials (Petrongolo *et al.*, 1974). Competitive inhibition studies (Barrett, 1972) show that the two classes of β-adrenergic agents, PEA and AOPA, act at the same receptor site; this provides biochemical support for those who pointed out structural features common to both series.

Thus, Ammon *et al.* (1975) have proposed that the ether fragment of AOPA can electronically and sterically simulate an aromatic ring. They justify this hypothesis on the basis of solid-state studies, showing that this fragment lies in the plane of the aryl ring; with this geometry the conjugation of the oxygen with the aromatic ring is maximum. Figure 33 illustrates how this potential ring may coincide with the propranolol ring bearing the ethanolamine side chain. This hypothesis was also recently developed by Leger *et al.* (1980, 1983).

A different solution was proposed by Jen and Kaiser (1977), who showed that propranolol salts may exist in a stable, almost rigid conformation involving two intramolecular hydrogen bonds to form a 6–5 bicyclic chelated structure as indicated in Fig. 34. In such a conformation, the two bulky substituents (Ar and R) are equatorial and the hydroxyl is in an axial position (with reference to the virtual six-membered ring). When this conformation is compared to the preferred

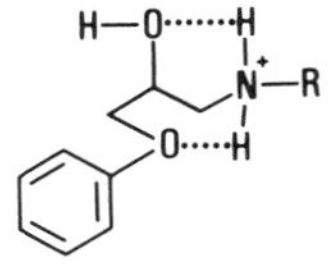

FIG. 34. The stable bicyclic chelated structure of AOPA as proposed by Jen and Kaiser (1977).

s-trans rotamer of adrenergic PEA molecules, it is observed that all positions of the phenyl ring, the phenyl-to-oxygen or phenyl-to-carbon bonds, as well as the terminal amino groups of both chemical classes, may be superimposed. The conformational features of the two series are visualized in Fig. 35; Fig. 36 shows how the corresponding pharmacophore is embedded in both structures.

Since, in this superposition, the two alcoholic hydroxyl groups are separated by about 2 Å, the authors have argued that a specific orientation of this alcoholic functionality may not be an absolute requirement. This is supported by the observation that the homolog **13** of *N-tert*-butylnorepinephrine, in which a meth-

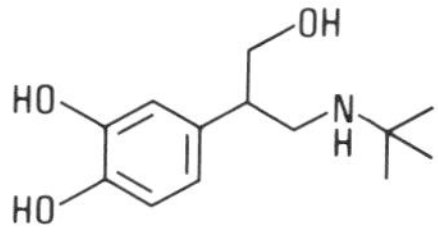

(13)

ylene group is inserted between the benzylic carbon and the hydroxyl group, also exhibits significant biological activity. Concerning the validity of the model proposed several arguments were put forward; in particular a precise analysis of the effects of substituents in both series permitted the same group to provide some convincing evidence (Kaiser *et al.*, 1977). This work was based on an analysis of the structure–activity relationships of substituted 1-phenoxy-3-(*tert*-butylamino)-2-propanols in the light of the two possible superpositions sketched in Fig. 37. On the left side of this figure the above-mentioned proposal is outlined (hypothesis a), while that appearing on the right side (hypothesis b) corresponds to the one proposed by Comer several years ago (1970). Reasoning on the basis of chemical structure of these phenylethanolamines and phenoxypropanolamines the substituent of a phenoxypropanolamine located para (p) to the ether oxygen should influence biological activity in a fashion similar to that

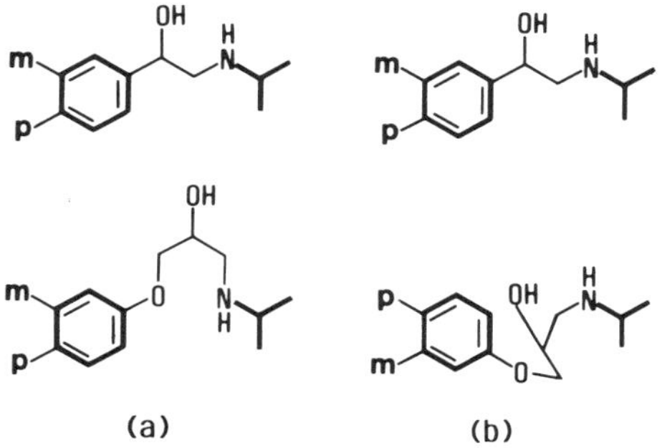

(a)   (b)

Fɪɢ. 37. Discrimination of superpositions a and b by the analysis of the effects of the substituents on the biological activities. (Kaiser *et al.*, 1977.)

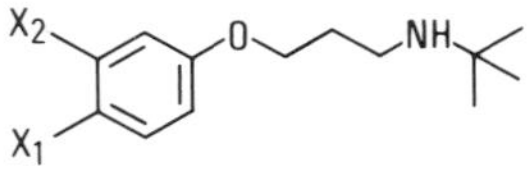

$$(14) \quad \begin{array}{l} \text{(a)} \quad X_1 = MeSO_2NH \; ; \; X_2 = OH \\ \text{(b)} \quad X_1 = OH ; \qquad\qquad X_2 = MeSO_2NH \end{array}$$

of a para (p) substituent of a phenylethanolamine in hypothesis a, whereas the same para (p) substitution of the former should be related to the meta (m) position of the latter. The results obtained are in favor of superposition a. For example, the *in vitro* biological actions of *m*-hydroxy-*p*-methylsulfonamido-substituted phenoxypropanolamine (**14a**) and its isomer (**14b**), in which the ring substituents have been interchanged, can be compared with those of the related PEA such as soterenol **9d** and its isomer **9e,** in which the same substituents have undergone the same interchange. The comparison shows a parallelism in the two series with regard to superposition of Fig. 37a (Kaiser *et al.,* 1977), where molecules **9d** and **14a** are much more active (*in vitro,* guinea pig tracheal and atrial tests) than their corresponding isomers **9e** and **14b.** These studies illustrate how traditional and recent approaches can be consistently combined with 3-D analysis in the comparison of different series of molecules.

5.2 β-LACTAM ANTIBIOTICS

5.2.1 D-Ala D-Ala *Mimetism*

The story of the discovery and the subsequent intensive research on penicillin (**15**), cephalosporins (**16**), and related β-lactam antibiotics is certainly among

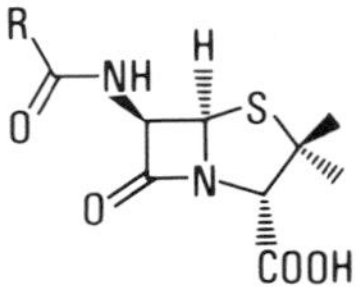

                    (15) 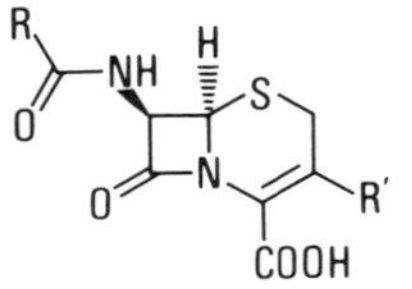   (16)

one of the most exciting therapeutic successes of the last few decades. It has mobilized unpredecented scientific and industrial effort, which is far from complete. The particular properties, the fascinating structures of the chemical entities involved, the strict stereochemical requirements observed for the biological activities, as well as great progress in the understanding, in molecular terms, of their mechanisms of action, have and will challenge the imaginations of medicinal chemists and biologists for more than another generation. The origin of the biological mode of action of these substances is thought to be based on the ability

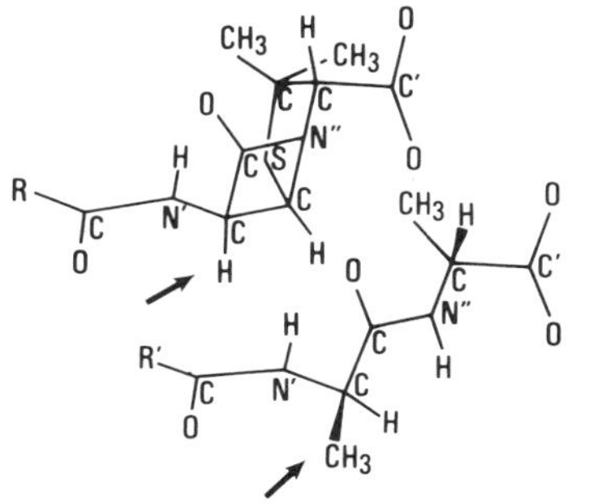

FIG. 38. Three-dimensional similarities between a penicillin (top) and a substituted D-Ala-D-Ala fragment. (From Strominger, and Tipper, 1965, with permission. Copyright 1965 by the Dun Donnelley Publishing Corporation.)

of the antibiotic to irreversibly acylate the active site of the transpeptidase enzyme involved in the biosynthesis of the peptidoglycan layer of bacterial cell wall. The bacteria is killed since the inhibition of cross-linking leads to the appearance of imperfections in its protecting 3-D cell wall, which eventually explodes under osmotic pressure. It has been suggested by Strominger and Tipper (1965) that the enzyme involved must normally recognize D-Ala-D-Ala terminal residues in order to operate the cross linking. This important step, which is inhibited by the antibiotic, may be understood by the drug's ability to mimic the same stereochemical features as the endogenous substrate. This interpretation, as visualized in Fig. 38, has led to the observation that this analogy would be even more enhanced if the antibiotic had had an additional methyl group appropriately located (see arrows on the figure). Following this idea through, Strominger and Tipper (1965) suggested that 6α-methylpenicillins (**17a**) and 7α-methylcephalosporins (**18a**) might show enhanced efficiency as antibacterials. Such analogs

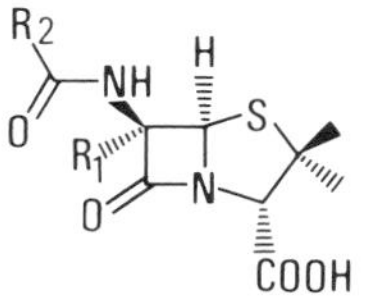

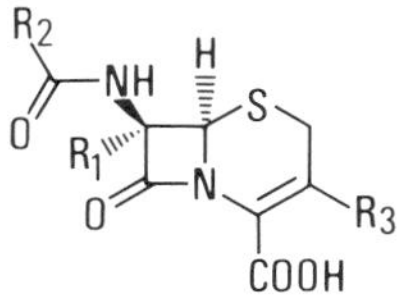

(17) (a) $R_1 = CH_3$

(b) $R_2 = OCH_3$

(18) (a) $R_1 = CH_3$

(b) $R_2 = OCH_3$

were synthesized in both series (Böhme et al., 1971), showing either very weak or no antibacterial activity. In a note added in proof the authors, however, drew the reader's attention to good gram-negative activities observed by the new methoxycephalophorin C (Nagarajan et al., 1971). It was later fully confirmed that the introduction of various groups on this position might lead to the improvement of some (mainly gram-negative) biological activities.

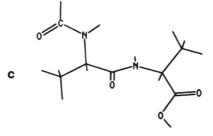

FIG. 39. Comparison of (a) a 6α-methyl substituted penicillin; (b) a 7α-methyl substituted cephalosporin; and (c) the D-Ala-D-Ala fragment.

The unexpected inactivities observed with the methyl analogs may, however, be interpreted as being consistent with the Strominger hypothesis as shown in the following paragraph.

When comparing the structural aspects of the bicyclic β-lactams with the proposed acyl-D-Ala-D conformation, one can detect two important features: (1) the proposed conformation for D-Ala-D-Ala is not a stable form, and (2) the

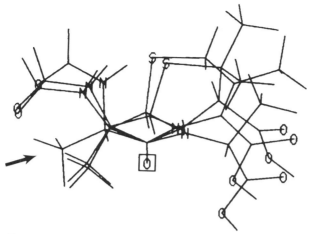

Fɪɢ. 40. Superposition of the three structures represented in Fig. 39.

difference of the valence angles between the β-lactam carbonyl group and the corresponding group in the unstrained peptidic fragment is around 25–30°.

Concerning the first point, the proposed model only shows how the substrate can mimic the drug, and not the reverse. The high flexibility of the peptidic terminal fragment obviously justifies the way the analysis proceeded for the superposition of the two molecules. However, had the other possibility not been rejected, it could have led to other interpretations. On the other hand, a more energetic form such as a transition state, as proposed by Lee (1971), can also be envisaged for the D-Ala-D-Ala conformation.

The second point relative to the difference in valence angles is worth noting. The 3-D features of a 6α-methylpenicillin, a 7α-methylcephalosporin, and the proposed D-Ala-D-Ala conformation are shown in Fig. 39 and it appears that the methyl groups of the two bicyclic β-lactams are not located in the same position as the corresponding one of the D-Ala-D-Ala fragment. This is shown in Fig. 40 where the three molecules are superimposed in such a way that their amide fragments coincide (the methyl group of the D-Ala-D-Ala is indicated by an arrow in the figure). The shift is due to the important difference observed between valence angles, as already mentioned. It is therefore not possible to conclude that Strominger's model is invalid only on the basis of the unexpected biological activities observed. Moreover, the good activities observed for the methoxy analogs permit another analysis to be envisaged, which is consistent with Strominger's hypothesis. The geometrical features of the methoxy bicyclic β-lactams are shown in Fig. 41, while the superposition of these two structures with that of D-Ala-D-Ala is visualized in Fig. 42. It now appears that the methyl groups of the three series of structures may be located in the same region. A

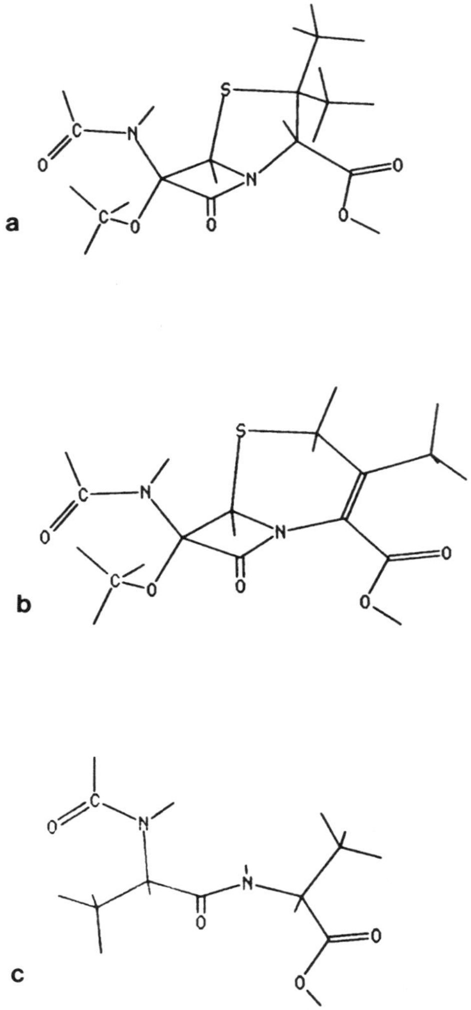

FIG. 41. Comparison of (a) a 6α-methoxy substitued penicillin; (b) a 7α-methoxy substituted cephalosporin; and (c) the D-Ala-D-Ala fragment.

superposition of the five molecules discussed here is presented in Fig. 43. The reader can also see in this view that there is a poor superposition of the carboxyl functions, which is caused by important local geometrical differences of the amide nitrogen atom: being pyramidal in the β-lactam structures, this atom becomes perfectly planar in the peptidic moiety. The stereochemical require-ments of the carboxyl group will be discussed in the next paragraph, though the

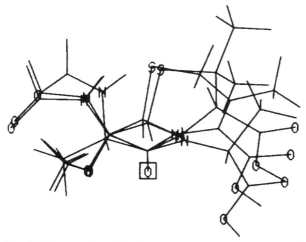

FIG. 42. Superposition of the three structures represented in Fig. 41.

analysis presented here aims only at showing that the results obtained with the substituted analogs may still be consistent with Strominger's suggestion.

5.2.2 Stereochemical Requirements of the Cyclic and Carboxy Moieties

The discovery of the cephalosporin antibiotics (**19**) opened up new perspectives by showing that relatively important structural modifications of the penicillin

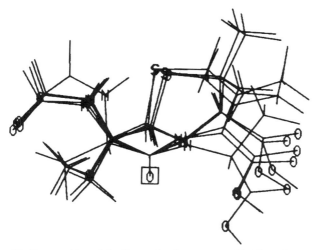

FIG. 43. Superposition of the five molecules represented in Figs. 39 and 41.

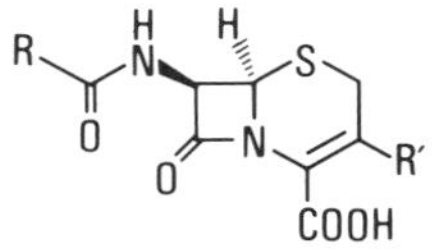

(19) 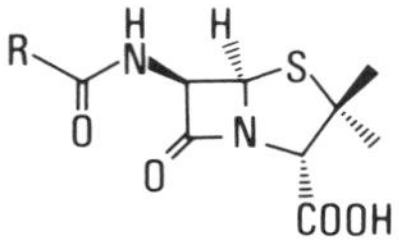   (20)

nucleus (**20**) are possible without loss of antibacterial properties. Despite the extensive work undertaken in both biology and medicinal chemistry for several decades, the understanding of the molecular requirements necessary for good biological activities is still limited and does not permit the rational design of new molecular structures to be confidently envisaged. Practical synthetic work in medicinal chemistry was therefore mainly restricted to the exploration of analogs using various empirical working hypotheses. It is observed in this area that precise stereochemical requirements are necessary for biological activity. For example, the stereochemical inversion of any of the substituted chiral carbon atoms belonging to the bicyclic nucleus of penicillin or cephalosporin leads to definitively inactive structures. The difficulty of integrating unexpected observations precluded the inclusion of the working rules of medicinal chemistry into a more general model which would have permitted the activities of new structures to be consistently predicted. An example of such difficulty is analyzed here and concerns the curious biological inactivities observed with Δ^2-cephalosporins (**21**).

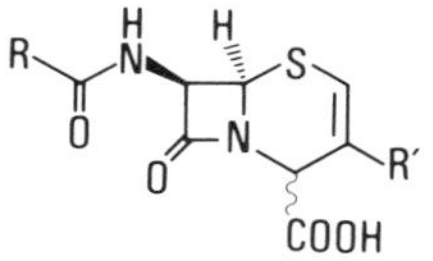

(21) 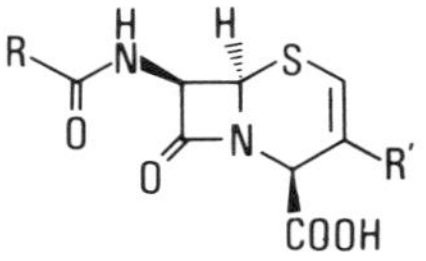   (22) 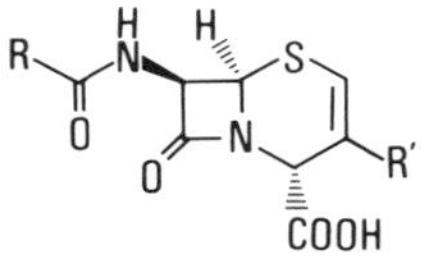   (23)

It was in the course of the study of cephalosporins that analogous compounds were prepared with a double bond in the Δ^2 position (**21**), and it was observed that these cephalosporins were devoid of any antibiotic action. This was quite surprising, since the structural differences existing between the two active families of compounds **19** and **20** are much greater than those existing between the two isomeric derivatives **19** and **21**, differing only by the position of the double bond. When this observation was made several years ago, some rational explanations were sought to justify the biological inactivities of the Δ^2-cephalosporins. The α stereochemistry of the carboxylic function in penicillin was already known, as opposed to Δ^2-cephalosporins, for which this stereochemistry was not yet established. It was therefore suspected (Van Heyningen and Ahern, 1968) that the biological inactivity of Δ^2-cephalosporins was due to a "wrong" β-configuration of this carboxylic function, as shown in **22**. Subsequent studies along these lines (Van Heyningen and Ahern, 1968) have shown that the config-

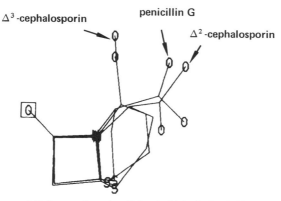

FIG. 44. No common 3-D features for rationalizing the biological activities observed in penicillins and cephalosporins. (From Sweet and Dahl, 1970.)

uration of the carboxy group is, in fact, α as in **23** and therefore identical with that of penicillins (**20**). A new attempt was made to analyze the geometrical aspects and was carried out on the basis of X-ray studies (Sweet and Dahl, 1970). The crystal structures of Δ^2- and Δ^3-cephalosporins were compared with that of penicillin G. Surprisingly, 3-D comparison of the cyclic moieties did not reveal obvious similarities between the active compounds, penicillin and Δ^3-cephalosporin. On the contrary, it showed that penicillin more closely resembles the inactive Δ^2-cephalosporin as shown in Fig. 44. Based on these observations it was concluded that the conformational requirements for the ligand recognition of the antibiotic by the enzyme are not very restrictive.

Similar features were recently observed following the discovery of thienamycin (**24**) (Albers-Schönberg *et al.*, 1978), as antibiotic possessing high antibacterial properties, and Δ^1-thienamycin (**25**), a double-bond isomer devoid of

(24)   (25)

any antibiotic activity (Shih and Ratcliffe, 1981). The antibacterial activities of even simpler but again highly strained β-lactams were also studied (Pfaendler *et al.*, 1981), showing that compounds **26** and **27** possess potential antibacterial activity whereas compound **28** is inactive.

(26)   (27)   (28)

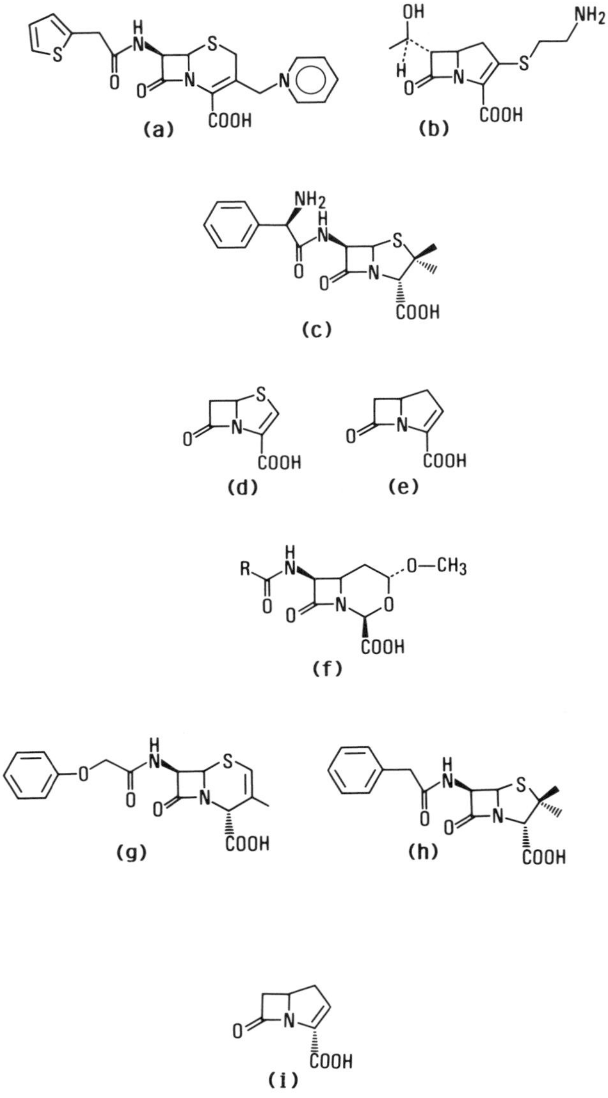

Fig. 45. Representative molecules chosen for 3-D comparison. (From Cohen, 1983a. Courtesy of the *American Chemical Society*.)

ACTIVE

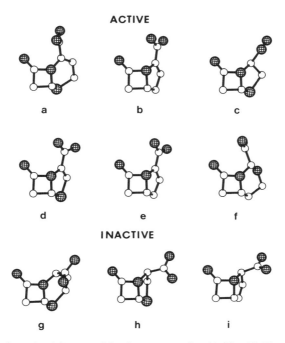

INACTIVE

FIG. 46. Three-dimensional features of the nine structures listed in Fig. 45. (From Cohen, 1983a. Courtesy of the *American Chemical Society*.)

The working hypothesis suggesting that the origin of the biological activity is found in the ease of base hydrolysis of the lactam amide bond was invoked to rationalize these results, and the observed biological inactivity of **23, 25,** and **28** was therefore ascribed to either a low or a high reactivity of the β-lactam ring (Van Heyningen and Ahern, 1968; Shih and Ratcliffe, 1981; Woodward, 1980). However, subsequent studies have shown the deficiencies of this model since the pyramidality of the β-lactam nitrogen atom as well as the chemical reactivity of the inactive molecule **28** are perfectly comparable to that of active compounds (Pfaendler *et al.*, 1981). Moreover, Frère and colleagues (1982) have analyzed in depth the chemical reactivity of a wide range of β-lactam structures and compared it with the kinetic parameters of their interaction with various enzymes (β-lactamases and peptidases). The intrinsic chemical reactivity is shown not to be correlated with the enzymes' activities. It is suggested as a result of this work that the primary parameters governing the biological action must be the goodness of fit of the β-lactam to the enzyme cavity.

Cohen (1983a) has recently shown that precise 3-D stereochemical features may exist in the recognition of the antibiotics by the enzymes. The geometrical features of a set of representative active and inactive structures (Fig. 45) were

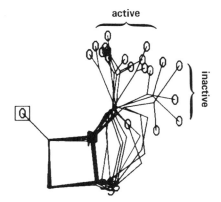

FIG. 47. Geometrical separation between active and inactive structures. (From Cohen, 1983a. Courtesy of the *American Chemical Society*.)

analyzed and demonstrate that active structures have very different 3-D features when compared to inactive ones, as shown in Fig. 46, where only the heavy atoms of the rings and those of the carboxy group are represented. The superposition of this set of representative structures shows how the carboxy groups of the active molecules are concentrated in the upper region (Fig. 47). In this model, the active form of the penam nucleus of penicillins is that with the carboxyl function in a pseudoequatorial position (conformer b in Fig. 48).

In a study of the broadness of the antibacterial spectrum of β-lactams, Balsamo *et al.* (1980) have proposed that the crystalline conformation of a given penicillin molecule (a or b in Fig. 48) may be associated with its antibacterial spectrum (narrow or broad), but indicated that the number of structures supporting this idea is too limited. Although the conformational flexibility associated to the pseudorotation of the five-membered ring can be envisaged in such molecules, the proposed hypothesis partly coincides with the preceding model.

This idea has led to the suggestion of minor chemical modifications in structures up to now considered as devoid of any therapeutic interest, in the hope of

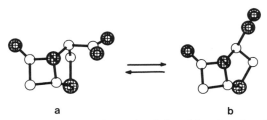

a   b

FIG. 48. Pseudorotation of the penam nucleus and variation of the orientation of the substituents. (From Cohen, 1983a. Courtesy of the *American Chemical Society*.)

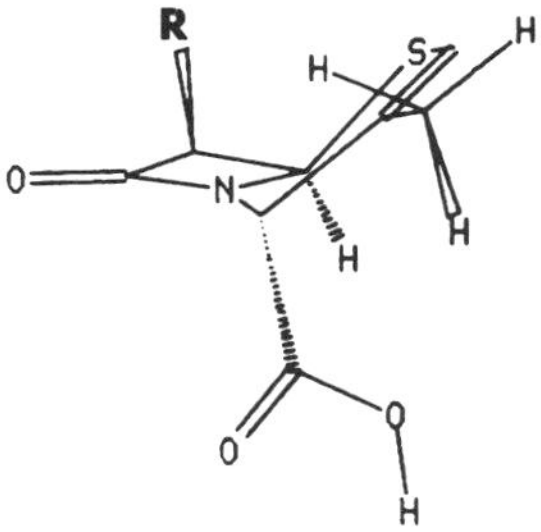

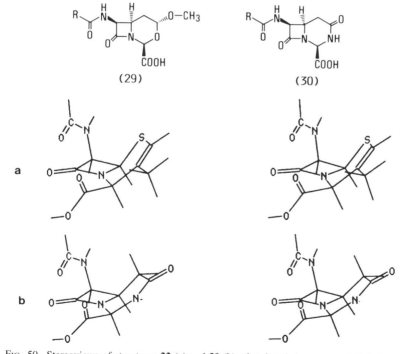

FIG. 49. Orientation of the α-carboxyl function in Δ²-cephalosporins.

restoring biological activities. Indeed, Δ²-cephalosporins having the carboxylic function in the "wrong" β-configuration (opposite to that in penicillin) appear as capable of presenting the appropriate 3-D requirements (Cohen, 1983a). Such an idea is consistent with the proposed model and the recent observation of the antibacterial properties of structures **29** (Gleason *et al.*, 1979) and **30** (Branch and Pearson, 1982) provides additional support to this proposal. The stereochemistry of Δ²-cephalosporins is shown in Fig. 49 whereas Fig. 50 illustrates the similar 3-D features of structures **22** and **30**.

FIG. 50. Stereoviews of structures **22** (a) and **30** (b), showing their common 3-D features.

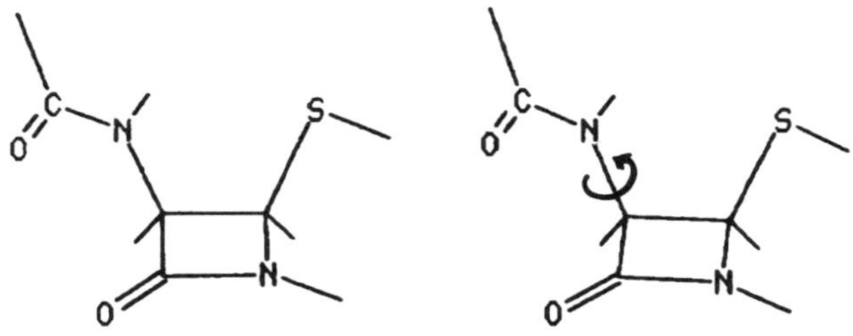

FIG. 51. Importance of the torsion angle of the side chain (stereoview).

5.2.3 Role of the Side Chain and Future Perspectives

The stereochemical requirements of the side chain of penicillins and cephalosporins are still poorly understood. Bocquet (1975) has calculated the preferred torsion angle (see Fig. 51) for a great variety of side chains in both series but a clear interpretation of the role of such moieties still remains to be established. The same side chain may lead to different activities when adjacent to penem or cephem nuclei. For example, mecillinam analogs of type **31** have shown good

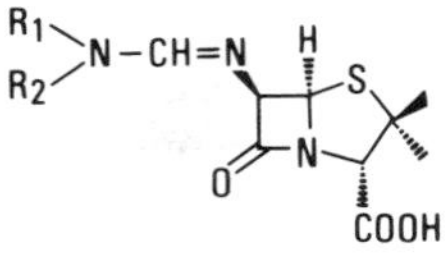

(31)

activities toward gram-negative microorganisms (Lund and Tybring, 1972) whereas poor activities were observed for the cephalosporin (**32**) derivatives

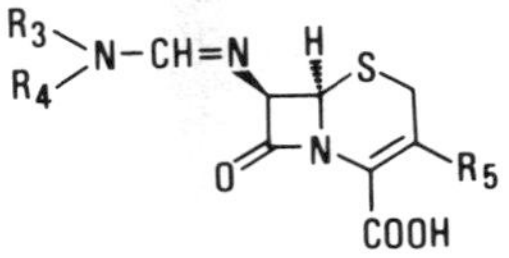

(32)

(Altman *et al.*, 1975). The inversion of stereochemistry observed in thienamycin (**25**) stresses the necessity of clarifying this question. The recent availability of the X-ray structure of a β-lactam-sensitive transpeptidase has opened up new perspectives in this field and should allow analysis of the geometric fit of each β-lactam antibiotic in correlation with its inhibitory strength (Kelly *et al.*, 1982). New designs (non-β-lactam antibiotics?) are expected to follow from these studies.

5.3 CENTRAL ANALGESICS

In recent years important information has accumulated on the stereochemical basis of structure–activity relationships at the central analgesic receptor level.

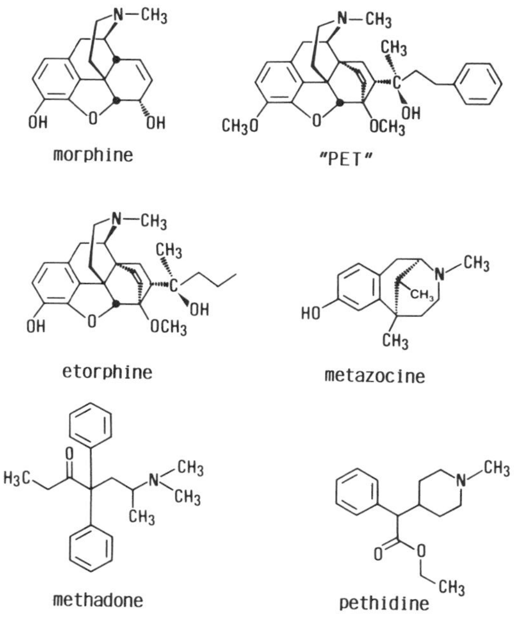

morphine "PET"

etorphine metazocine

methadone pethidine

FIG. 52. Some representative analgesic structures.

Among the various chemical classes of narcotic analgesics, the structural features which appear to be related to biological activity include the presence of a phenyl ring together with that of a nitrogen atom. Structure–activity analyses have revealed a 3-D pharmacophore to be common to all the known active structures interacting with the same binding site (Beckett and Casy, 1954; Casy, 1978).

From the analysis of various structurally related active compounds (see Fig. 52) the common pharmacophore could be most simply described as a 4-phenyl piperidine moiety having the piperidine ring in a chair conformation and the phenyl ring in an axial orientation.

This model, however, is too restricted since it does not include some extremely potent azabicycloalkanes such as **33**, having the phenyl substituent

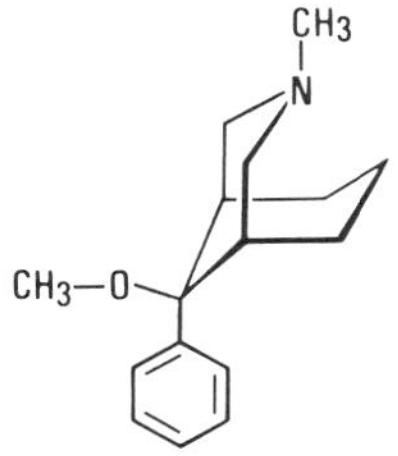

(33)

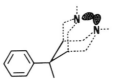

FIG. 53. Axial and equatorial 4-phenyl piperidines may interact with a common binding site. (According to Fries and Portoghese, 1976.)

blocked in an equatorial orienation, or the well-known 4-phenyl piperidine ana-logs pethidine (see Fig. 52) whose favored conformation places the phenyl group in an equatorial position.

   To account for these observations and also to interpret more sophisticated stereoselective effects observed in the biological activity of these structures, Fries and Portoghese have shown that the apparent contradiction is in fact one of reference frames more than of molecular structures (Fries and Portoghese, 1976). Whatever the orientation (axial or equatorial) of the phenyl group, both mo-lecular structures can interact with a common binding site. Figure 53 shows how the nitrogen lone electron pair of both conformers converge to a common area in space. Molecular modeling studies recently confirmed the validity of this model (Humblet and Marshall, 1981). Another approach, still consistent with the pre-ceding one, was proposed by Belleau and colleagues on the basis of studies on morphinan analogs. In an attempt to analyze the stereoelectronic factors govern-ing the binding of these compounds, several lines of evidence have been present-ed showing that the precise orientation of the nitrogen lone pair may be of crucial importance for productive interactions with the opiate receptor (Dimaio *et al.*, 1979). One of the lines of evidence concerned the unexpected contrasting biolog-ical activities between morphinan and D-normorphinan derivatives. When the six-membered piperidine ring of the active morphinan molecule **34** was con-tracted to a five-membered ring as shown in **35** it was observed that the latter

(34)   (35)

molecule is devoid of any receptor affinity (Belleau *et al.*, 1974). The proposed explanation was based on X-ray data of the hydrobromide salt of a D-nor-morphinan showing that in this structure the nitrogen lone pair projects toward the phenyl ring whereas in the classical morphinan derivatives this lone electron pair projects away from the benzene ring (Belleau *et al.*, 1974) (see Fig. 54).

   These results were recently confirmed using the SCRIPT molecular modeling

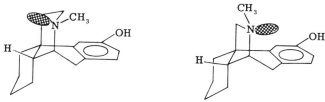

Fig. 54. Comparison of the conformations of (a) morphinan (**34**) and that of (b) D-normorphinan (**35**) as revealed by X-ray analysis. (Belleau *et al.*, 1974.)

system (Cohen and Lemoine, unpublished). In structure **34** the conformer having its lone pair orientated away from the benzene ring is favored and the difference of energy between the two forms is 1.6 kcal/mol. In contrast, the stable form of **35** has its lone pair orientated toward the benzene and in this case the difference of energy between the two forms is 2.7 kcal/mol (see Fig. 55).

Another line of evidence provided by Belleau *et al.* to account for this model concerns the two epimeric molecules of 16,17-butanomorphinan (**36**) (Dimaio *et al.*, 1979).

It was observed that the configuration of carbon number 16 is of crucial importance for biological activity. When the configuration of the hydrogen is α the molecule exhibits agonist activities whereas its β epimer has neither agonist nor antagonist activity. These observations were also analyzed in terms of the specific orientation of the electron lone pair. X-Ray studies have confirmed (Ahmed, 1981) the following interpretation: A chair conformation is possible for the piperidine ring D of the α epimer whereas, due to a combination of contradictory stereochemical and cyclic constraints, this conformation is rigorously prohibited in the β epimer where the piperidine ring D is forced to adopt a boat conformation. Figure 56 shows the 3-D molecular structures of these two molecules and visualizes how the electron lone pair has completely different orientations in the two compounds. It is orientated away from the benzene ring in the active structure **37** whereas in the inactive epimer it is oriented toward this ring. The generality of this model is not definitively established as the crystal structure of the two nonmorphinan derivatives **37** and **38** has been found not to conform to the above requirements (Shiotani *et al.*, 1978).

Some explanations were proposed aiming at a reconciliation of such contradictions (Dimaio *et al.*, 1979). However, recent advances in biology have also

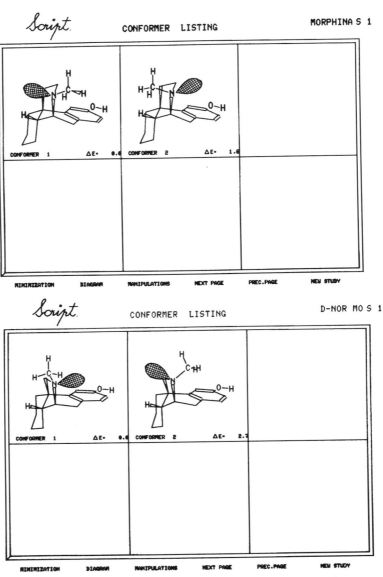

FIG. 55. Orientation of the lone pair and relative stability of the two conformations of morphinan (34) (top) and of D-normorphinan (35) (bottom) as calculated with the SCRIPT molecular modeling system. (Cohen and Lemoine, unpublished.)

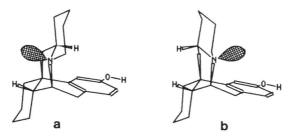

FIG. 56. Stable forms of the two epimeric molecules of 16,17-butanomorphinan (36): the (a) 16α and (b) 16β epimers.

(37)

(38)

drawn attention to the necessity of taking receptor multiplicity into account. New insights in this field should soon lead to appropriate operational models allowing a greater control of the design of new substances with specific actions at different subpopulations of opiate receptors.

5.4 ANTICONVULSANTS

Anticonvulsant drugs are useful in the treatment of epilepsy, with some of these drugs being more specific for certain types of epilepsy. Although the precise site of action for this effect is not known, the GABA (39) neurotransmitter system

NH₂ ⌇ COOH

(39) GABA

plays a key role. Tentative classifications of the drugs in terms of clinical properties have been made together with concomitant attempts to interpret their anticonvulsant action in terms of stereochemical features.

In a series of studies, Camerman and Camerman (1970, 1971a,b, 1972a,b, 1974, 1977; Fawcett *et al.*, 1977) analyzed the crystal structures of anticonvulsant compounds apparently having few chemical similarities (see Fig. 57) and suggested that the anticonvulsant action of these molecules may occur via the same mechanisms. The evidence was based on the observation that all the structures studied had two hydrophobic regions, and these authors have shown that when these regions were superimposed, each compound appeared to possess two electron donor groups situated in similar position and orientation (summarized by

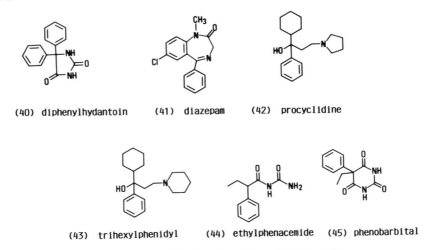

(40) diphenylhydantoin   (41) diazepam   (42) procyclidine

(43) trihexylphenidyl   (44) ethylphenacemide   (45) phenobarbital

FIG. 57. Some clinically active anticonvulsant structures.

Camerman and Camerman, 1974). The corresponding stereochemical similarities are visualized in Fig. 58 for diphenylhydantoin (40), diazepam (41), and procyclidine (42).

Recent results on cannabidiol (46) are consistent with this model (Tamir et al., 1980). The latter, however, has been criticized (Jones and Kennard, 1978) on the ground that the published atomic coordinates do not show a consistent orientation of the hydrophobic rings in the different compounds, and that two benzodiazepine analogs (Sternbach et al., 1974; Gilli et al., 1978), which are almost superimposable on diazepam, exhibit no anticonvulsant activity. These argu-

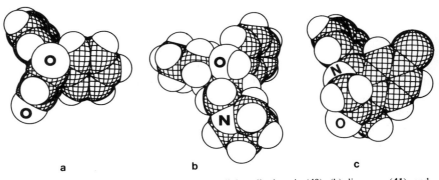

a   b   c

FIG. 58. Stereochemical similarities between (a) diphenylhydantoin (40), (b) diazepam (41), and (c) procyclidine (42) anticonvulsants according to the Camerman model. (Adapted from Camerman and Camerman, 1971b, with permission. Copyright 1971 by the American Society for Pharmacology and Experimental Therapeutics.)

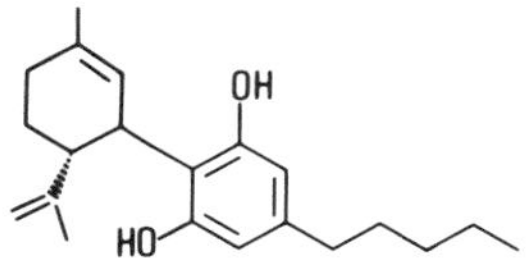

(46) cannabidiol

ments were recently refuted by Andrews and Lloyd (1982), who recalled (Camerman and Camerman, 1974) that the term ''stereochemistry'' refers not only to the 3-D geometry of a molecule, but also to the electronic properties of its functional groups in space. Inactive structures therefore cannot permit one to conclude on the invalidity of this approach. Concerning the orientation of the hydrophobic rings, it has been shown (Andrews and Lloyd, 1982) that consistency may exist within the series, provided that the corresponding absolute configurations are compared. These authors have shown that when the calculated stable or mirror image conformations are used, not only one, but two alternative stereochemical models for anticonvulsant activity can be envisaged. Mentioning unpublished results, they indicate that if anticonvulsant substances with a single hydrophobic ring substituent are considered, the stereochemical features for anticonvulsant activity can be reduced to the following two requirements: (1) a phenyl ring or equivalent hydrocarbon substituent, and (2) a carbonyl or other electronegative group adjacent to the phenyl ring. Additional stereochemical features may enhance the biological activity, e.g., a nitrogen atom able to participate in hydrogen bonding on the opposite side of the electronegative group, or a second electronegative group diagonally opposite the first electronegative region. The same group (Andrews et al., 1983) indicates that clear-cut stereochemical and conformational differences exist in a series of barbiturates with regard to their convulsant or anticonvulsant activities. The corresponding proposed features should enable one on the basis of this model to predict the ability of a new barbiturate to exhibit convulsant or anticonvulsant activities.

5.5 ANTIPSYCHOTICS AND DOPAMINE AGONIST AGENTS

5.5.1 Antipsychotics and Neuroleptics

The central postulate that governs much of the current research concerned with the understanding and treatment of schizophrenia remains the dopamine hypothesis. It is well established that all clinically effective antipsychotic agents act by modulating central dopaminergic activity. This action is interpreted essentially by the ability of these substances to act as antagonists at dopamine receptors in the CNS.

Dopamine has a very simple chemical structure (**47**). The early illuminating

HO—⟨benzene⟩—CH2—CH2—NH2
|
OH
(47) dopamine

observation of Horn and Snyder (1971) that the structure of dopamine is superimposable on the corresponding portion of the chlorpromazine molecule (48) (see

(48) chlorpromazine

Fig. 59) has stimulated extensive chemical and biological work in understanding structure–activity relationships.

The dopamine moiety has been incorporated in a great variety of structures and it was found that the rigidity of this fragment, as well as its stereochemical aspects, were of crucial importance for the biological properties of the molecules concerned. Systematic work was therefore undertaken in order to explore the stereochemical requirements of these dopamine receptors. One central question concerns the conformational preference of the dopamine substrate at its receptor sites. As summarized by Horn and Rodgers (1980), the conformational analysis of the receptor-preferred conformation of dopamine is a threefold problem due to the following aspects:

1. Dopamine can exist in a trans (extended) or two gauche forms (see Fig. 60a).

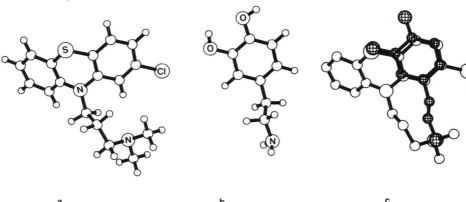

a   b   c

FIG. 59. Common 3-D features: (a) chlorpromazine (48), (b) dopamine (47), and (c) their superposition. (Adapted from Horn and Snyder, 1971, with permission.)

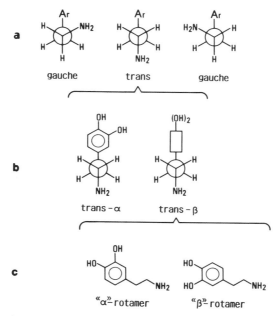

FIG. 60. Conformational features of dopamine and attempts to identify active forms.

2. There are two possibilities for the trans form, for which the aromatic ring can be either perpendicular (trans-α) or coplanar (trans-β) to the amino side chain (Fig. 60b).
3. When the benzene ring is coplanar with the amino side chain, two conformations can be envisaged (they are currently referred as the "α" and "β" rotamers) (Fig. 60c).

The energy difference between these conformations is small, and either of them could therefore be envisaged to be responsible for the biological activity of dopamine at a given receptor.

(−)-Apomorphine (**49**) is a potent dopamine agonist in which the location of the hydroxyl substituents is of great importance: for example, the complete loss of receptor affinity is observed with isoapomorphine (**50**).

(49)   apomorphine   (50)   isoapomorphine

The simple comparison of these structures with that of the α and β rotamers of dopamine may lead to the conclusion that the α rotamer should be the biologically relevant one; unfortunately the problem is not so simple, as evidenced by the numerous data which are not consistent with this interpretation. Although most pharmacological results are compatible with the existence of a trans conformation for dopamine (reviewed by Horn and Rodgers, 1980) the difficulty is to clearly establish which of the α or β rotamers is preferred.

In a series of papers, Cannon *et al.* (1975, 1976, 1983) have analyzed this question and proposed a preference for the α rotamer (Cannon *et al.*, 1977; Costall *et al.*, 1982); on the contrary, Horn and Rodgers (1980) proposed the β rotamer. In both studies the biological properties of the two isomeric aminotetralins (**51**) and (**52**) were different, but *in vivo* results were opposite to *in vitro* results.

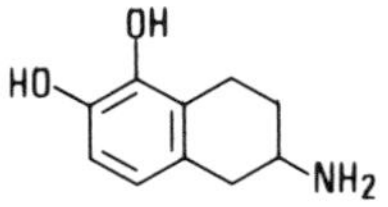

(51) 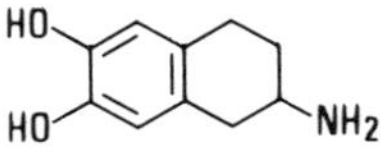   (52)

Costall and Naylor have stressed (1981) that attempts to define a single definitive answer to this question may be an "illusory quest" since receptor-labeling studies indicate that this preference may change *within* a chemical series (depending, in particular, on the degree of N-alkylation)!

More recent results obtained with the two aminoindan analogs (**53**) and (**54**)

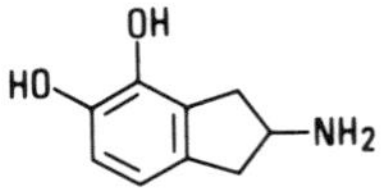

(53) 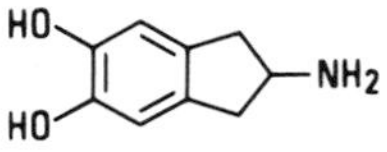   (54)

revealed that this series markedly differs from the aminotetralin series (Cannon *et al.*, 1982), thus confirming the necessity to refine the strategies of research in this direction.

Due to the continuous accumulation of results obtained in this field a number of "models" have been envisaged in order to account for the biological properties observed.

In attempts to design dopaminergic agonists which lack adrenergic effects Grol and Rollema (1977) and Goldberg *et al.* (1978) have outlined some requirements of the renal vascular dopamine receptor. Considering the inability of the proposed models to account for the vascular effects displayed by compounds such as **55** (largely inactive) and **56** (as potent as dopamine), Cannon *et al.* (1981) stressed the fact that the requirements for renal vascular dopaminergic

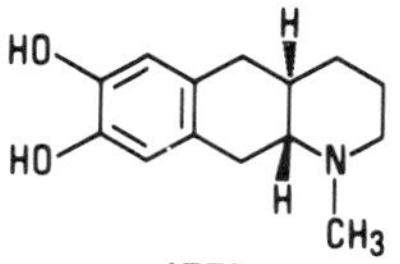

(55) 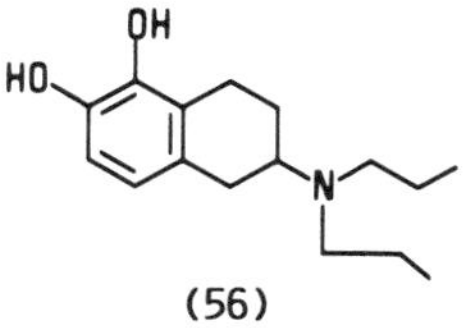   (56)

agonist activity are as yet poorly understood. However, Erhardt (1980) has improved these models by considering novel chemical series such as the inactive phenylcyclopropylamine analogs (57).

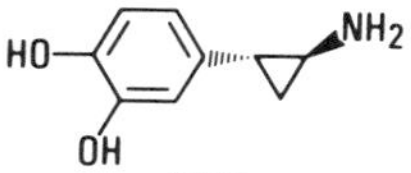

(57)

Concerning dopaminergic receptors in the central nervous system, Tollenaere *et al.* (1980) have analyzed a wide range of neuroleptics by means of X-ray crystallographic data, molecular orbital calculations (PCILO), and least-squares superposition methods. Using the rigid dopamine antagonist butaclamol (58a) as

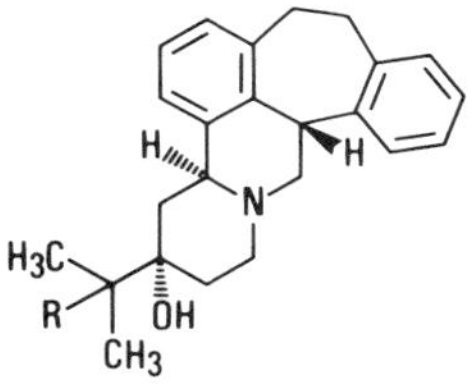

(a) R= CH₃ (+)-butaclamol
(58) (b) R= H   (+)-dexclamol

a probe, and low-energy conformations (less than 3 kcal/mol) of various anti-psychotics, least-squares procedures were conducted to fit each molecule with that of the reference probe. The set of antipsychotics studied included the following chemical series: butyrophenones [represented by benperidol (59)], phenothi-

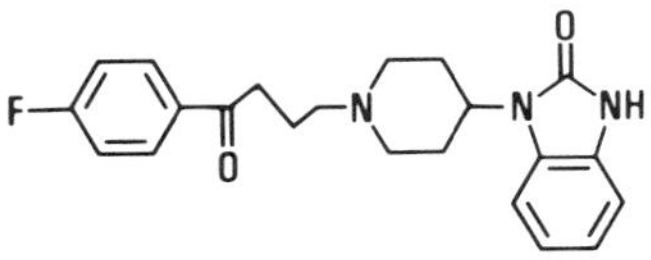

(59) benperidol

azines [chlorpromazine (48)], thioxanthenes [piflutixol (60)], clozapine (61), and octoclothepine (62). The matching treatment was aimed at maximizing the overlap between corresponding groupings such as phenyl rings, nitrogen atoms, and the orientation of the nitrogen lone electron pair. The resulting superposi-

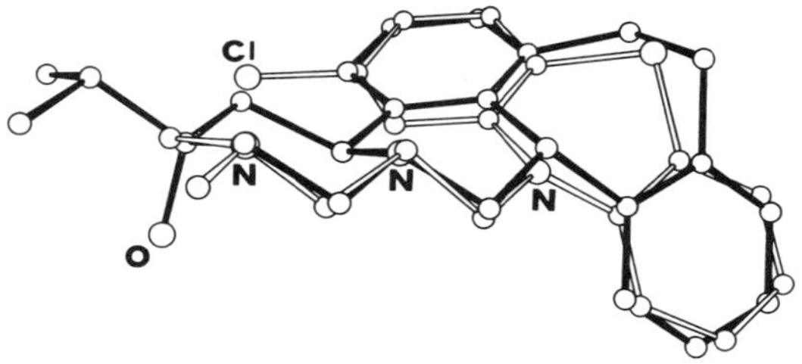

FIG. 61. The fit of the structures of chlorpromazine (48) and dexclamol (58b). (According to Moereels and Tollenaere, 1978, copyright 1978 by Pergamon Press.)

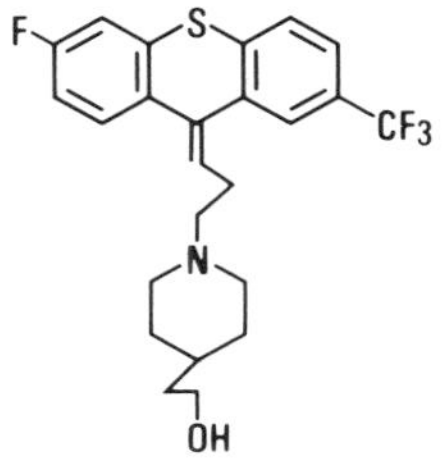

(60) piflutixol 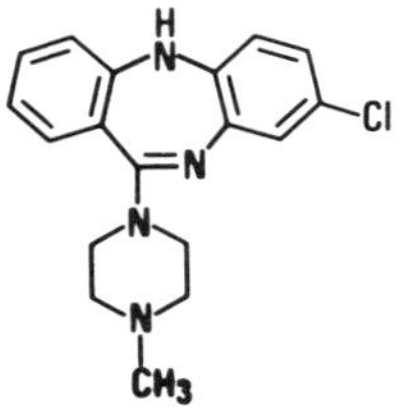   (61) clozapine 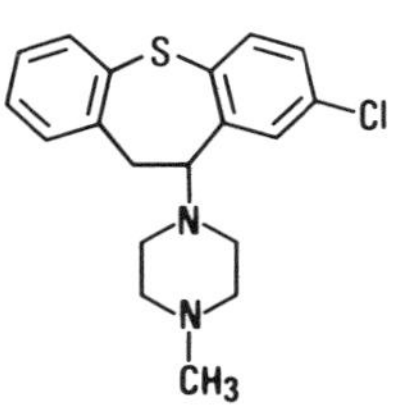   (62) octoclothepine

tions therefore suggest possible biologically relevant conformations of the molecules concerned. Figure 61, for example, illustrates the superposition of dexclamol (58b) with chlorpromazine (48) [the more accurate X-ray data of dexclamol (Bird *et al.*, 1976) was used for the superposition instead of butaclamol].

One of the weaknesses of this model is the assumption that carbon-2 of dexclamol could mimic the important nitrogen atom of the side chain in neuroleptic structures, a postulate not entirely consistent with what is known about the particular role of this atom. However, this attempt must not be rejected. While not giving a global interpretation of this as yet unclarified question, it has merit in proposing a number of excellent fits which can be used for further improvement and design.

In order to establish a topographic map of the central dopamine receptor, Humber *et al.* (1979) have paid particular attention to (−)-apomorphine (63), a

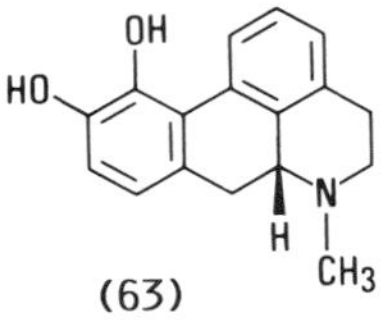

(63)

(-)-apomorphine

dopamine receptor agonist, and to the antagonist butaclamol (58a). Assuming that both types of ligands bind to the same receptor sites, they proposed the

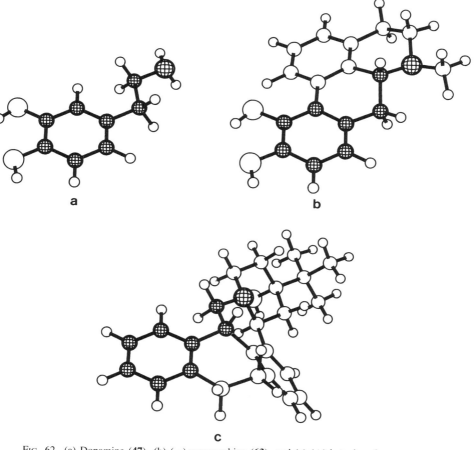

FIG. 62. (a) Dopamine (**47**), (b) (−)-apomorphine (**63**), and (c) (+)-butaclamol: common stereochemical features according to Humber *et al.* (1979).

common stereochemical features visualized in Fig. 62 for dopamine, (−)-apomorphine and (+)-butaclamol.

The conformation proposed for butaclamol is not that observed in the crystalline state (conformation A) but another one where the seven-membered ring assumes a geometry (conformer B) which should be of higher energy. Following on along these lines, Humber *et al.* (1979) compared various antagonists such as (+)-isobutaclamol (**64**) and octoclothepine (**62**), and derived a topographic map summarizing the requirements proposed for the central dopaminergic receptor (Fig. 63). It contains a planar primary aromatic (naphthalenic) binding site, a primary nitrogen binding site with its complementary hydrogen bond donor site, as well as a lipophilic accessory binding site able to accomodate the *tert*-butyl or

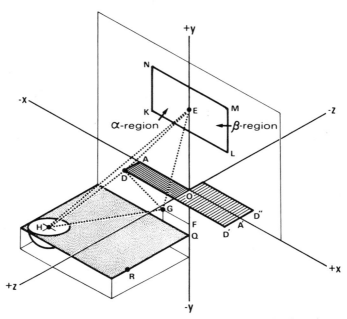

FIG. 63. Representation of primary and accessory binding sites on the dopamine receptor according to Humber. (Humber *et al.*, 1979, with permission. Copyright 1979 by the *American Chemical Society*.)

(64)

(+)-isobutaclamol

similar bulky groups. The aromatic binding site contains α and β regions (Fig. 63) which can be understood from the superposition of (+)-butaclamol (**58a**) and (+)-isobutaclamol (**64**) (see Fig. 64).

The model has been criticized (Andrews and Lloyd, 1982) in that it does not account for the effect of electronic substituents of classical tricyclic neuroleptics since halogenation of butaclamol in an analogous position to that of phenothiazines did not produce the anticipated increase in activity (Humber *et al.*, 1978). From another point of view, the model has been also criticized by Cannon *et al.* (1981), who argued that it is risky to define a dopamine receptor on the basis of features that accomodate both agonist and antagonist molecules. This question is still under dispute, and there is experimental evidence in favor

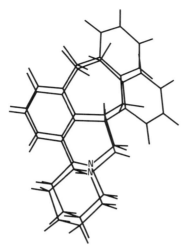

Fig. 64. Superimposed Dreiding models of B conformers of (+)-butaclamol and (+)-iso-butaclamol. (From Humber *et al.*, 1979, with permission. Copyright 1979 by the *American Chemical Society.*)

(Tedesco *et al.*, 1979) and against (Seeman *et al.*, 1979) the identity of the "neuroleptic receptor" with the receptor binding the agonist apomorphine (for recent reviews see Kaiser and Kebabian, 1983; Carlsson and Nilsson, 1983). However, as far as attempts to design new agents are concerned, no practical working hypothesis should be rejected. It is well known from experience that simple working hypotheses may lead to compounds of great utility in therapy and in clarifying biological investigations.

5.5.2 Dopamine Receptor Agonists

In the field of dopamine agonists ergot alkaloids have been the starting point of extensive series of semisynthetic and synthetic analogs. These derivatives belong to the class of indole alkaloids having, in general, the condensed four-ring structure of ergoline. One of the most studied molecules is bromocriptine (**65**),

(65) bromocriptine

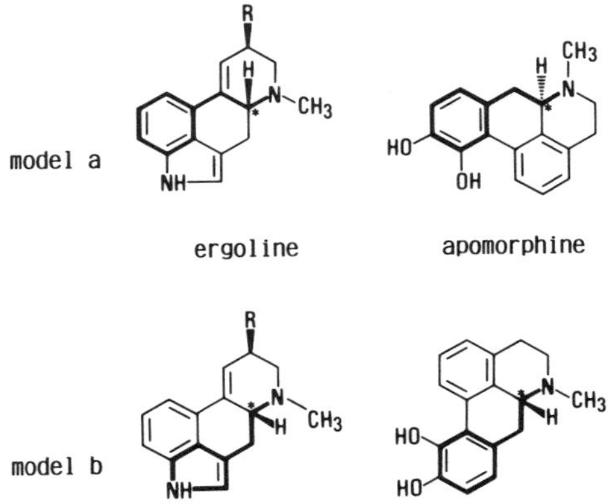

model a

ergoline   apomorphine

model b

FIG. 65. Two alternative ways (a and b) of recognizing the phenethylamine dopamine moiety of apomorphine in the ergoline nucleus.

whose chemical structure is also related to that of lysergic acid. In such structures the phenylethylamine moiety of dopamine is fixed in a rigid extended conformation. Although it lacks the phenolic group of catecholamines, bromocriptine has potent dopamine agonist activities. This property is useful in the therapy of a number of diseases, including Parkinsonism, acromegaly, and galactorrhea–amenorrhea syndrome. The compound is preferred to apomorphine due to the drawbacks of the latter with respect to its short duration of action and its poor oral absorption. Isosteric entities mimicking the phenethylamine moiety existing in dopamine and apomorphine can be found in the chemical structure of bromocriptine. Actually it is possible to envisage the recognition of this fragment in two different ways, depending on whether the benzene or the pyrrol ring of bromocriptine mimics the phenolic ring of apomorphine (Figure 65). Both interpretations were actually explored. On the one hand, model a symbolizes the strategy used in the thorough work of Cannon *et al.* (summarized by Bach *et al.*, 1980). On the other hand, Bach, *et al.* (1980) have explored the second alternative. Considering the question from the point of view of model a they have designed simplified bicyclic and tricyclic ergoline structures such as (**66**) and

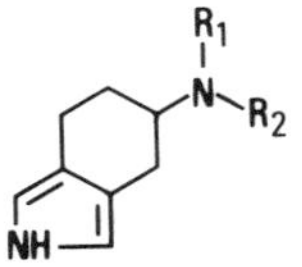

(66) 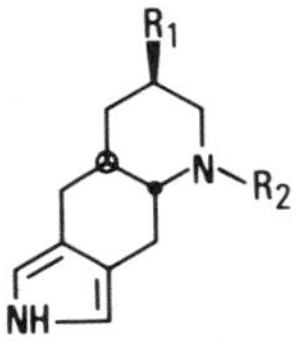   (67)

(**67**). These series exhibited potent dopaminergic activities and therefore proved that the benzene ring of an ergoline is not essential for dopaminergic activity. In

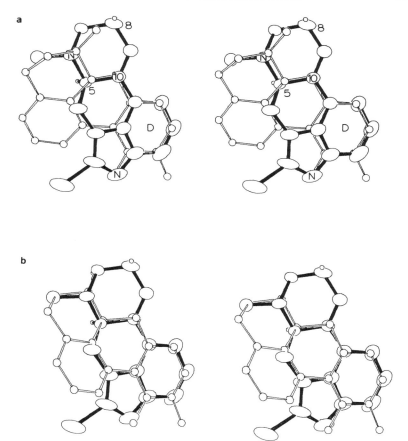

FIG. 66. Stereoscopic view of the tetracyclic ring system of bromocriptine (**65**) (dark bonds) superimposed on (a) $R(-)$-apomorphine, and (b) $S(+)$-apomorphine (light bonds) so that dopamine-like parts of the molecules are maximally fitted. (From Camerman *et al.*, 1979, with permission. Copyright 1979 by the *American Society for Pharmacology and Experimental Therapeutics*).

support of this hypothesis the authors have stressed that there is a greater stereochemical consistency in model b (hydrogens on carbon atoms indicated in Fig. 65 by an asterisk have the same configuration) than in model a (the configurations are opposite). Since apomorphine with the R absolute configuration at this carbon is active whereas the S enantiomer is inactive, the potential possibilities of model b appear even more convincing and further studies are expected to open new horizons on this question.

Camerman *et al.* (1979) compared the X-ray structures of bromocriptine and apomorphine and have indicated a good fit in the superposition of the two molecules (model a). However, they were surprised to observe that the degree of fit was better with the inactive S-apomorphine rather than with the active R enantiomer (see Fig. 66)!

In this article the inactivity of S-apomorphine is ascribed to the existence of the two additional rings of apomorphine (when compared to dopamine) which might block the approach of the pharmacophore to the receptor. Although this interpretation should not be rejected, the relative bad fit observed for S-apomorphine reflects only the stereochemical inconsistency as indicated in model a. The comparison of the 3-D features of the two active molecules remains to be done, and in any case must not be overlooked in the light of model b. This example illustrates how simple questions may not have simple (and unique) answers and that one important aspect of the answers is also that the question should be formulated in a different way.

5.5.3 Multiplicity of Dopamine Receptors

It is well established that there exist (in animals and presumably in humans) more than one type of dopamine receptor (Kebabian and Calne, 1979; Seeman, 1980;

ACTIVE   ANALOGS

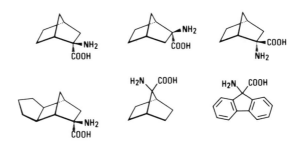

INACTIVE   ANALOGS

FIG. 67. Active and inactive analogs used to analyze the "enzyme excluded" and "enzyme-essential" regions. (From Sufrin et al., 1981, with permission. Copyright 1981 by the American Society for Pharmacology and Experimental Therapeutics.)

FIG. 68. Enzyme-excluded volume map constructed with the six active analogs represented in Fig. 67. (From Sufrin et al., 1981, with permission. Copyright 1981 by the American Society for Pharmacology and Experimental Therapeutics.)

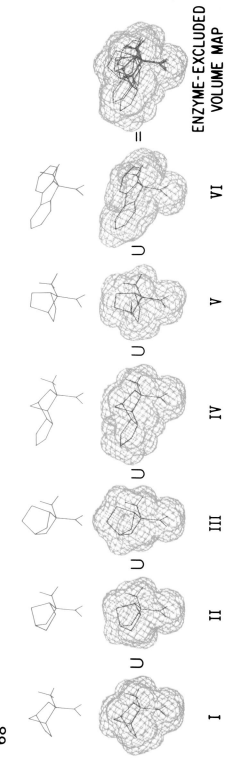

ENZYME-EXCLUDED
VOLUME MAP

II

VI

∪

V

∪

IV

∪

III

∪

II

∪

I

68

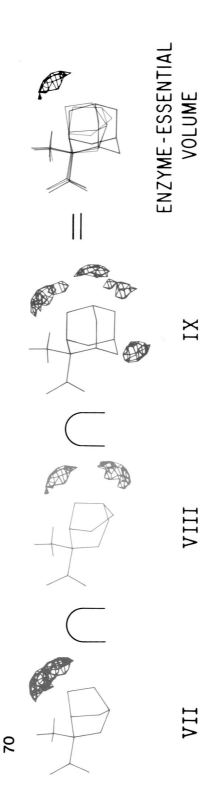

VII

VIII

IX

ENZYME-ESSENTIAL
VOLUME

70

Sokoloff *et al.*, 1980; Costall and Naylor, 1981). Attempts to classify the numerous dopamine receptor subtypes include biochemical, behavioral, and electrophysical responses toward natural or synthetic ligands. It appears useful to distinguish between D_1 and D_2 receptors: D_1 receptors are those whose stimulation activates adenylate cyclase whereas D_2 receptors are not or are negatively linked to this enzyme. It is now also necessary to distinguish between pre- and postsynaptic receptors. Among numerous intriguing observations is the fact that some dopaminergic agonists can either stimulate or inhibit the activity of a dopaminergic neuron depending upon a predominant or exclusive pre- or postsynaptic locus of action. Despite the large number of synthetic dopamine analogs which have been studied it has not yet been possible either to design substances which are consistently specific for the various subtypes of receptors, or to achieve a fully satisfactory dopamine receptor classification. It will be most instructive and fruitful for drug design to follow breakthroughs in this challenging area.

5.6 INHIBITORS OF THE ENZYMATIC SYNTHESIS OF S-ADENOSYL-L-METHIONINE

Methionine adenosyltransferase catalyzes the biosynthetic conversion of L-methionine and ATP to S-adenosyl-L-methionine the principal biological methyl donor. From inhibition studies with various amino acid analogs, Talalay and co-workers have deduced the conformation of L-methionine (**68**) at the active site

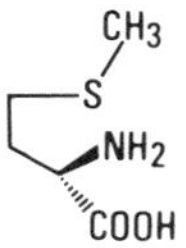

$$\text{CH}_3$$

(68) L-methionine

(Sufrin *et al.*, 1979). In an attempt to design chemotherapeutic agents capable of inhibiting adenosyltransferase activity, conformational rigid amino acid analogs were studied according to the ''enzyme-excluded volume'' and ''enzyme-essential volume'' concepts as defined by Marshall *et al.* (1979). In this formulation the enzyme-excluded volume map defines that region of the enzyme-active site available for binding by ligands, whereas the enzyme-essential volume is the volume occupied by the enzyme, (a molecule requiring volume in this region would be unable to bind to the surface of the enzyme's active site and would therefore be inactive). The six active analogs indicated in Fig. 67 permitted the construction of the enzyme-excluded volume (a volume not occupied by the enzyme itself).

FIG. 70. The ''enzyme-essential'' volume as obtained using the individual inactive analogs. (From Sufrin *et al.*, 1981, with permission. Copyright 1981 by the *American Society for Pharmacology and Experimental Therapeutics*.)

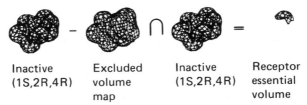

Inactive	Excluded	Inactive	Receptor
(1S,2R,4R)	volume	(1S,2R,4R)	essential
	map		volume

FIG. 69. Definition of an active site-essential volume as revealed by one inactive analog:

$$<V_I - (V_{EX} \cap V_I) = V_{ESS}^{(I)} >$$

with the subtraction of the favorable V_F volume from that of the inactive analog one obtains a volume which could be responsible for negative interactions with the receptor site. (From Marshall *et al.*, 1979, with permission. Copyright 1979 by the *American Chemical Society*.)

Such a resulting volume is shown in Fig. 68. It is obtained as the union of the six individual volumes of the active structures in providing the volume available for binding the methionine site.

Inactive analogs can be used to provide information about possible enzyme-essential regions in the active site. A given inactive compound reveals such a region in the following way (Fig. 69): V_I and V_{EX} are, respectively, the volume of the inactive substance and that of the excluded volume. The intersection $V_{EX} \cap V_I$ defines a "favorable" volume V_F existing in the inactive analog. By subtraction of this volume from that of the inactive analog ($V_I - V_F$) one gets for this inactive compound the volume which could be responsible for negative interaction with the receptor. The intersection of such volumes for all the inactive structures analyzed provides the enzyme-essential volume. In Fig. 70 it is shown how such a volume has been obtained on the basis of the three inactive molecules from Fig. 67.

Such a model offers a rational basis for the interpretation of the strict stereochemical requirements observed for activity. The knowledge of the different spatial regions involved can serve as a starting point for predicting the chances of activity for new analogs and also for improving the 3-D features of the working model. Such an approach can be useful only where there are strong reasons to interpret the biological inactivity on the basis of steric effects. Otherwise it can only be considered as a working hypothesis, leaving room to other interpretations.

5.7 NONSTEROIDAL ANTIINFLAMMATORY AGENTS

It is now well established that the molecular mechanism accounting for the biological properties of nonsteroidal antiinflammatory drugs (NSAID) such as indomethacin (**69**) is due to the ability of these substances to inhibit the bio-synthesis of prostaglandins (PG). One of the first steps of PG biosynthesis involves cyclooxygenase, a PG synthetase. As a wide range of nonsteroidal antiinflammatory drugs inhibit this enzyme, several attempts have been made to compare the stereochemical features of the natural substrates such as arachidonic acid (**70**) or its peroxy analog (**71**) (Fig. 71) with that of known inhibitors. For example, on the basis of a comparison between indomethacin (**69**) and arach-idonic acid (**70**), Gund and Shen (1977) have proposed conformational sim-ilarities as shown in Fig. 72. These stereoviews illustrate how the two ligands can fit the same receptor site on PG cyclooxygenase. The actual conformation of arachidonic acid was constructed in a way permitting not only the fit of this substrate on the proposed receptor site, but aiming also at being consistent with the precise known stereospecificity of the transformation of arachidonic acid into the cyclic endoperoxide PGG_2 (**72**).

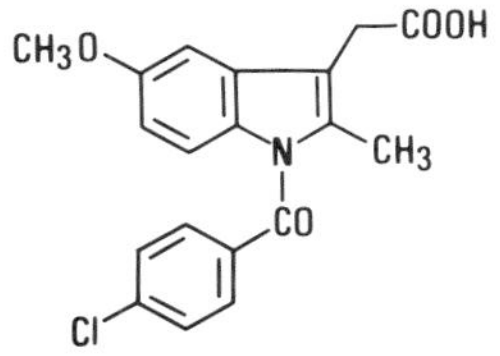

(69) indomethacin 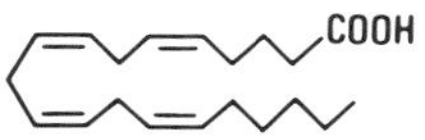 (70) arachidonic acid

In this interpretation, as well as in that previously proposed by Scherrer (1974), the mechanism accounting for the inhibition by antiinflammatory agents requires that the carboxyl group of the drugs binds at a cationic site of the enzyme, a region normally occupied by the carboxyl group of the substrate.

Appleton and Brown (1979) studied the peroxy radical (**71**) and compound **73** as representative models for cyclooxygenase substrates and inhibitors, respec-tively. Following a similar approach they revealed new 3-D similarities as out-

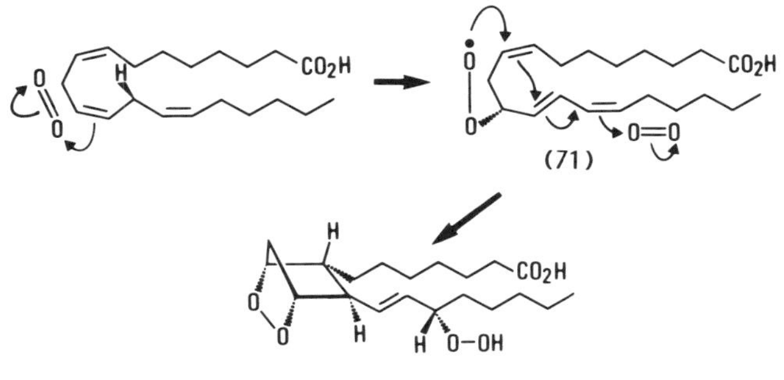

(71)

(72)

Fig. 71. The prostaglandin cyclooxygenase pathway.

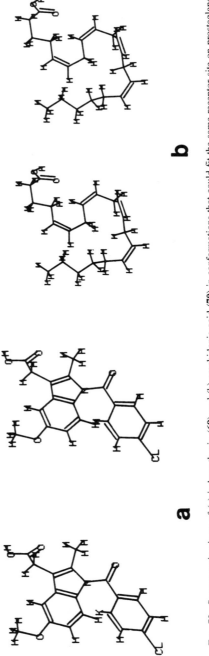

FIG. 72. Stereoscopic views of (a) indomethacin (**69**) and (b) arachidonic acid (**70**) in conformations that could fit the same receptor site on prostaglandin cyclooxygenase. (From Gund and Shen, 1977. Copyright 1977 by the *American Chemical Society*.)

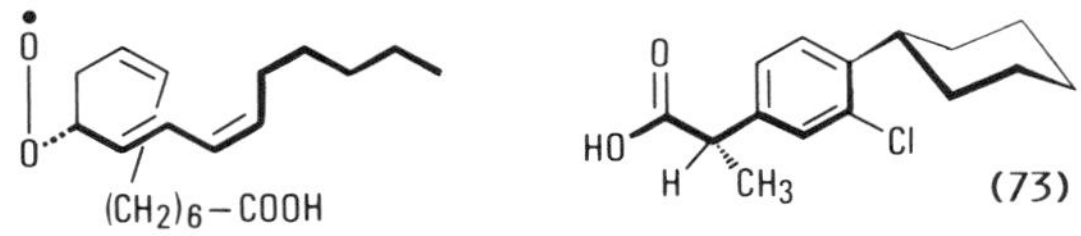

(CH2)6—COOH (73)

Fig. 73. Three-dimensional similarities proposed by Appleton and Brown (1979) between the peroxy radical **71** and molecule **73**. (With permission, copyright 1979 by Geron-X, Inc.)

lined in Fig. 73. In this model, the carboxyl group of the antiinflammatory drug is assumed to bind to an oxygenation site of the enzyme which is different from Gund's interpretation. The structures of other inhibitors such as indomethacin (**74**), ketoprofen (**75**), fenopren (**76**), alclofenac (**77**), naproxen (**78**), and ibuprofen (**79**), were shown to be able to fit this model. New derivatives such as FPL 58302 (**80**) were designed on the basis of these features and exhibited

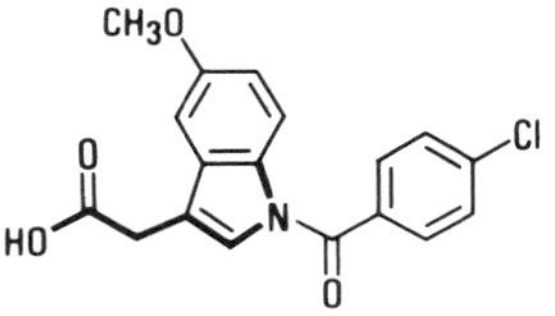

(74) indomethacin 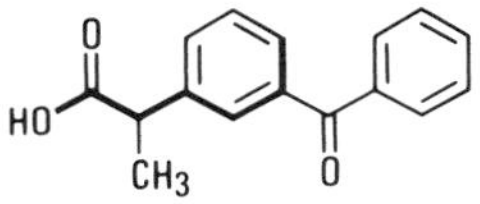   (75) ketoprofen 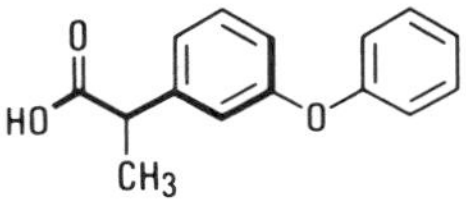   (76) fenopren

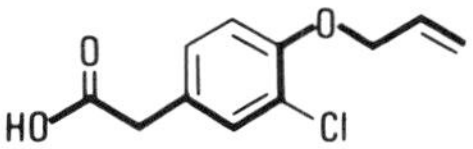

(77) alclofenac   naproxen (78) 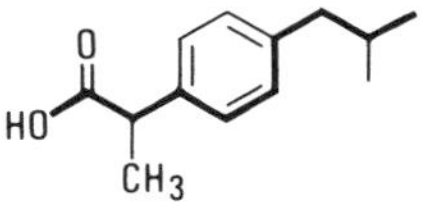   (79) ibuprofen

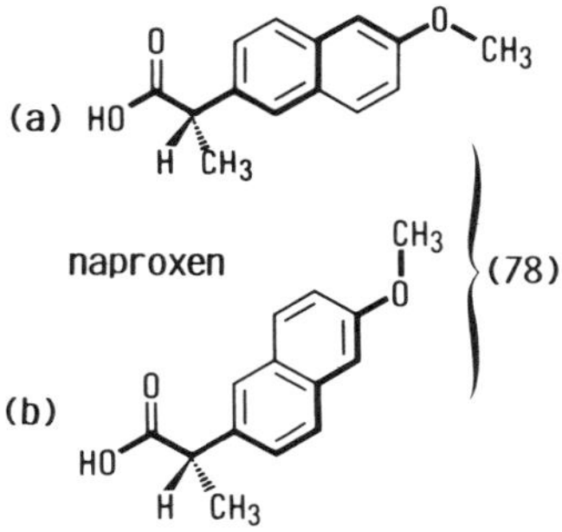

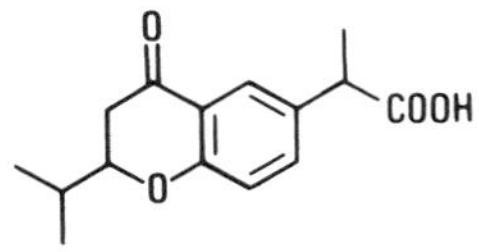

(80) FPL 58302

moderately good antiinflammatory properties (Blackham *et al.*, 1979a,b). Recently, Salvetti *et al.* (1981) compared the geometrical features of indoprofen, another PG synthetase inhibitor, and calculated a low-energy conformation of arachidonic acid mimicking the stereochemical features of the drug. Although

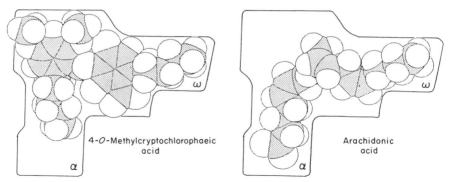

FIG. 74. Conformations of arachidonic acid (**70**) and *m*-depside (**81**) defining the receptor site model proposed by Sankawa *et al.* (1982). (With permission, copyright 1982 by Geron-X, Inc.)

the actual conformation is quite different from that proposed by Gund and Shen (1977), the general features of the cyclooxygenase active site remain similar.

Recently a new active site model was proposed for this enzyme by Sankawa *et al.* (1982) subsequent to the discovery of natural products (lichen depsides) such as 4-*O*-methylcryptochlorophaeic acid (**81**) (see Fig. 75). It was observed that such a compound binds competitively with respect to arachidonic acid or indomethacin and other nonsteroidal antiinflammatory drugs. Starting from the X-ray structure of this molecule a new cyclooxygenase active site was proposed (see Fig. 74). The model consists of four regions, designated α, ω, A, and B. The α region contains a cationic center trapping the carboxyl group of arachidonic acid, and an ω region accommodating the terminal alkyl group. A and B regions are π electron acceptor regions functioning as the catalytic sites for C-11 and C-15 of arachidonic acid.

The corresponding mechanism of inhibition is similar to that of Appleton and Brown (1979) and the newly proposed interpretation is consistent with a wide range of very different chemical classes of drugs including indomethacin (**82**), flurbiprofen (**83**), ketoprofen (**84**), a yet unnamed molecule (**73**), clidanac (**91**), mefenamic acid (**86**), and flufenamic acid (**87**) (Fig. 75).

As we can see from this analysis several explanatory models have been proposed, the comparison of which reveals that they are not always consistent with one another. This is not surprising when one recalls the several millions of possible low-energy conformations of the natural substrates as well as the great variety of reference lead structures which may be considered as a basic set in the search for stereochemical similarities. Moreover, the reduction of the inflammation process to a mere PG synthesis, although useful for SAR purposes, remains an approximation. The merit of the various models which were, and will be, proposed is to broaden the horizon by allowing consideration of the wide range of accumulated data in the light of useful empirical working hypotheses. These

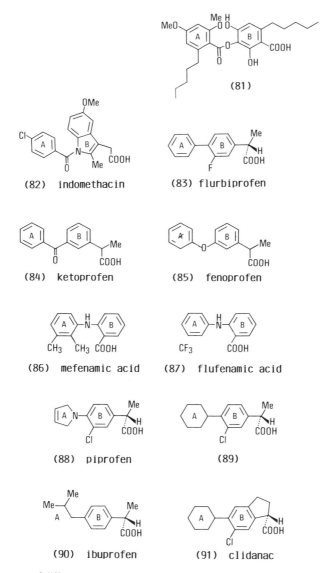

FIG. 75. Structures of different classes of nonsteroidal antiinflammatory agents considered in the Sankawa *et al.* (1982) model. (With permission Copyright 1982 by Geron-X, Inc.)

working hypotheses, being continuously improved, provide practical guidelines in the search for novel antiinflammatory drugs while new insights are obtained in our understanding of detailed mechanisms of inflammation or of the topography of active sites in the various enzymes involved.

5.8 INHIBITORS OF DIHYDROFOLATE REDUCTASE

5.8.1 QSAR Approaches

The enzyme dihydrofolate reductase (DHFR) is used by all living organisms in the activation of dihydrofolic acid (92) to tetrahydrofolic acid which acts in the

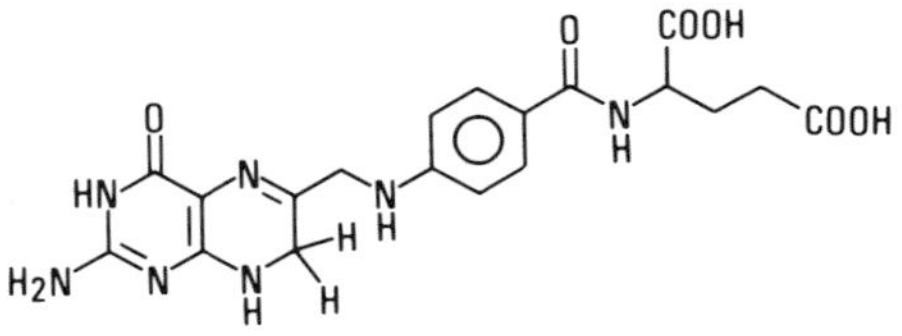

(92) dihydrofolic acid

synthesis of the heterocyclic bases that are necessary to build DNA. Inhibition of DHFR can therefore prevent cell division, explaining why inhibitors are of great therapeutic interest in the control of disease processes, including bacterial infections and tumors.

Trimethoprim (93) and methotrexate (94) are both inhibitors of DHFR; the

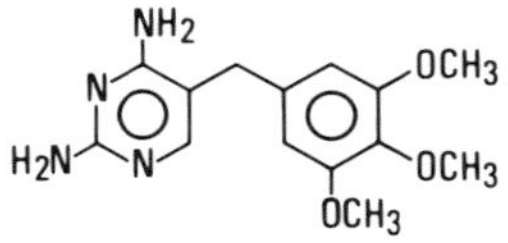

(93) trimethoprim 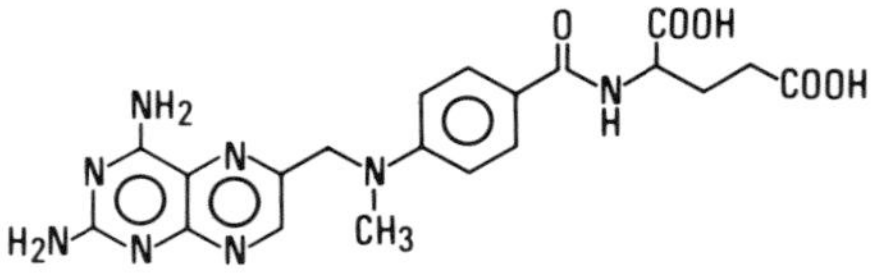   (94) methotrexate

former is an antibacterial while the latter is used in anticancer chemotherapy.

Extensive studies initiated by Baker (summarized by Hansch et al., 1977) on triazine analogs (95) have led Hansch's group to establish QSAR for various

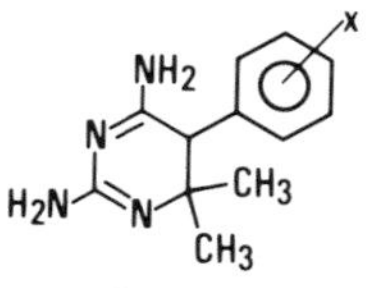

(95)

series of inhibitors and enzymes (reviewed by Hansch, 1981). Indeed, the DHFR group of enzymes exhibits considerable species-to-species variability in sen-

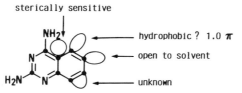

FIG. 76. Structural features established by QSAR analyses. (From Hansch *et al.*, 1977, with permission. Copyright 1977 by the *American Chemical Society.*)

sitivity toward different inhibitors. The general features revealed in the *Escherischia coli* DHFR are outlined in Fig. 76. Hopfinger envisaged the use of novel molecular shape descriptors where the 3-D common overlap volume between pairs of molecules are considered in a QSAR analysis (Hopfinger, 1980). This parameter may be considered as a representation of relative shape similarity. The analysis of the bovine liver DHFR inhibitory activity of a series of substituted 5-benzyl-2,4-diaminopyrimidines has led to the following equation (Hopfinger, 1981):

$$\log(1/C) = -21.31V_0 + 2.39V_0^2 + 0.44\,(\pi_3 + \pi_4) + 52.23 \qquad (1)$$

$$n = 23 \qquad r = 0.931 \qquad s = 0.137$$

where V_0 represents the common overlap steric volume between each molecule of the series and a reference standard compound. The term $\pi_3 + \pi_4$ is the sum of hydrophobic constants of the 3- and 4-position substituents.

This equation can be compared with that obtained in the Hansch group (Blaney *et al.*, 1979) as indicated in Eq. (2):

$$\log(1/C) = 0.622\pi_3 + 0.322\,\Sigma\sigma^+ + 4.99 \qquad (2)$$

$$n = 23 \qquad r = 0.931 \qquad s = 0.146$$

Both correlations have the same statistical quality; however, the physical model associated with molecular shape descriptors is shown to carry a better description of the SAR since the corresponding equation appeared to be identical in form in the analysis of a set of quinazoline derivatives (Hopfinger, 1980). Using molecular shape analysis correlations the activities of several compounds were predicted and fully confirmed (Hopfinger, 1980). New improvements were recently introduced by expressing the shape descriptor in terms of differences in molecular potential energy fields (Hopfinger, 1983). The Hansch group continues to develop new QSAR equations in order to reveal more selective antitumor and antimicrobiological agents having a relative low effect toward DHFR of human cells (Hathaway *et al.*, 1984). Molecular graphics is now being used by this group in order to provide new guidelines in this respect (Hansch *et al.*, 1982, 1984; Li *et al.*, 1982).

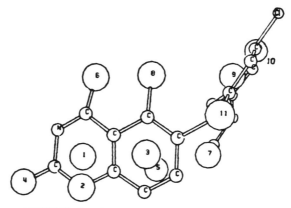

Fig. 77. Proposed DHFR binding site established by distance geometry analyses. (From Crippen, 1980, with permission. Copyright 1980 by the *American Chemical Society*.)

Using the distance geometry approach, Crippen has proposed a binding geometry as described in Fig. 77 (Crippen, 1980). Further investigations following this nonclassical QSAR approach led to improved results and suggested geometrical interpretations (Ghose and Crippen, 1982, 1983).

5.8.2 X-Ray Structures of the Enzymes and ''Direct'' Design

As stressed by Gund (1982) it is most instructive to compare insights provided by each of these approaches in the investigation of this question. There is no doubt that approaches based on crystal structures of the enzyme with bound inhibitors will permit one to explore new lead inhibitors in a more rational way. The first such crystal structure analysis was done by Matthews *et al.* (1977) for methotrexate bound to *E. coli* DHFR. New X-ray studies of enzyme–ligand complexes have been reported by Matthews *et al.* (1979) for *Lactobacillus casei* DHFR, NADPH, and methotrexate; by Matthews (1981) for chicken liver DHFR, NADPH, and a series of inhibitors including trimethoprim; by Baker *et al.* on *E. coli* DHFR complexes with trimethoprim (1981a) and two analogs (1981b). Differences have been detected in the orientation of the various ligands in the receptor cleft, and ongoing studies with mammalian enzymes are expected to explain why methotrexate, unlike trimethoprim, inhibits mammalian DHFR much more than bacterial DHFR.

Subsequent to the analysis of a crystal structure revealing the existence of possible additional binding sites, Poe *et al.* (1981; see also Gund, 1982) have designed potent DHFR inhibitors. A similar approach permitted Kuyper *et al.* (1982) to observe that appropriate substituents on the structure of trimethoprim could lead to an increase in inhibitory binding. The following basic residues of

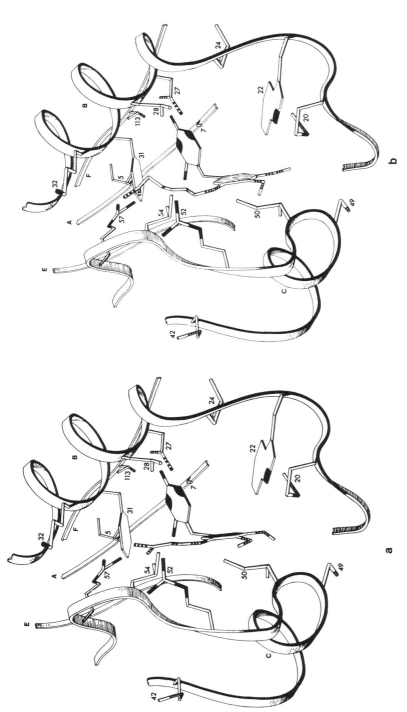

FIG. 78. Schematic illustration of the binding site for (a) compound **96b** and (b) **96e** in *E. coli* DHFR. (From Kuyper *et al.*, 1982, with permission. Copyright 1982 by the *American Chemical Society*.)

the enzyme, Arg-57, Lys-32, and Arg-52, appeared as possible additional anchoring sites. To compare the situation with that of methotrexate, a carboxyl function was introduced for exploratory purposes in the chemical structure of trimethoprim (96).

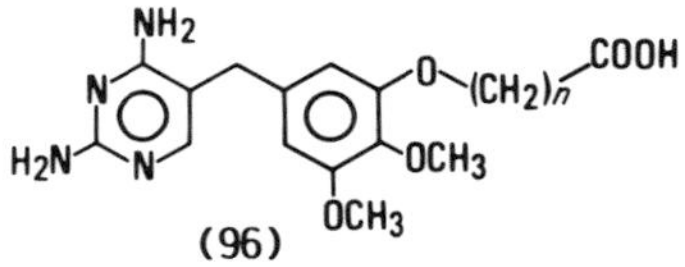

$$n = \begin{array}{cccccc} a & b & c & d & e & f \\ 1 & 2 & 3 & 4 & 5 & 6 \end{array}$$

An ionic linkage was expected to be created with one or more of the positively charged sites involving the above-mentioned basic residues. As some acid analogs such as 96c–f exhibited a significantly higher affinity for DHFR than that of trimethoprim, it was concluded that the desired ionic interaction could have occurred (Kuyper *et al.*, 1982). The X-ray study of two enzyme complexes with 96b and 96e revealed that the carboxylic acid substituent was interacting with Arg-57 as visualized in Fig. 78.

These analyses also confirmed the prediction that Arg-57 would be preferable for binding rather than Lys-32 or Arg-52. Because the guanidinium moiety of Arg-57 is deeply buried in a hydrophobic region of the enzyme, it was expected that it would form stronger ionic bonds than the two other residues, which are located on the enzyme surface with side chains extending into the solvent (Kuyper *et al.*, 1982).

As we can see, great progress has been made in this direction, ''molecular modeling experiments'' being likely to dramatically widen the horizon of medicinal chemistry in the next decades. Initiated several years ago on a very empirical basis, the design of new inhibitors can now proceed in a more rational way. The potential interest of this new methodology is illustrated and discussed in the next section.

6 Applied Three-Dimensional Drug Design: Toward the Rational Design of New Leads

6.1 DIRECT AND INDIRECT MOLECULAR MODELING

As outlined in the previous example it is possible to envisage an ideal drug design approach for which the molecular features of the receptor sites are known with precise 3-D details (in general, determined by X-ray diffraction analysis). In this perspective the efficiency of the design should be improved in an approach which can be called direct or *ab initio* drug design (Meyer, 1980; Cushman and Ondetti, 1982). Controlled 3-D structures can therefore be designed for direct and optimal interactions with the receptor site. Several years ago, Beddell and co-workers (1976) considered the crystallographic coordinates of atoms in human hemoglobin and used molecular models to design compounds which should bind and stabilize the deoxy conformation of the enzyme. As expected, the compounds behaved as expected and promoted oxygen liberation. These molecules (**97**) actually had a completely different chemical type from the known 2,3-diphosphoglycerate (DPG) ligand (**98**).

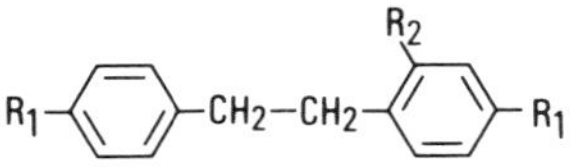

$$R_1-\langle\rangle-CH_2-CH_2-\langle\rangle-R_1$$
$$\overset{R_2}{}$$

(97)

(a) $R_1 = CHO$; $R_2 = O-CH_2-COOH$

(b) $R_1 = CHOH-SO_3H$; $R_2 = H$

(c) $R_1 = CHOH-SO_3H$; $R_2 = O-CH_2-COOH$

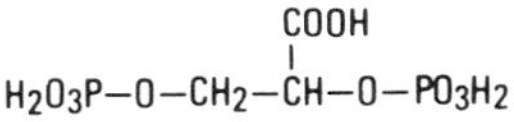

$$H_2O_3P-O-CH_2-\overset{\overset{\textstyle COOH}{|}}{CH}-O-PO_3H_2$$

(98) (DPG)

The use of this new approach was a success in the sense that it proved the possibility to design novel compounds not closely related to the known (natural) starting substance.

Conceptually, captopril (**99**) was also created partly along these lines. This

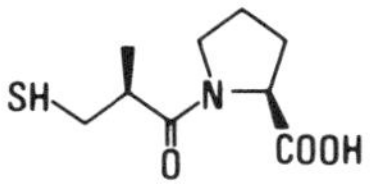

(99) captopril (SQ 14225)

substance lowers blood pressure by specific inhibition of the angiotensin-converting enzyme (ACE). A nonapeptide SQ 20881 was shown to have great potential interest, but this was limited by lack of oral activity. The geometrical features of the ACE active site are not yet known, but the chemical and enzymatic properties of the enzyme permitted Ondetti, Cushman, and colleagues to anticipate hypothetical features by analogy with pancreatic carboxypeptidase A (Fig. 79) (Cushman *et al.*, 1977; Ondetti *et al.*, 1977).

Unfortunately, in most therapeutic areas of interest the 3-D structures of target macromolecules are not yet known. It has been common practice to design new substances by modifying the structure of a known reference molecule which has the desired biological property. Most examples reviewed in the following paragraphs show how even in such a situation it is still possible to avoid using conventional procedures and to design new compounds using working models consistent with the ''lock and key'' views of molecular biology.

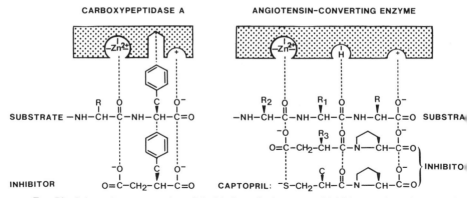

FIG. 79. Schematic representation of the binding of substrates and inhibitors at the active site of pancreatic carboxypeptidase A, and at the hypothetical active site of angiotensin-converting enzyme. (From Ondetti *et al.*, 1977, with permission. Copyright 1977 by the *American Association for the Advancement of Science.*)

6.2 DESIGN OF NEW ANTIPSYCHOTICS

6.2.1 Comparison of Dopamine Agonists and Antagonists

Particular attention has been paid to the identification of the stereochemical requirements of the dopamine receptor(s) and several topographic maps of the central dopamine receptors were envisaged on the basis of the comparison of the stereochemical features of $(-)$-apomorphine (**100**) (a dopamine receptor agonist) and $(+)$-butaclamol (**101a**) (an antagonist). As mentioned in previous sections,

(100)	(101)
(R)-apomorphine	(a) (+)-butaclamol R= C(CH₃)₃
	(b) (+)-dexclamol R= CH(CH₃)₂

doubts have been shed on the proposed models since it was not at all proven that the "neuroleptic receptor" is the same as the one which binds apomorphine. However, the principle of their identity was assumed as a working hypothesis by several groups who tried to design new dopamine antagonists and succeeded in discovering novel antipsychotics of potential interest.

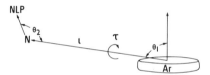

FIG. 80. Angular parameters used for the definition of the pharmacophores of drugs acting at dopamine receptors. (From Olson *et al.*, 1981, with permission. Copyright 1981 by the *American Chemical Society.*)

6.2.2 Receptor Model and Design of Pyrroloisoquinolines

Olson *et al.* (1981) have hypothesized a model of the central dopamine receptor starting from the active conformation of butaclamol (**101a**) and dexclamol (**101b**) as proposed by Humber *et al.* (1979) (the ''B-conformer'' mentioned in Section V and resulting from the comparison of butaclamol and apomorphine). A classical pharmacophore consisting of a basic nitrogen atom separated by a 5- to 7-Å chain or framework from an aromatic ring was considered. Figure 80 outlines this pharmacophore and its associated geometrical parameters. Assuming that the two groups are bound to complementary functionalities on the receptor protein, the latter were considered for simplicity to be a carboxylate group (likely to give a $COO^- \cdots H-N^+$ bond with the amine nitrogen) and a phenyl group π_1 (likely to form a $\pi-\pi$ stacking interaction with the ligand's aromatic moiety). When other classes of antipsychotic compounds such as haloperidol (**102**), pimozide (**103**), sulpiride (**104**), or molindone (**105**) were fitted to bind with

(102) haloperidol

(103) pimozide

(104) sulpiride

(105) molindone

these two sites, a possible second aromatic binding site π_2 emerged from the analysis. The superposition of these various dopamine antagonists actually re-

N. CLAUDE COHEN

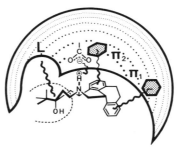

FIG. 81. Interaction of (+)-butaclamol with the receptor model of Olson *et al*. (1981). (Adapted with permission. Copyright 1981 by the *American Chemical Society*.)

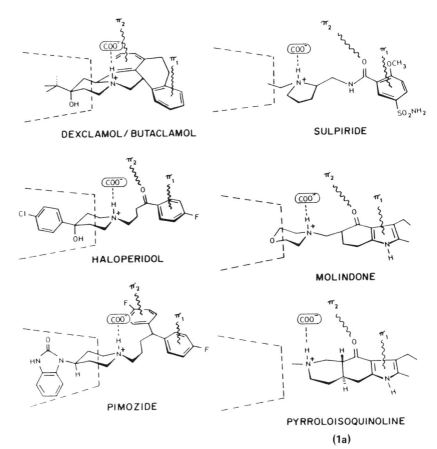

FIG. 82. Interaction of different classes of ligands with the receptor model of Olson *et al*. (1981) (With permission. Copyright 1981 by the *American Chemical Society*.)

vealed the coincidence of common structural features such as a phenyl ring or a ketone carbonyl permitting $\pi-\pi$ or $n\ \pi$ ligand–receptor interactions to be envisaged in this region. A possible fourth binding site, consisting of a lipophilic site L of low structural specificity, was also identified. The interaction of butaclamol with this receptor site is outlined in Fig. 81. The arrangement of various classes of antagonists (Fig. 82) shows that a ligand can interact with the π_2 site through either a phenyl or a carbonyl group. Olson *et al.* suggested that electronegative groups binding to this site may lead to antagonist activity whereas its occupation might not be a prerequisite for agonist activity.

The receptor model consisting of one auxiliary lipophilic site L and three essential binding sites π_1, π_2 and COO^- permitted the analysis of its 3-D features and the design of pyrroloisoquinolines such as **106**. It is apparent that the

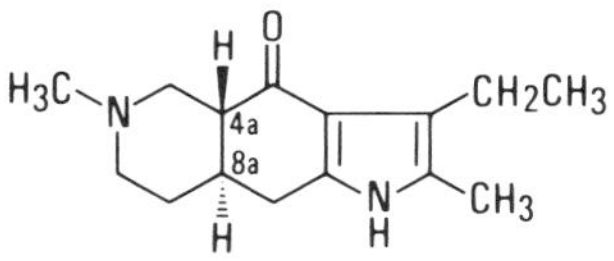

(106)   Ro 22–1319

authors drew their inspiration from the chemical frame of molindone (**105**) in which appropriate constraints were introduced leading to a structure conforming well to the desired stereochemical requirements. It is worth noting that only the 4aR,8aR configuration (the trans fusion of the two six-membered rings in **106**) was predicted to have the expected biological properties, and this was fully confirmed. Biochemical studies indicated that this compound is a specific D-2 dopamine antagonist, and pharmacological tests have shown that it exhibits potent neuroleptic-like activity. In the avoidance blockade (AB) test compound **106** is in the potency range of haloperidol and over five times as potent as molindone. Its biological activity is highly stereoselective since it resides entirely in the $(-)$-**106** enantiomer. Preliminary clinical trials confirmed that **106** is a good antipsychotic agent with minimal extrapyramidal effects (Olson *et al.*, 1981; Keller, 1983).

6.2.3 Design of Phenylquinolizidines

Using almost the same set of known active molecules, Imhof *et al.* (1982, 1984) have conceived a slightly different model. In terms of the requirements of the substrate, the starting model likewise consists of an aromatic (or heteroaromatic) ring, and a basic nitrogen atom located 5–6 Å away from the center of the ring. Two additional features are also proposed: a ''bulky moiety'' (in place of π_2 in the preceding model) and a second aromatic group (in place of L), but they are only considered as optional. The fused ring system **107** was then designed. In this structure one can recognize some of the chemical features of butaclamol. Additional studies have enabled this new family to be optimized and have led to **108,** in which some functionalities of pimozide **103** can also be recognized. This compound is more potent than haloperidol (pole climbing, catalepsy, and continuous avoidance tests). In this series the biological activity also appears as highly stereoselective since only the (+)-enatiomer of **108** is active. The modification of configuration either in position 2 or 7 considerably reduces activity.

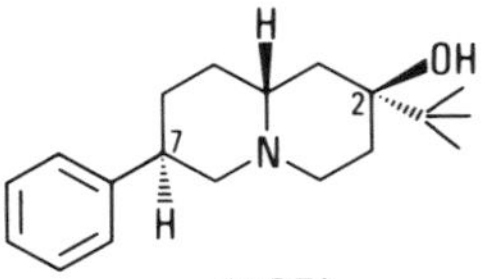

(107) 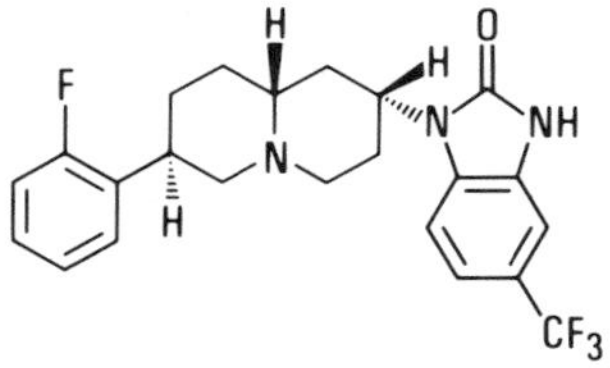   (108)   Ro 14-8625

Although the two models outlined above are not entirely consistent with one another, they have proven their utility in guiding the design of new series of antipsychotic agents. Concerning the actual features of the dopamine receptor, further studies remain to be done in order to provide a more complete understanding of the recognition and discrimination processes involved as well as the precise orientation of the various antagonists in the active site.

6.3 DESIGN OF NONTRICYCLIC ANTIDEPRESSANTS

Depression seems to be due to a functional underactivity or deficiency of the biogenic amines noradrenaline (**109**) and serotonin (**110**). The exact mechanism of action of tricyclic antidepressants [e.g., imipramine (**111**) and amitriptyline (**112**)] is not yet fully known and the current hypothesis states that these drugs

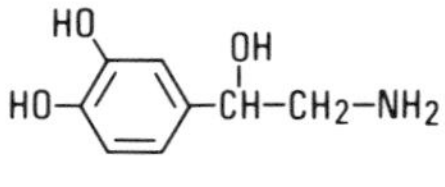

(109)   noradrenaline 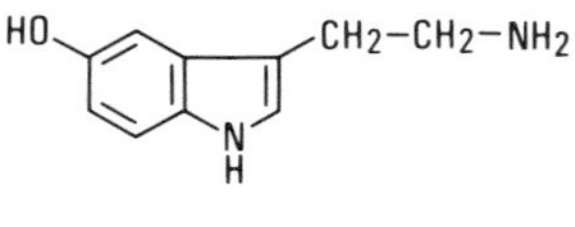   (110)   serotonin

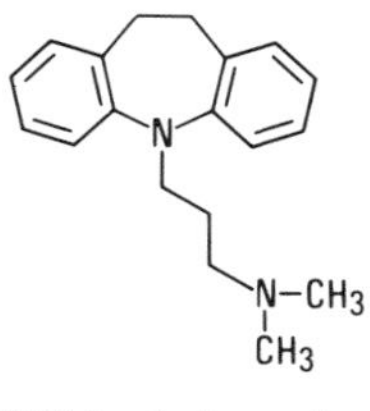

(111)   imipramine 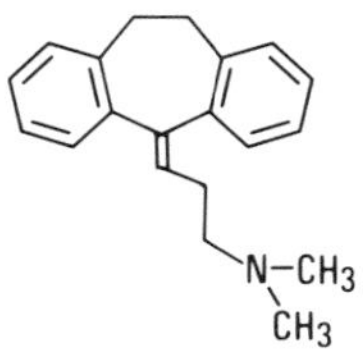   (112)   amitriptyline

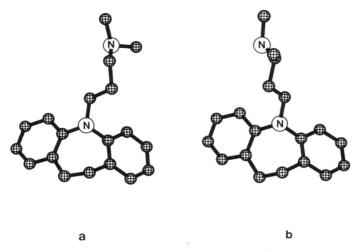

a   **b**

FIG. 83. Two conformations of imipramine (X ray of the hydrochloride salt analysis by Post *et al.*, 1975).

increase the functional activity of noradrenaline and serotonin (Berger, 1978). Tricyclics are reuptake inhibitors of noradrenaline and serotonin. Inhibiting the uptake of these neurotransmitters by the neuron that released them into the synaptic cleft increases their concentration in the synapse and counteracts deficiency-associated depressive illness. It was shown that tricyclics are competitive inhibitors of noradrenaline uptake, and several models have been proposed to account for the structural features of a relevant pharmacophore. Maxwell *et al.* (1969) have shown that the phenethylamine moiety of the neurotransmitter may be superimposed to the 3-D structure of the tricyclics. These authors also suggested that in the tricyclic structure the angle between the two aromatic rings may be linked to the potency of uptake inhibition.

Imipramine (**111**), a fairly flexible molecule, was found to exist in two different conformations in the crystal (Post *et al.*, 1975) (Fig. 83). Martin *et al.* (1980) designed conformationally locked analogs of imipramine such as **113** for which

(113)

the cis and the trans isomers actually mimic the folded (Fig. 83a) and extended (Fig. 83b) imipramine conformations, respectively. Both isomers were inactive in inhibiting of serotonin uptake whereas they showed moderate activity in inhibiting noradrenaline uptake.

Although various ways of superimposing the phenyl ring of a tricyclic antidepressant on the phenyl group of noradrenaline continue to be postulated (Sundaram and Mahajan, 1981) recent potent new structures do not seem to conform to such requirements. The conformational features of the potent spiro inhibitor **114** suggested that apparent competitive antagonism between tricyclics and nor-

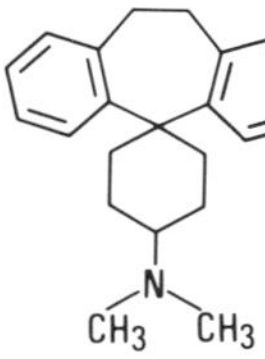

$$\overset{|}{\underset{\underset{CH_3 \quad CH_3}{N}}{}}$$

(114)

adrenaline can be understood on the assumption that two different conformational states may exist for the receptor site involved. (De Paulis *et al.*, 1978) In this hypothesis, the structural requirements for inhibiting uptake of a neurotransmitter do not need to fit the actual stereochemical features of the biogenic amine considered. The model proposed is based on the comparison of a set of various antagonists and is defined with the aid of four distances characterizing the spatial relationships of two benzene rings and a nitrogen atom. As mentioned above, noradrenaline does not fit the proposed requirements. The model is also not consistent with that of Maxwell *et al.* (1969).

In a similar perspective, the "Psychotropes GEMO" project was initiated in 1970 in collaboration with Nédélec, Kannengiesser, and Lemoine (unpublished, summarized by Cohen, 1983b), aiming at the discovery of nontricyclic antidepressant molecules on the basis of detailed potential energy calculations using the GEMO program (Cohen, 1971). Starting from the set of known antidepressants represented in Fig. 84, GEMO calculations provided sets of minimized conformations for each of these compounds. Low-energy conformers (less than 1 kcal/mol) were analyzed in order to reveal common possible stereochemical features. The great variation in the angles between the two aromatic rings invalidates Maxwell's hypothesis (Maxwell *et al.*, 1969) on the role of this structural parameter. A deeper analysis showed that a simple pharmacophore made up of only one aromatic ring and a nitrogen atom could be envisaged. The molecules were analyzed in terms of two geometrical parameters characterizing the relative position of the two pharmacophoric elements: parameter d represents the distance between the nitrogen atom and the center of the benzene ring, and parameter h the height of the nitrogen relative to the plane of this ring (see Fig. 85, top). The various stable conformations were represented on a coordinate system (d,h) (Fig. 85) which revealed the existence of two distinct regions M_1 and M_2. All the

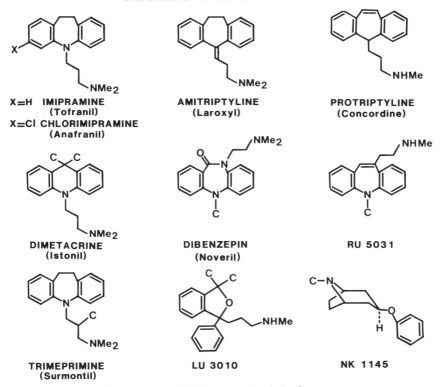

X=H IMIPRAMINE
     (Tofranil)
X=Cl CHLORIMIPRAMINE
     (Anafranil)

AMITRIPTYLINE
(Laroxyl)

PROTRIPTYLINE
(Concordine)

DIMETACRINE
(Istonil)

DIBENZEPIN
(Noveril)

RU 5031

TRIMEPRIMINE
(Surmontil)

LU 3010

NK 1145

FIG. 84. "Psychotropes GEMO": basic chemical reference structures.

molecules analyzed appear to have at least one stable form in the vicinity of each region, except for NK 1145, which is only present in region M_1. The two regions correspond to the following dimensions:

$$M_1: d=5.9 \text{ Å}, h=3.4 \text{ Å} (\pm 0.4 \text{ Å})$$

$$M_2: d=6.7 \text{ Å}, h=0.9 \text{ Å} (\pm 0.6 \text{ Å})$$

This means that the molecules could share common 3-D features in two different ways with, however, a preference for model M_1. Figure 85 also shows that noradrenaline and serotonin are not able to conform to model M_1 requirements. When a model is obtained it becomes possible to visualize the essential pharmacophore on any of the molecules studied provided its appropriate conformation(s) is considered. Figure 86 shows for example how the M_1 pharmacophore is embedded in the molecular structure of imipramine.

The imipramine conformation represented in this figure is actually very similar to the folded conformation observed in the crystal (see Fig. 83a) and was found to have an energy of 0.1 kcal/mol above that of the more stable, extended form.

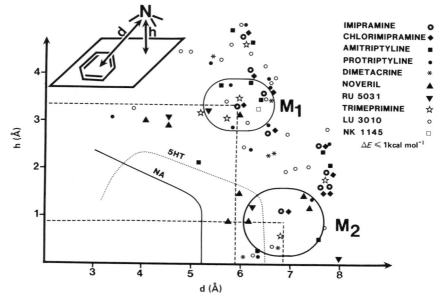

N. CLAUDE COHEN

FIG. 85. Common 3-D features: models M_1 and M_2 revealing possible conformations of the different antidepressant molecules analyzed that could fit the same receptor site. NA, noradrenaline; 5HT, serotonin.

(115)

(a) $R_1 = CH_3$ $R_2 = CH_3$ RU 21033

(b) $R_1 = CH_3$ $R_2 = H$ RU 22249

The potential value of model M_1 was explored and led to the design of nontricyclic chemical structures such as **115** (Nédélec *et al.*, 1975a,b). They appeared to conform well to the desired requirements (in the case of **115a**, stable

FIG. 86. The proposed active folded conformation of imipramine and its corresponding M_1 ($\Delta E = 0.1$ kcal/mol) pharmacophore.

FIG. 87. Superposition of the proposed active conformation of imipramine represented in Fig. 86 with that of molecule **115b**.

conformation with $d=6.1$ Å and $h=3.7$ Å), and the newly synthesized molecules exhibited specific serotonergic activities *in vitro* (inhibition of serotonin reuptake) as well as *in vivo* (potentiation of the behavioral effects induced by the administration of 5-hydroxytryptophan in mice). An illustration of the stereochemical similarities between imipramine (folded conformation of model M_1) and **115b** (RU 22249) is given in Fig. 87.

Various analogs were synthesized to explore the possibilities of this family of compounds and to optimize their biological properties. Although the clinical studies have not yet been completed for the selected analogs, the project allowed the validity of this approach to be tested and confirmed.

Analyzing the role of the aromatic rings in the tricyclic structures, Grunewald *et al.* (1979) have observed that the saturation of one or both rings did not significantly affect the inhibition of serotonin uptake but substantially reduced the inhibition of noradrenaline uptake.

6.4 DESIGN OF SIMPLIFIED SOMATOSTATIN ANALOGS

Somatostatin (**116a**) is a peptide hormone which is sometimes considered to function also as a neurotransmitter. The substance is involved in various biological systems, and its potential therapeutic applications involve principally the treatment of diabetes (reduced gluconeogenesis by inhibition of insulin and glucagon release), but also the treatment of acromegaly (by inhibition of growth hormone release) and of ulcers and related gastrointestinal disorders (by inhibition of gastric acid secretion). The short duration of action of somatostatin limits its use as a drug and has prompted the search for analogs with greater metabolic stability. It was the Salk group who first showed (Rivier *et al.*, 1975) that the complete molecule of somatostatin is not necessary for full activity. This was later confirmed when extensive computerized molecular design studies resulted in the discovery of simple potent compounds such as **118** (Merck), **119** (Salk), or **120** (Sandoz).

Somatostatin (a) = H-Ala-Gly -Cys-Lys-Asn-Phe-Phe-Trp-Lys-Thr-Phe-Thr-Ser-Cys-O
                 1   2   3   4   5   6   7   8   9 10 11 12 13 14

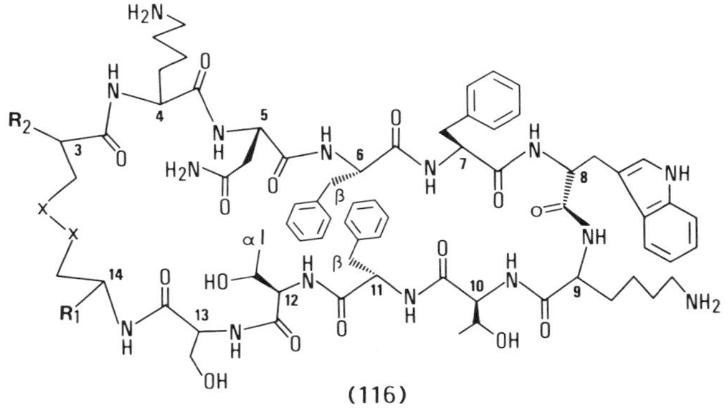

(116)

(a) X = S R_1 = COOH R_2 = H-Ala-Gly
(b) X = C R_1 = H R_2 = H

It was actually at Merck that continuous studies in this area led Veber and colleagues (summarized by Veber, 1981) to stress the importance of conformational aspects and to derive a strategy toward the development of potent and long-acting somatostatin analogs.

Starting from the primary structure–activity relationships observed with various somatostatin analogs and considering a β-turn conformation from Phe-7 to Thr-10, Veber *et al.* hypothesized a possible active conformation (Fig. 88). The model permitted, in the first place, to design conformationally restricted analogs (Veber *et al.*, 1978, 1979; Veber and Saperstein, 1979) such as the bicyclic derivative **117,** which was three times more potent than somatostatin in inhibit-

cyclo (Aha-Cys-Phe-D-Trp -Lys-Thr-Cys)
            6   7   8   9 10 11

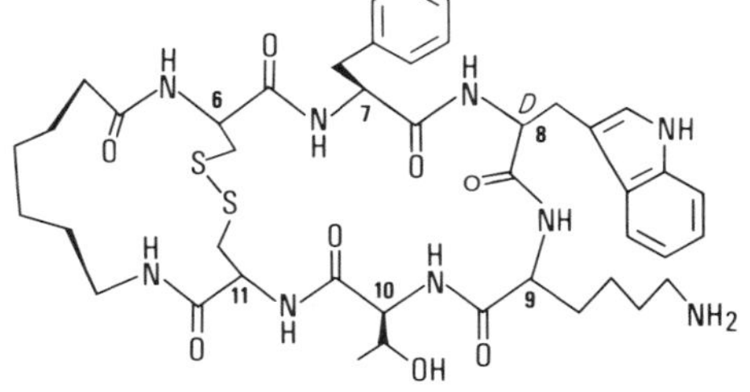

(117)

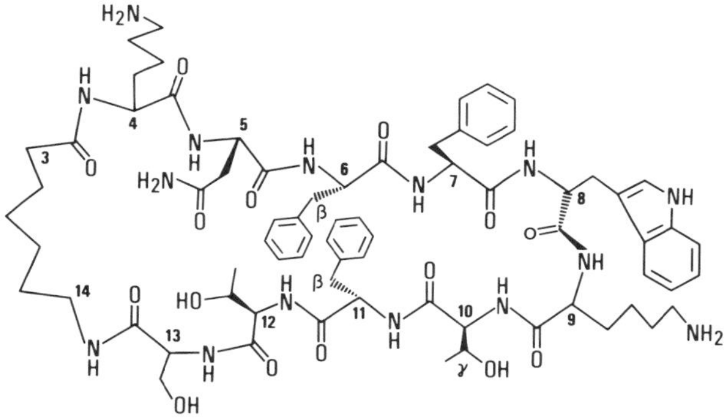

FIG. 88. A dicarba[3,14] somatostatin analog and corresponding conformation visualizing the proposed β-turn involving Phe-7, Trp-8, Lys-9, and Thr-10. (From Veber *et al.*, 1978, with permission.)

ing insulin secretion and markedly more selective (one-twentieth of the activity of somatostatin in the inhibition of gastric secretion). A second breakthrough was obtained when additional studies led to the design of even simpler chemical structures (Veber *et al.*, 1981) such as the cyclic peptide **118**, which is 50–100

cyclo (Pro -Phe-D-Trp -Lys-Thr -Phe)

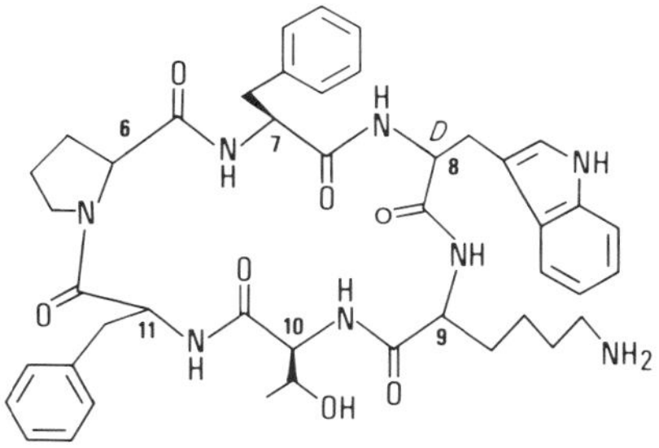

(118)

times more potent than somatostatin in the inhibition of insulin, glucagon, and growth hormone. These results permitted the authors to interpret structure–activity relationships in terms of only 4 of the 14 amino acid residues of somatostatin. It is proposed that the sequence of residues 7, 8, 9, and 10 (Fig. 89) contains all the elements necessary for expression of the full activity spectrum. A folded conformation (with residues 8 and 9 at the corner of a β-turn) is consistent with the biological activities of the various series studied. Figure 90 shows the proposed active conformation of the cyclic hexapeptide **118.** Likewise a high

-Phe-Trp-Lys-Thr-
  7   8   9   10

FIG. 89. The four amino acid residues containing the elements for expression of somatostatin activities.

FIG. 90. Stereoviews of the proposed active conformation of the cyclic hexapeptide **118**. (From Veber, 1981, with permission. Copyright 1981 by Pierce Chemical Company.)

activity was reported for a simple cyclic heptapeptide of structure **119** (reviewed by Veber and Saperstein, 1979). Using the same approach, Bauer *et al.* (1982) have designed other series of simplified analogs such as the octapeptide **120** which has more than 20 times the potency of somatostatin. Figure 91 shows a proposed low-energy conformation of this compound which mimics the pharmacophoric fragment of somatostatin. The substance was found to be metabolically stable and orally active and is currently undergoing clinical trials.

H–Cys–Phe–D–Trp–Lys–Thr–Phe–Cys–OH

6   7   8   9   10   11   12

(119)

H–D–Phe–Cys–Phe–D–Trp–Lys–Thr–Cys–Thr (OL)

6   7   8   9   10   11

(120)

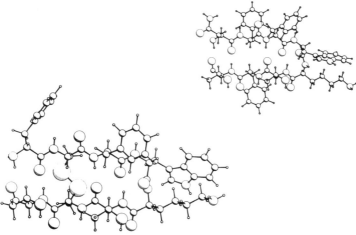

FIG. 91. The proposed active and low-energy conformation of the octapeptide **120** (bottom) as compared with (top) the corresponding fragment of somatostatin. (From Bauer *et al.*, 1982, with permission. Copyright 1982 by Pergamon Press.)

Based mainly on the identification of relevant conformational features, this approach permitted the design of simple analogs of somatostatin through elimination of unnecessary amino acids and introduction of appropriate geometrical constraints. New designs and increased internal consistency of the current model were efficiently combined as demonstrated by the successful results obtained. A good combination of chemical imagination and molecular modeling led to the proposal of an active conformation for somatostatin, a molecule which may adopt several thousands of different conformations. The identification of a simple pharmacophore of only four residues is the fruit of this effort composed of intuition, patience, and perseverance. Even simpler structures mimicking the stereochemical features of this fragment are expected to be successfully designed.

6.5 DESIGN OF NEW HYPOLIPEMIC AGENTS

Epidemiological studies have shown that an intimate correlation exists between the occurrence of arteriosclerotic disease and elevated levels of cholesterol and/or triglycerides in blood plasma. This disease is characterized by the deposition of cholesterol esters in the inner layers of the arterial wall. Therapeutic approaches to arteriosclerosis have therefore centered on the reduction of cholesterol and serum lipoprotein levels.

Clofibrate (**121**), a hypocholesterolemic agent principally effective in lowering serum triglycerides, has been largely used in the last 20 years in the treatment of arteriosclerotic diseases (Witiak *et al.*, 1977). The drug was envisaged as a

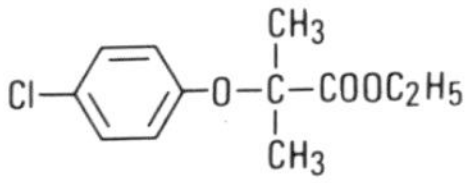

$$Cl-\langle\bigcirc\rangle-O-\underset{\underset{CH_3}{|}}{\overset{\overset{CH_3}{|}}{C}}-COOC_2H_5$$

(121) clofibrate

mass medication in the prevention of ischemic diseases but extensive studies have shed doubts on its actual benefit. However, hypolipemic agents related to clofibrate continue to be used in current therapy. Future insights should improve our understanding of the etiology of arteriosclerosis, thus leading to better treatment and prevention.

A great variety of clofibrate analogs were studied (Witiak *et al.*, 1977), showing that the introduction of a second benzene ring as well as precise conformational constraints enhance potency. For example, treloxinate (**122**) is a potent

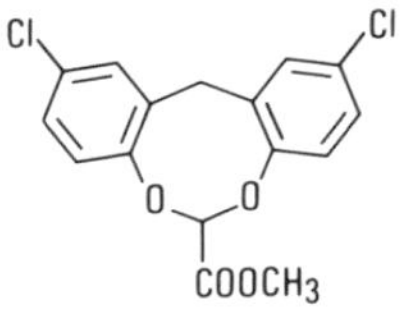

$$\text{(structure of treloxinate)}$$

COOCH₃

(122)   treloxinate

hypolipemic agent which has been shown to be more active than clofibrate in lowering both cholesterol and triglycerides levels in the rat (Grisar *et al.*, 1972; Kariya *et al.*, 1972). The design of a structure such as **123** (Humbert *et al.*, 1983)

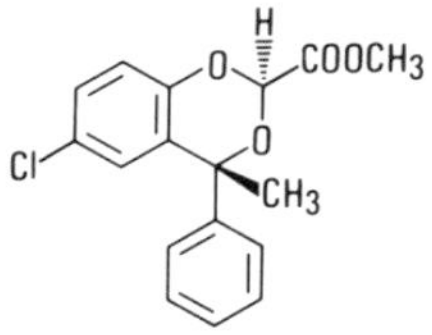

$$\text{(structure of RU 25247)}$$

(123)   (RU 25247)

has led to the discovery of a series of potent hypolipidemic agents exhibiting remarkable 3-D similarities with the stable conformation of treloxinate (Humbert *et al.*, 1983; Cohen, 1979). Molecule **123** has been shown to exist with the phenyl substituent in an axial orientation. Analysis of 3-D features revealed that the mimetism with the molecular structure of treloximate would be even more enhanced when the axial phenyl is substituted with a chlorine atom. Superposi-

FIG. 92. Conformations of the acid forms of **123** (a), **124** (b), and **122** (c) that might interact with the same receptor site. (From Humbert *et al.*, 1983.)

FIG. 93. "Mimetism in 4-D": common stereochemical features of the acid forms of **124** (a) and **122** (b) using CNDO/2 electronic densities. Numerical values associated to the electrostatic contour lines are in kcal/mol. Extended Hückel electronic densities exhibit the same features. (Cohen, 1979.)

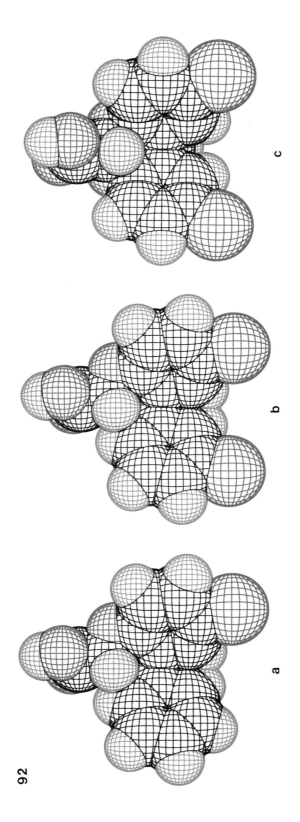

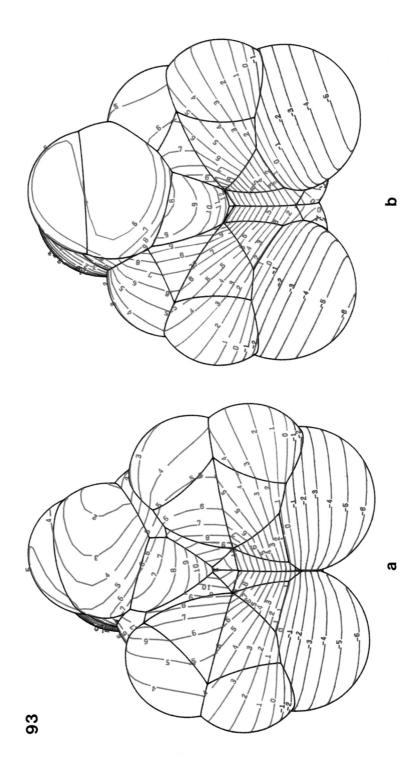

a

b

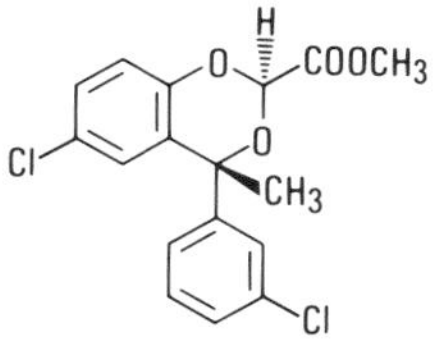

(124)   (RU 25961)

tion analyses revealed that meta substitution (molecule **124**) was preferable to para substitution although both are possible, the ideal orientation being located between these two positions with, however, a preference for the former.

Compounds **123** and **124** displayed hypolipemic activities in doses from 2–5 mg/kg in the rat. Figure 92 visualizes the mimetism existing between the acid forms of these two esters together with the structure of the acid form of treloxinate (it is the free carboxylic acid entities which are the active forms in this series of compounds, as shown by Witiak *et al.*, 1968; Pichardo *et al.*, 1977; and Humbert *et al.*, 1983). The different series retain mimetism in 4-D when the molecular electrostatic potentials are considered (see Fig. 93).

These representations rationalize the enhanced pharmacological hypolipidemic potency observed in analog **124**. Preliminary clinical studies have confirmed that the **123** derivative is an effective hypocholesterolemic agent (Cunha-Monteiro, 1980).

6.6 DESIGN OF NEW LIGANDS FOR THE BENZODIAZEPINE RECEPTOR

Considerable work has been done on synthetic molecules belonging to the 1,4-benzodiazepine series of which diazepam (**125**) is a typical representative. The

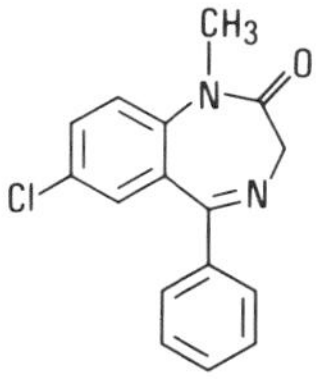

(125)   diazepam

existence of "benzodiazepine receptors" has been proven (Braestrup and Squires, 1977) in different parts of the brain. The endogenous ligands of these receptors have not yet been identified, but their discovery may lead to considerable understanding in relevant biochemical processes. It is now known that the benzodiazepine receptor is coupled with that of GABA and associated with a chloride channel (summarized by Tallman *et al.*, 1980).

An increasing number of synthetic nonbenzodiazepine chemical entities have been recently found to bind specifically to this receptor in the nanomolar range, e.g., zopiclone (**126**), suriclone (**127**), and compounds **128, 129,** or **130.** *In vitro* [^{3}H]diazepam binding assays permit measurement of the affinity of a substance in terms of IC_{50} with comparison to diazepam, which has a IC_{50} of about 5–10 nM. The IC_{50} values of molecules **126, 127, 128, 129,** and **130** are about 43, 2, 140, 160, and 14 nM, respectively [reviewed by Effland and Försch, 1981, 1982; for suriclone (**127**) see Blanchard and Julon, 1983].

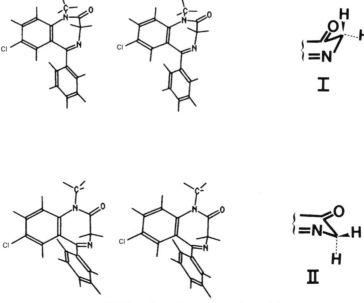

Preliminary attempts have been made to establish common 3-D features between different structures binding to the same receptor (Crippen, 1982). More

FIG. 94. Two alternative conformations of diazepam.

convincing evidence has been recently proposed where the probable active form of benzodiazepine actually recognized by the receptor has been identified (Blount *et al.*, 1983). As shown in this work, diazepam can exist in either of the two conformations I and II as illustrated in Fig. 94, the change in conformation resulting from a "flipping" of the methylene group of the seven-membered ring through the plane of the aromatic "A" chlorinated ring. These two forms are mirror images and the authors suggest that conformation I should be the active form binding to the chiral active site of the benzodiazepine receptor.

This proposal is supported by the structure–activity features of enantiomeric 3-methyl-1,4-benzodiazepines such as **131** and **132**.

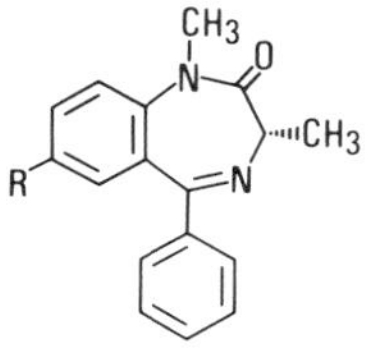

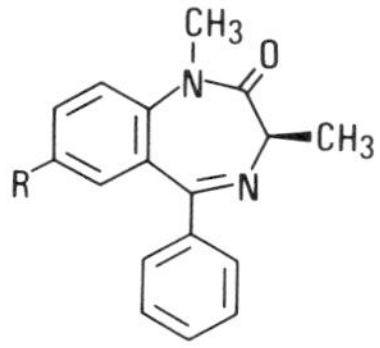

(131)   (a) R= NO$_2$ (132)
              (b) R= Cl

Contrasting biological activities were observed in these series. For example, **131a** is much more active than **132a** (*in vivo*, pentylenetetrazole test), and these observations were also well correlated with *in vitro* [^{3}H]diazepam binding assays (IC$_{50}$ of 7 nM for **131a** and >1000 nM for **132a**). Analysis of the conformational features of the two enantiomeric series, either in the solid state (Blount *et al.*, 1983) or in solution (Sunjic *et al.*, 1979), showed that the preferred conformation of **131** analogs is of type I whereas structure **132b** was found in a type II form. In both series the methyl group is in an equatorial orientation and eclipses the adjacent keto function. Both analyses have led to the same conclusion proposing that the benzodiazepine conformation I should be the active form recognized by the receptor site. Consistent with this, it was shown (Fryer, 1983; Fryer and Gilman, 1983; Blount *et al.*, 1983) that the biological activities observed of anthramycin analogs in enantiomers such as **133–134** or **135–136** can be per-

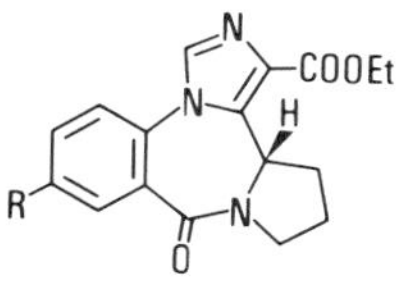

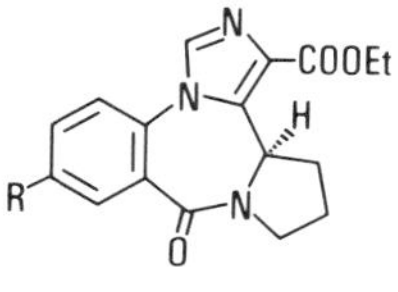

(133)   (a) R= H   (134)
              (b) R= Cl

fectly understood on the same basis. For example, **133a** was found to have an IC$_{50}$ of about 6.4 nM whereas **134a** was completely inactive. Contrasting biolog-

diazepam   midazolam   Ro 21-8384

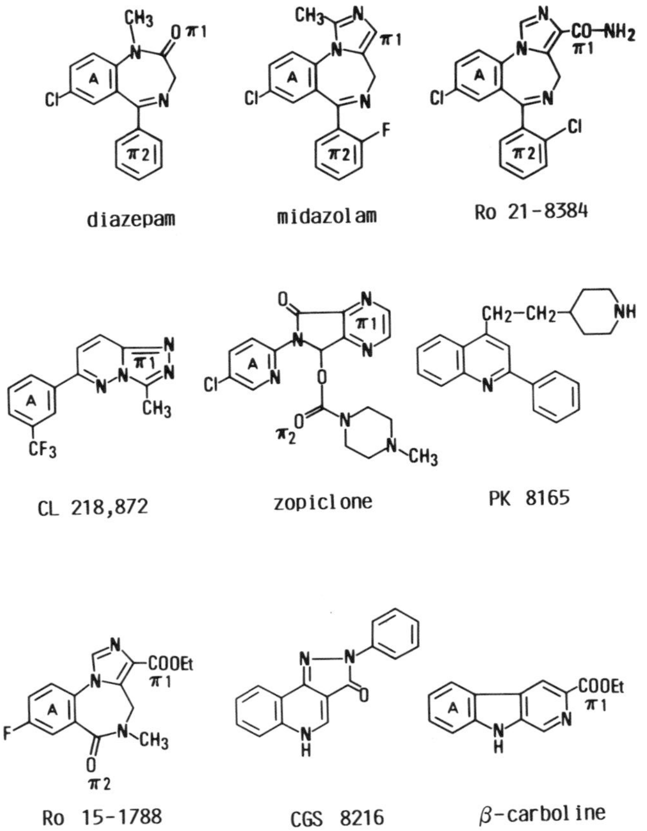

CL 218,872   zopiclone   PK 8165

Ro 15-1788   CGS 8216   β-carboline

FIG. 95. Representative chemical structures binding to the benzodiazepine receptor and envisaged for revealing common 3-D features. (From Fryer and Gilman, 1983.)

(135)   (a) R= H   (136)

(b) R= Cl

ical activities were also observed in **135a** and **136a** enantiomers where only isomer **135a** exhibited antipentetrazole activity. It was shown, for example, that **136b** can be perfectly superimposed on the proposed active conformation of diazepam (Fryer, 1983). Following on these lines, the same authors have revealed common 3-D features as sketched in Fig. 95 and have deduced a generalized model of the stereochemical requirements for binding to the ben-

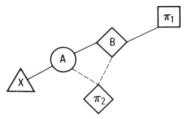

FIG. 96. Fryer and Gilman proposed model for binding to the benzodiazepine receptor. X, substituent, i.e., halogen; A, aromatic or heteroaromatic ring; B, a double bond (either formal or in a resonance form); π_1 and π_2, a π system (electronegative atom or part of an aromatic ring system).

zodiazepine receptor (Fryer and Gilman, 1983). The model consists of five separate binding sites (see Fig. 96) of which A, B, and π_1 are considered to be essential and the two others, X and π_2, permit modulation of the intensity of this binding. For example, molecule CL218.872 and the β-carboline depicted in Fig. 95 exhibit good affinities for the benzodiazepine receptor and have no π_2 system. The 3-D correspondence between the binding sites and representative structures is indicated in Fig. 96 where the distance between the center of the ''A'' ring and the π_1 system is evaluated to be around 6 Å with the π_1 group located ''in front'' (see the chemical formulas) of the ''A'' ring plane.

In agreement with this model, new chemical entities were designed and found to be active. For example, structures such as **137, 138,** and **139** (among others

(137)   (138)   (139)

which are yet to be disclosed) showed IC_{50} values of 79, 25, and 24 nM, respectively (Fryer and Gilman, 1983).

These studies are still in progress for new designs and for refinement of the model. In particular, 3-D considerations and electrostatic potentials are expected to characterize some molecular features permitting one to differentiate between agonists and antagonists.

7 Conclusion

The great majority of drugs presently in use were developed in a classical manner through extraction of natural products and variation of known active compounds carried out by synthetic methods. During the last decades many laboratories devoted a major effort to screening investigations with the hope of duplicating the successes of substances such as reserpine or penicillin. The low number of advances with respect to original useful medicinal agents has prompted an intensive effort conducted in the last 15 years to place structure–activity relationships on a quantitative basis. Although the hopes which have been raised with QSAR methodologies have materialized only partly, a progressive evolution in the conceptualization of new drugs now unavoidably unfolds, and the purely heuristic and empirical methods are being replaced by more rational approaches. New knowledge of the electronic, hydrophobic, and steric nature of molecular interactions together with the availability of efficient computer graphic devices has created new conditions allowing the molecular modelist to be in a position to recognize and envisage methods for the prediction of the biological activity of not yet synthesized or tested prototype chemical compounds.

Typical examples of recent 3-D drug design have been discussed in this article. They show how the consolidation of this line of research is now in progress and how medicinal chemistry is beginning to employ elegant and innovative concepts.

Beyond the particular examples presented here, it is now clear that the successful results already obtained are triggering the development of sophisticated computerized molecular design projects opening up perspectives invaluable to pharmaceutical research.

This novel way of dealing with the task has proven to encompass an unexpectedly high capacity to enlarge the view and unify the innovative stimuli of both medicinal chemists and biologists involved in this ambitious multidisciplinary goal. They permit us to anticipate with optimism a new generation of well executed and much safer drugs carrying higher information content than those that have yet been at our command.

Acknowledgments

It is a pleasure to acknowledge the collaboration of my former co-workers G. Lemoine and Dr. P. Colin (Roussel-Uclaf) for their collaboration in some of the work reviewed in this article and for their valuable help in preparing some of the computer-drawn illustrations. I am indebted to my Ciba-Geigy colleagues for helpful comments on the manuscript as well as stimulating discussions. I am particularly grateful to Dr. G. L. Olson for a preprint of his article on antipsychotic pyrroloisoquinolines, to Dr. I. Fryer and Dr. N. W. Gilman for preprints of their work on the recognition of ligands by the benzodiazepine receptor as well as their recent and yet unpublished results in the design of new anxiolytics. The kind help of many individuals who provided drawing material is appreciated: Dr. N. Camerman, Dr. L. Humber, Dr. L. F. Kuyper, Dr. G. R. Marshall, Dr. H. Moereels, Dr. T. S. Petcher, Dr. C. Petrongolo, Dr. U. Sankawa, Dr. J. P. Tollenare, Dr. D. F. Veber, and Dr. P. Wiener. The assistance of Dr. Wiener is particularly acknowledged for having reproduced the color drawing cited in this article concerning fragments of DNA.

The valuable and kind help of Dr. Ph. Levin-Andrea in correcting the English style and errors of the manuscript is gratefully acknowledged. Especially appreciated is the expert assistance of Mrs. E. Robison for her secretarial help in preparing the manuscript.

References

Agresti, A., Buffoni, F., Kaufman, J. J., and Petrongolo, C. (1980). *Mol. Pharmacol.* **18**, 461–467.

Ahmed, F. R. (1981). *Acta Crystallogr.* B **37**, 188–192.

Albers-Schönberg, G., Arison, B. H., Hensens, O. D., Hirshfield, J., Hoogsteen, K., Kaczka, E. A., Rhodes, R. E., Kahan, J. S., Kahan, F. M., Ratcliffe, R. W., Walton, E., Ruswinkle, L. J., Morin, R. B., and Christensen, B. G. (1978). *J. Am. Chem. Soc.* **100**, 6491–6499.

Allen, F. H., Bellard, S., Brice, M. D., Cartwright, B. A., Doubleway, A., Higgs, H., Hummelink, T., Hummelink-Peters, B. G., Kennard, O., Motherwell, W. D. S., Rodgers, J. A., and Watson, D. G. (1979). *Acta Crystallogr.* B **35**, 2331–2339.

Allen, F. H., Kennard, O., and Taylor, R. (1983). *Acc. Chem. Res.* **16**, 146–153.

Allinger, N. L. (1977). *J. Am. Chem. Soc.* **99**, 8127–8134.

Allinger, N. L., and Sprague, J. T. (1973). *J. Am. Chem. Soc.* **95**, 3893–3907.

Allinger, N. L., and Yuh, Y. H. (1980a). *Quantum Chem. Program Exchange* **11**, 318.

Allinger, N. L., and Yuh, Y. H. (1980b). *Quantum Chem. Program Exchange* **11**, 395.

Altman, J., Karoly, E., and Maoz, N. (1975). *J. Med. Chem.* **18**, 627–630.

Ammon, H. L., Balsamo, A., Macchia, B., Macchia, F., Howe, D.-B., and Keefe, W. E. (1975). *Experientia* **31**, 644–646.

Andose, J. D., Engler, E. M., Collins, J. B., Hummel, J. P., Mislow, K., and Schleyer, P.v.R. (1980). *Quantum Chem. Program Exchange* **11**, 348.

Andrews, P. R., and Lloyd, E. J. (1982). *Med. Res. Rev.* **2**, 355–393.

Andrews, P. R., Mark, L. C., Winkler, D. A., and Jones, G. P. (1983). *J. Med. Chem.* **26**, 1223–1229.

Appleton, R. A., and Brown, K. (1979). *Prostaglandins* **18**, 29–34.

Bach, N. J., Kornfeld, E. C., Jones, N. D., Chaney, M. O., Dorman, D. E., Paschal, J. W., Clemens, J. A., and Smalstig, E. B. (1980). *J. Med. Chem.* **23**, 481–491.

Baker, D. J., Beddell, C. R., Champness, J. N., Goodford, P. J., Norrington, F. E. A., Smith, D. R., and Stammers, D. K. (1981a). *FEBS Lett.* **126**, 49–52.

Baker, D. J., Beddell, C. R., Champness, J. N., Goodford, P. J., Norrington, F. E. A., Roth, B., and Stammers, D. K. (1981b). *Acta Crystallogr.* A **37** (Suppl.), C-58.

Baldwin, S., Kier, L. B., and Shillady, D. (1980). *Mol. Pharmacol.* **18**, 455–460.

Balsamo, A., Domiano, P., Macchia, B., Macchia, F., and Nardelli, M. (1980). *Eur. J. Med. Chem.* **15**, 559–562.

Barrett, A. M. (1972). *In* "Drug Design" (E. J. Ariens, ed.), Vol. 3, pp. 205–228. Academic Press, New York.

Bauer, W., Briner, V., Doepfner, W., Haller, R., Huguenin, R., Marback, P., Petcher, T. J., and Pless, J. (1982). *Life Sci.* **31**, 1133–1140.

Beckett, A. H., and Casy, A. F. (1954). *J. Pharm. Pharmacol.* **6**, 986–1001.

Beddell, C. R. (1984). *Chem. Soc. Rev.* **13**, 279–319.

Beddell, C. R., Goodford, P. J., Norrington, F. E., Wilkinson, S., and Wootton, R. (1976). *Br. J. Pharmacol.* **57**, 201–209.

Belleau, B., Conway, T., Ahmed, F. R., and Hardy, A. D. (1974). *J. Med. Chem.* **17**, 907–908.

Berger, P. A. (1978). *Science* **200**, 974–981.

Bernstein, F. C., Koetzle, T. F., Williams, G. J. B., Meyer, E. F., Jr., Brice, M. D., Rodgers, J. R., Kennard, O., Shimanouchi, T., and Tasumi, M. (1977). *J. Mol. Biol.* **112**, 535–542.

Bird, P. H., Bruderlein, F. T., and Humber, L. G. (1976). *Can. J. Chem.* **54**, 2715–2722.

Blackham, A., Hall, D. E., Mann, J., and Woods, A. M. (1979a). *Agents Actions Suppl.* **AAS4**, 193–201.

Blackham, A., Hall, D. E., Mann, J., and Woods, A. M. (1979b). *Int. J. Tissue React.* **1**, 85–94.
Blanchard, J.-C., and Julon, L. (1983). *J. Neurochem.* **40**, 601–607.
Blaney, J. M., Dietrich, S. W., Reynolds, M. A., and Hansch, C. (1979). *J. Med. Chem.* **22**, 614–617.
Blount, J. F., Fryer, R. I., Gilman, N. W., and Todaro, L. J. (1983). *Mol. Pharmacol.* **24**, 425–428.
Bocquet, G. (1975). Doctorate Thesis. Paris University.
Böhme, E. H. W., Applegate, H. E., Toeplitz, B., Dolfini, J. E., and Gougoutas, J. Z. (1971). *J. Am. Chem. Soc.* **93**, 4324–4326.
Bonaccorsi, R., Scrocco, E., and Tomasi, J. (1970). *J. Chem. Phys.* **52**, 5270–5281.
Bonaccorsi, R., Pullman, A., Scrocco, E., and Tomasi, J. (1972). *Chem. Phys. Lett.* **12**, 622–625.
Boyd, D. B., and Marsh, M. M. (1982). *Am. Chem. Soc. Natl. Meet., 183rd, Las Vegas* Asbtract COMP-9.
Braestrup, C., and Squires, R. F. (1977). *Nature (London)* **266**, 732–734.
Branch, C. L., and Pearson, M. J. (1982). *Tetrahedron Lett.* **23**, 3003–3006.
Breon, T. L., Petersen, H., and Paruta, A. N. (1978). *J. Pharm. Sci.* **67**, 73–83.
Camerman, A., and Camerman, N. (1970). *Science* **168**, 1457–1458.
Camerman, A., and Camerman, N. (1971a). *Acta Crystallogr. B* **27**, 2205–2211.
Camerman, N., and Camerman, A. (1971b). *Mol. Pharmacol.* **7**, 406–412.
Camerman, N., and Camerman, A. (1972a). *J. Am. Chem. Soc.* **94**, 8553–8556.
Camerman, A., and Camerman, N. (1972b). *J. Am. Chem. Soc.* **94**, 268–272.
Camerman, A., and Camerman, N. (1974). *In* "Molecular and Quantum Pharmacology" (E. D. Bergmann and B. Pullman, eds.), pp. 213–228. Reidel, Dordrecht.
Camerman, A., and Camerman, N. (1977). *Proc. Natl. Acad. Sci. U.S.A.* **74**, 1264–1266.
Camerman, N., Chan, L. Y. Y., and Camerman, A. (1979). *Mol. Pharmacol.* **16**, 729–736.
Cannon, J. G. (1975). *Adv. Neurol.* **9**, 177–183.
Cannon, J. G., Smith, R. V., Aleem, M. A., and Long, J. P. (1975). *J. Med. Chem.* **18**, 108–110.
Cannon, J. G., Hatheway, G. J., Long, J. P., and Sharabi, F. M. (1976). *J. Med. Chem.* **19**, 987–993.
Cannon, J. G., Lee, T., Goldman, H. D., Costall, B., and Naylor, R. J. (1977). *J. Med. Chem.* **20**, 1111–1116.
Cannon, J. G., Long, J. P., and Bhatnagar, R. (1981). *J. Med. Chem.* **24**, 1113–1118.
Cannon, J. G., Perez, J. A., Bhatnagar, R. K., Long, J. P., and Sharabi, F. M. (1982). *J. Med. Chem.* **25**, 1442–1446.
Cannon, J. G., Perez, Z., Long, J. P., and Ilhan, M. (1983). *J. Med. Chem.* **26**, 813–816.
Carhart, R. E., Dixon, J. S., Dunn, D. A., and Venkataraghavan, R. (1981). *Am. Chem. Soc. Natl. Meet., 181st, Atlanta* Abstract MEDI-10.
Carlsson, A., and Nilsson, J. L. G., eds. (1983). "Dopamine Receptor Agonists." Swedish Pharmaceutical Press, Stockholm.
Casy, A. F. (1978). *Prog. Drug Res.* **22**, 149–227.
Cohen, N. C. (1971). *Tetrahedron* **27**, 789–797.
Cohen, N. C. (1979). *ACS Symp. Ser.* **112**, 371–381.
Cohen, N. C. (1983a). *J. Med. Chem.* **26**, 259–264.
Cohen, N. C. (1983b). *Trends Pharmacol. Sci.* **4**, 503–506.
Cohen, N. C. (1985). "Drugs of the Future," in press.
Cohen, N. C., and Régnier, G. (1976). *Bull. Soc. Chim. Fr.* 2034–2038.
Cohen, N. C., Colin, P., and Lemoine, G. (1981). *Tetrahedron* **37**, 1711–1721.
Cole, G. M., Meyer, E. F., Swanson, S. M., and White, W. G. (1979). *ACS Symp. Ser.* **112**, 189–204.
Comer, W. T. (1970). *ACS Symp.* (Ref. 7 of Kaiser *et al.*, 1977).
Costall, B., and Naylor, R. (1981). *Life Sci.* **28**, 215–229.

Costall, B., Lim, S. K., Naylor, R. J., and Cannon, J. G. (1982). *J. Pharm. Pharmacol.* **34**, 246–254.

Cramer, R. (1982). *Am. Chem. Soc. Natl. Meet., 183rd, Las Vegas* Abstract COMP-11.

Crandell, C. W., and Smith, D. H. (1983). *J. Chem. Inf. Comput. Sci.* **23**, 186–197.

Crippen, G. M. (1979). *J. Med. Chem.* **22**, 988–997.

Crippen, G. M. (1980). *J. Med. Chem.* **23**, 599–606.

Crippen, G. M. (1981). *J. Med. Chem.* **24**, 198–203.

Crippen, G. M. (1982). *Mol. Pharmacol.* **22**, 11–19.

Crippen, G. M. (1983). *Quant. Struct.-Act. Relat.* **2**, 95–100.

Cunha Monteiro, A. L. (1980). *Nom. Med. (Suppl.)* **June**, 23–27.

Cushman, D. W., and Ondetti, M. A. (1982). *Am. Chem. Soc. Natl. Meet., 183rd Las Vegas* Abstract MEDI-56.

Cushman, D. W., Cheung, H. S., Sabo, E. F., and Ondetti, M. A. (1977). *Biochemistry* **16**, 5484–5491.

Dauber, P., Osguthorpe, D. J., and Hagler, A. T. (1982). *Biochem. Soc. Trans.* **10**, 312–318.

De Paulis, T., Kelder, D., Ross, S. B., and Stjernström, N. E. (1978). *Mol. Pharmacol.* **14**, 596–606.

Dewar, M. J. S. (1969). "The Molecular Orbital Theory of Organic Chemistry." McGraw-Hill, New York.

Dewar, M. J. S., and Ford, G. P. (1979). *J. Am. Chem. Soc.* **101**, 5558–5561.

Dimaio, J., Ahmed, F. R., Schiller, P., and Belleau, B. (1979). *In* "Recent Advances in Receptor Chemistry" (F. Gualtieri, M. Giannella, and C. Melchiorre, eds.), pp. 221–234. Elsevier, Amsterdam.

Diner, S., Malrieu, J.-P., and Claverie, P. (1969a). *Theor. Chim. Acta* **13**, 1–17, 18–45.

Diner, S., Malrieu, J.-P., Jordan, F., and Gilbert, M. (1969b). *Theor. Chim. Acta* **15**, 100–110.

Effland, R. C., and Försch, M. F. (1981). *Annu. Rep. Med. Chem.* **16**, 31–40.

Effland, R. C., and Försch, M. F. (1982). *Annu. Rep. Med. Chem.* **17**, 11–19.

Erhardt, P. W. (1980). *J. Pharm. Sci.* **69**, 1059–1061.

Esaki, T. (1982). *Chem. Pharm. Bull.* **30**, 3657–3661.

Fawcett, J. K., Camerman, A., and Camerman, N. (1977). *Can. J. Chem.* **55**, 3631–3635.

Frère, J. M., Kelly, J. A., Klein, D., and Ghuysen, J. M. (1982). *Biochem. J.* **203**, 223–234.

Fries, D. S., and Portoghese, P. S. (1976). *J. Med. Chem.* **19**, 1155–1158.

Fryer, R. I. (1983). *In* "The Benzodiazepines: From Molecular Biology to Clinical Practice" (E. Costa, ed.), pp. 7–20. Raven, New York.

Fryer, R. I., and Gilman, N. W. (1983). Personal communication.

Ghose, A. K., and Crippen, G. M. (1982). *J. Med. Chem.* **25**, 892–899.

Ghose, A. K., and Crippen, G. M. (1983). *J. Med. Chem.* **26**, 996–1010.

Giessner-Prettre, C., and Pullman, A. (1972). *Theor. Chim. Acta* **25**, 83–88.

Gilli, G., Bertolasi, V., Sacerdoti, M., and Borea, P. A. (1978). *Acta Crystallogr. B* **34**, 2826–2829.

Gleason, J. G., Buckley, T. F., Holden, K. G., Bryan, D. B., and Siler, P. (1979). *J. Am. Chem. Soc.* **101**, 4730–4732.

Goldberg, L. I., Kohli, J. D., Kotake, A. N., and Volkman, P. H. (1978). *Fed. Proc. Fed. Am. Soc. Exp. Biol.* **37**, 2396–2402.

Goodford, P. J. (1984). *J. Med. Chem.* **27**, 557–564.

Grisar, J. M., Parker, R. A., Kariya, T., Blohm, T. R., Fleming, R. W., Petrow, V., Wenstrup, D. L., and Johnson, R. G. (1972). *J. Med. Chem.* **15**, 1273–1278.

Grol, C. J., and Rollema, H. (1977). *J. Pharm. Pharmacol.* **29**, 153–156.

Grunewald, G. L., Reitz, T. J., Ruth, J. A., Vollmer, S., Eiden, L. E., and Rutledge, C. O. (1979). *Biochem. Pharmacol.* **28**, 417–421.

Gund, P. (1979). Ann. Rep. Med. Chem. **14**, 299–308.

Gund, P. (1982). *Trends Pharmacol. Sci.* **3,** 56–58.
Gund, P., and Shen, T. Y. (1977). *J. Med. Chem.* **20,** 1146–1152.
Gund, P., Andose, J. D., Rhodes, J. B., and Smith, G. M. (1980). *Science* **208,** 1425–1431.
Halgren, T. A., Kleier, D. A., Hall, J. H., Jr., Brown, L. D., and Lipscomb, W. N. (1978). *J. Am. Chem. Soc.* **100,** 6595–6608.
Hansch, C. (1981). *Drug. Dev. Res.* **1,** 267–309.
Hansch, C., Fukunaga, J. Y., and Jow, P. Y. C. (1977). *J. Med. Chem.* **20,** 96–102.
Hansch, C., Li, R.-L., Blaney, J. M., and Langridge, R. (1982). *J. Med. Chem.* **25,** 777–784.
Hansch, C., Hathaway, B. A., Guo, Z. R., Selassie, C. D., Dietrich, S. W., Blaney, J. M., Langridge, R., Voltz, K. W., and Kaufman, B. T. (1984). *J. Med. Chem.* **27,** 129–143.
Hathaway, B. A., Guo, Z. R., Hansch, C., Delcamp, T. J., Susten, S. S., and Freisheim, J. H. (1984). *J. Med. Chem.* **27,** 144–149.
Hoffmann, R. (1963). *J. Chem. Phys.* **39,** 1397–1412.
Hopfinger, A. J. (1971). *Macromolecules* **4,** 731–737.
Hopfinger, A. J. (1980). *J. Am. Chem. Soc.* **102,** 7196–7206.
Hopfinger, A. J. (1981). *J. Med. Chem.* **24,** 818–822.
Hopfinger, A. J. (1983). *J. Med. Chem.* **26,** 990–996.
Horn, A. S., and Rodgers, J. R. (1980). *J. Pharm. Pharmacol.* **32,** 521–524.
Horn, A. S., and Snyder, S. H. (1971). *Proc. Natl. Acad. Sci. U.S.A.* **68,** 2325–2328.
Humber, L. G., Sideridis, N., Asselin, A. A., Bruderlein, F. T., and Voith, K. (1978). *J. Med. Chem.* **21,** 1225–1231.
Humber, L. G., Philipp, A. H., Bruderlein, F. T., and Voith, K. (1979). *ACS Symp. Ser.* **112,** 227–241.
Humbert, D., Dagnaux, M., Cohen, N. C., Fournex, R., and Clemence, F. (1983). *Eur. J. Med. Chem.* **18,** 67–78.
Humblet, C., and Marshall, G. R. (1980). *Annu. Rep. Med. Chem.* **15,** 267–276.
Humblet, C., and Marshall, G. R. (1981). *Drug Dev. Res.* **1,** 409–434.
Imhof, R., and Kyburz, E. (1982). *North Am. Med. Chem. Symp., Toronto* Poster Session 1, Abstract 59.
Imhof, R., Kyburz, E., and Daly, J. J. (1984). *J. Med. Chem.* **27,** 165–175.
Jen, T., and Kaiser, C. (1977). *J. Med. Chem.* **20,** 693–698.
Jones, G., and Kennard, O. (1978). *J. Pharm. Pharmacol.* **30,** 815–817.
Jones, T. A. (1978). *J. Appl. Crystallogr.* **11,** 268–272.
Jones, T. A. (1982). *In* "Computational Crystallography" (D. Sayre, ed.), pp. 303–317. Clarendon, Oxford.
Jurs, P. C., Chou, J. T., and Yuan, M. (1979). *ACS Symp. Ser.* **112,** 103–129.
Kaiser, C., and Kebabian, J. W., eds. (1983). Dopamine Receptors. *ACS Symp. Ser.* **224.**
Kaiser, C., Jen, T., Garvey, E., Bowen, W. D., Colella, D. F., and Wardell, J. R. (1977). *J. Med. Chem.* **20,** 687–692.
Kariya, T., Blohm, T. R., Grisar, J. M., Parker, R. A., Martin, J. R., Holmes, W. R., Paoletti, R., and Kritchevsky, D. (1972). *Adv. Exp. Med. Biol.* **26,** 302–303.
Kebabian, J. W., and Calne, D. B. (1979). *Nature (London)* **277,** 93–96.
Keller, H. H. (1983). *Naunyn-Schmiedeberg's Arch. Pharmacol.* **324** (Suppl.), R 19, Abstract 74.
Kelly, J. A., Moews, P. C., Knox, J. R., Frère, J. M., and Ghuysen, J. M. (1982). *Science* **218,** 479–481.
Kennard, O., Watson, D., Allen, F., Motherwell, W., Town, W., and Rodgers, J. (1975). *Chem. Br.* 213–216.
Kier, L. B., and Aldrich, H. E. (1974). *J. Theor. Biol.* **46,** 521–527.
Kuyper, L. F., Roth, B., Baccanari, D. P., Ferone, R., Beddel, C. R., Champness, J. N., Stammers, D. K., Dann, J. G., Norrington, F. E. A., Baker, D. J., and Goodford, P. J. (1982). *J. Med. Chem.* **25,** 1120–1122.

Langridge R. (1980). *Chem. Ind.* June 21, 475–477.

Langridge, R., Ferrin, T. E., Kuntz, I. D., and Connolly, M. L. (1981). *Science* **211**,661–666.

Lee, B. (1971). *J. Mol. Biol.* **61**, 463–469.

Leger, J. M., Gadret, M., and Carpy, A. (1980). *Mol. Pharmacol.* **17**, 339–343.

Leger, J. M., Colleter, J. C., and Carpy, A. (1983). *Eur. J. Med. Chem.* **18**, 559–562.

Lesk, A. M. (1979). *Commun. ACM* **22**, 219–224.

Li, R.-L., Hansch, C., Matthews, D., Blaney, J. M., Langridge, R., Delcamp, T. J., Susten, S. S., and Freisheim, J. H. (1982). *Quant. Struct.-Act. Relat.* **1**, 1–17.

Lipinski, C. A. (1983). *J. Med. Chem.* **26**, 1–6.

Lund, F., and Tybring, L. (1972). *Nature (London)* **236**, 135–136.

Marshall, G. R., Bosshard, H. E., and Ellis, R. A. (1974). *In* "Computer Representation and Manipulation of Chemical Information" (W. T. Wipke, S. R. Heller, R. J. Feldmann, and E. Hyde, eds.) pp. 203–237. Wiley, New York.

Marshall, G. R., Barry, C. D., Bosshard, H. E., Dammkoehler, R and Dunn, D. A. (1979). *ACS Symp. Ser.* **112**, 205–226.

Martin, A. R., Paradkar, V. M., Peng, G. W., Speth, R. C., Yamamura, H. I., and Horn, A. S. (1980). *J. Med. Chem.* **23**, 865–873.

Martin, Y. C. (1981). *J. Med. Chem.* **24**, 229–237.

Matthews, D. A. (1981). *Proc. Congr. 12th, Int. Union Crystallogr. Assoc. Meet., Mol. Struct. Biol. Activ., Buffalo N.Y.*

Matthews, D. A., Alden, R. A., Freer, S. T., Xuong, N., and Kraut, J. (1979). *J. Biol. Chem.* **254**, 4144–4151.

Matthews, D. A., Alden, R. A., Bolin, J. T., Freer, S. T., Hamlin, R., Xuong, N., Kraut, J., Poe, M., Williams, M., and Hoogsteen (1977). *Science* **197**, 452–455.

Mautner, H. G. (1974). *In* "Molecular and Quantum Pharmacology" (E. D. Bergmann and B. Pullman, eds.), pp. 119–125. Reidel, Dordrecht.

Maxwell, R. A., Keenan, P. D., Chaplin, E., Roth, B., and Eckhardt, S. B. (1969). *J. Pharm. Exp. Ther.* **166**, 320–329.

Meyer, E. F. (1980). *In* "Drug Design" (E. J. Ariens, ed.), Vol. 9, pp. 267–298. Academic Press, New York.

Moereels, H., and Tollenaere, J. P. (1978). *Life Sci.* **23**, 459–464.

Morffew, A. J. (1983). *J. Mol. Graphics* **1**, 17–23.

Murray-Rust, P., and Motherwell, S. (1978). *Acta Crystallogr.* B **34**, 2518–2526.

Nagarajan, R., Boeck, L. D., Gorman, M., Hamill, R. L., Higgins, C. E., Hoehn, M. M., Stark, W. M., and Whitney, J. G. (1971). *J. Am. Chem. Soc.* **93**, 2308–2310.

Nédélec, L., Pierdet, A., Dumont, C., and Kannengiesser, M. H. (1975a). Fr. patent 75/25,398 (CA **87**:102093W).

Nédélec, L., Pierdet, A., Dumont, C., and Kannengiesser, M. H. (1975b). Fr. patent 2,337,127 (CA **88**:136376b).

Nordby, D. H., and Hodges, D. (1975). *Am. Chem. Soc. Natl. Meet., 169th, Philadelphia* Abstract COMP-16.

O'Donnel, T. J., Martin, Y. C., and Koschmann, T. (1982). *Am. Chem. Soc. Natl. Meet., 183rd, Las Vegas* Abstract COMP-14.

Olson, G. L., Cheung, H.-C., Morgan, K. D., Todaro, L., Berger, L., Davidson, A. B., and Boff, E. (1981). *J. Med. Chem.* **24**, 1026–1034.

Olson, G. L., Cheung, H.-C., and Berger, L. (1983). *ACS Symp. Ser.* **224**, 251–274.

Ondetti, M. A., Rubin, B., and Cushman, D. W. (1977). *Science* **196**, 441–444.

Osawa, E., and Musso, H. (1982). *In* "Topics in Stereochemistry" (N. L. Allinger, E. L. Eliel, and S. H. Wilen, eds.), Vol. 13, pp. 117–193. Wiley, New York.

Pensak, D. A. (1979). *ACS/CSJ Chem. Congr., Honolulu* Abstract COMP-21.

Petrongolo, C., Tomasi, J., Macchia, B., and Macchia, J. (1974). *J. Med. Chem.* **17**, 501–507.

Pfaendler, H. R., Gostelli, J., Woodward, R. B., and Rihs, G. (1981). *J. Am. Chem. Soc.* **103**, 4526–4531.

Pichardo, R., Boulet, L., and Davignon, J. (1977). *Atherosclerosis* **26**, 573–582.

Poe, M., Springer, J. P., and Hoogsteen, K. (1981). *Annu. Meet. Am. Soc. Biol. Chem.*, *72nd, St. Louis* May 31–June 4. *Fed. Proc. Fed. Am. Soc. Exp. Biol.* **40**, 1837.

Politzer, P., and Daiker, K. C. (1977). *Int. J. Quant. Chem.* **QBS4**, 317–323.

Pople, J. A., and Segal, G. A. (1966). *J. Chem. Phys.* **44**, 3289–3296.

Post, M. L., Kennard, O., and Horn, A. S. (1975). *Acta Crystallogr. B* **31**, 1008–1013.

Pullman, A., Pullman, B., and Lavery, R. (1983). *J. Mol. Struct.* **93**, 85–91.

Rein, R., Swissler, T. J., Renugopalkrishnan, V., and Pack, G. R. (1972). *In* "Conformation of Biological Molecules" (E. D. Bergmann and B. Pullman, eds.), pp. 761–780. Israël Acad. Sci. Human., Jerusalem.

Rindone, W. P., and Kush, T. (1980). "User's Guide to the Molecule Facilities of the PROPHET System." Bolt Beranek & Newman, Cambridge, Mass.

Rivier, J., Brazeau, P., Vale, W., and Guillemin, R. (1975). *J. Med. Chem.* **18**, 123–126.

Salvetti, F., Buttinoni, A., Ceserani, R., and Tosi, C. (1981). *Eur. J. Med. Chem.* **16**, 81–90.

Sankawa, U., Shibuya, M., Ebizuka, Y., Noguchi, H., Kinoshita, T., Iitaka, Y., Endo, A., and Kitahara, N. (1982). *Prostaglandins* **24**, 21–34.

Scherrer, R. A. (1974). *In* "Antiinflammatory Agents: Chemistry and Pharmacology" (R. A. Scherrer and M. W. Whitehouse, eds.), Vol. 1, pp. 29–43. Academic Press, New York.

Scrocco, E., and Tomasi, J. (1973). *Fortschr. Chem. Forsch.* **42**, 95–170.

Scrocco, E., and Tomasi, J. (1978). *Adv. Quantum Chem.* **11**, 115–193.

Seeman, P. (1980). *Pharmacol. Rev.* **32**, 229–313.

Seeman, P., Westman, K., Protiva, M., Jilek, J., Jain, P. C., Saxena, A. K., Anand, N., Humber, L., and Philipp, A. (1979). *Eur. J. Pharmacol.* **56**, 247–251.

Shih, D., and Ratcliffe, R. W. (1981). *J. Med. Chem.* **24**, 639–643.

Shiotani, S., Kometani, T., Iitaka, Y., and Itai, A. (1978). *J. Med. Chem.* **21**, 153–154.

Sokoloff, P., Martres, M. P., and Schwartz, J. C. (1980). *Naunyn-Schmiedeberg's Arch. Pharmacol.* **315**, 89–102.

Srebrenik, S., Weinstein, H., and Pauncz, R. (1973). *Chem. Phys. Lett.* **20**, 419–423.

Sternbach, L. H., Sancilio, F. D., and Blount, J. F. (1974). *J. Med. Chem.* **17**, 374–377.

Strominger, J. L., and Tipper, D. J. (1965). *Am. J. Med.* **39**, 708–721.

Strominger, J. L., Izaki, K., Matsuhasi, M., and Tipper, D. (1967). *Fed. Proc., Fed. Am. Soc. Exp. Biol.* **26**, 9–22.

Sufrin, J. R., Coulter, A. W., and Talalay, P. (1979). *Mol. Pharmacol.* **15**, 661–677.

Sufrin, J. R., Dunn, D. A., and Marshall, G. R. (1981). *Mol. Pharmacol.* **19**, 307–313.

Sundaram, K., and Mahajan, S. (1981). *Physiol. Chem. Phys.* **13**, 387–406.

Sunjic, V., Lisini, A., Sega, A., Kovac, T., Kajfez, F., and Ruscic, B. (1979). *J. Heterocycl. Chem.* **16**, 757–761.

Surcouf, E. (1982). Doctorate Thesis. Paris University.

Surcouf, E., and Mornon, J. P. (1983). *In* "Biotechnologie et Conception Asssitée par Ordinateur" (J. Janin, ed.), pp. 23–26. Proceedings of a Colloqium held at the Pasteur Institute, Paris, Jan. 25–26.

Surcouf, E., Rimsky, A., and Mornon, J. P. (1982). *J. Appl. Crystallogr.* **15**, 636–637.

Sweet, R., and Dahl, L. F. (1970). *J. Am. Chem. Soc.* **92**, 5489–5507.

Tallman, J. F., Paul, S. M., Skolnick, W., and Gallager, D. W. (1980). *Science* **207**, 274–281.

Tamir, I., Mechoulam, R., and Meyer, A. Y. (1980). *J. Med. Chem.* **23**, 220–223.

Tedesco, J. L., Seeman, P., and McDermed, J. D. (1979). *Mol. Pharmacol.* **16**, 369–381.

Tollenaere, J. P., Moereels, H., and Raymaekers, L. A. (1980). *In* "Drug Design" (E. J. Ariens, ed.), Vol. 10, pp. 71–118. Academic Press, New York.

Tomasi, J. (1980). *In* "Quantum Theory of Chemical Reactions" (R. Daudel, ed.), Vol. 1, pp. 191–228. Reidel, Dordrecht.

Van Heyningen, E., and Ahern, L. K. (1968). *J. Med. Chem.* **11**, 933–936.

Veber, D. F. (1981). *Proc. Am. Peptide Symp, 7th* Pierce Chem. Co. 685–694.

Veber, D. F., and Saperstein, R. (1979). *Annu. Rep. Med. Chem.* **14**, 209–218.

Veber, D. F., Holly, F. W., Paleveda, W. J., Nutt, R. F., Bergstrand, S. J., Torchiana, M., Glitzer, M. S., Saperstein, R., and Hirschmann, R. (1978). *Proc. Natl. Acad. Sci. U.S.A.* **75**, 2636–2640.

Veber, D. F., Holly, F. W., Nutt, R. F., Bergstrand, S. J., Brady, S. F., Hirschmann, R., Glitzer, M. S., and Saperstein, R. (1979). *Nature (London)* **280**, 512–514.

Veber, D. F., Freidinger, R. M., Perlow, D. S., Paleveda, W. J., Holly, F. W., Strachan, R. G., Nutt, R. F., Arison, B. H., Homnick, C., Randall, W. C., Glitzer, M. S., Saperstein, R., and Hirschmann, R. (1981). *Nature (London)* **292**, 55–58.

Verloop, A., Hoogenstraaten, W., and Tipker, J. (1976). *In* "Drug Design" (E. J. Ariens, ed.), Vol. 11, pp. 165–207. Academic Press, New York.

Weiner, P. K., and Kollman, P. A. (1981). *J. Comput. Chem.* **2**, 287–303.

Weiner, P. K., Langridge, R., Blaney, J. M., Schaefer, R., and Kollman, P. A. (1982). *Proc. Natl. Acad. Sci. U.S.A.* **79**, 3754–3758.

Weinstein, H., and Osman, R. (1977). *Int. J. Quantum Chem.* **QBS4**, 253–268.

Weinstein, H., Osman, R., Topiol, S., and Green, J. P. (1981). *Ann. N.Y. Acad. Sci.* **367**, 434–451.

Weintraub, H. J. R. (1975). Ph.D. Dissertation. Case Western Reserve University, Cleveland Ohio. (Univ. Microfilms, Ann Arbor, Mich., No 75-19.257).

Weintraub, H. J. R. (1979). *ACS Symp. Ser.* **112**, 353–370.

Weintraub, H. J. R., and Hopfinger, A. J. (1975). *Int. J. Quantum Chem., Quantum Biol. Symp.* **2**, 203–208.

Wertz, D. H., and Allinger, N. L. (1974). *Tetrahedron* **30**, 1579–1586.

Wilson, S. R., and Huffman, J. C. (1980). *J. Org. Chem.* **45**, 560–566.

Witiak, D. T., Chun-Lun-Ho, T., and Hackney, R. E. (1968). *J. Med. Chem.* **11**, 1086–1089.

Witiak, D. T., Newman, H. A., and Feller, D. R. (1977). *In* "Clofibrate and Related Analogs. A Comprehensive Review," Medicinal Research Series, Vol. 7. Dekker, New York.

Woodward, R. B. (1980). *Philos. Trans. R. Soc. London Ser. B* **289**, 239–250.

Mechanisms of Action of Antiinflammatory Drugs

WILLIAM E. M. LANDS

Department of Biological Chemistry
University of Illinois at Chicago
College of Medicine
Chicago, Illinois

1 Effector Cells and Effector Molecules at Inflammatory Sites

Inflammation is generally regarded to be a local disorder that involves increased numbers of leukocytes at the immediate site with increased local release of inflammatory mediator molecules. The many different cells and effector molecules involved in the complex network of processes that we call inflammation permit a variety of strategies in developing antiinflammatory therapies. The cellular interactions appear to change throughout the progression of the inflammatory processes so that one form of cellular interaction may dominate at an early stage whereas that interaction may be of little significance at a later stage, and other cellular interactions dominate. As in all series of sequential events, successful attack at the rate-limiting step gives a better opportunity for success in preventing the overall process than would be obtained by modifying steps that are not rate limiting. Some intended antiinflammatory agents may act at steps

ADVANCES IN DRUG RESEARCH, VOL. 14
0-12-013314-8

that are not always rate limiting and therefore are not always very successful, depending on the stage to which a given inflammatory condition has progressed. Investigators in this area find it important to appreciate that reducing a catalytic step that is necessary but not rate limiting by 80% may have little influence on the overall process. Thus, experimental models designed to test the efficacy of antiinflammatory agents must satisfy two principal requirements. First, the assay model must have a rate-limiting step upon which the agent to be examined can exert an influence. Second, the rate-limiting steps in the experimental model should bear some relationship to the rate-limiting steps in the human inflammatory disorder being modeled. The latter requirement appears to be a particularly vexing problem for investigators, since inflammatory conditions in humans still have many processes that are poorly understood. We need a much more systematic investigation of the rate-limiting steps in these complex inflammatory disorders. It seems likely that better interpretations of the regulation of inflammatory processes will come as we transfer knowledge from studies of asthma, thrombosis, and atherogenesis, in which similar networks of cell–cell signaling by eicosanoid modulators are now recognized to occur. Many cases of inflammation have imprecise origins, and the initial stimulus or signal that provokes the chain of cellular processes remains uncertain even though the overall results of the processes are clearly evident. The following discussion considers three aspects of inflammatory processes: the effector cells that mediate and amplify the signal, the effector molecules released by those cells, and cell–cell signaling processes.

1.1 CELLS MEDIATING INFLAMMATION

The four major types of cell involved at the site of an inflammatory condition are polymorphonuclear leukocytes (or neutrophils), macrophages, lymphocytes, and mast cells. A general overall characteristic of the inflammatory process is that some triggering event stimulates the inward migration of neutrophils to the inflammatory site, and these cells are subsequently followed by macrophages (Di Rosa et al., 1971). During and after these events, some signaling occurs that activates mast cells to release other inflammatory mediator molecules that create the principal symptoms of inflammation: erythema, edema, hyperthermia, hyperalgesia, and loss of function. The cell–cell signaling among these cell types that amplifies the initial signal represents an important network of information that must be modified by successful antiinflammatory strategies. For example, the appearance of increased numbers of mediator-releasing cells at an inflammatory site might be diminished greatly by agents that decrease either the release or the effectiveness of chemotactic factors. Without appreciable numbers of inflammatory cells at the site, little inflammation occurs. Thus an inhibition of the earliest chemotactic signals may succeed conveniently before the amplifying processes have created a condition that requires more drastic treatment.

1.2 EFFECTOR MOLECULES IN INFLAMMATION

Attempting to counteract the results of the bewildering set of released effector molecules at a fully developed inflammatory site poses almost insurmountable problems. The symptoms of erythema, edema, hyperthermia, and hyperalgesia result from mediators derived from both tissue and vascular components. The mast cells release histamine and eosinophil chemotactic factor (ECF) from their granules and also form and release prostaglandins (PGD_2, PGE_2), leukotrienes (LTB_4, LTC_4, LTD_4), platelet activating factor (PAF), and hexosaminidase.

Neutrophils release LTB_4, a potent chemotactic agent for stimulating and recruiting more neutrophils (Bray *et al.*, 1981a). They also release several neutral and acid proteases as well as a cationic protein that stimulates the release of the contents of mast cell granules. Additional proteins from the neutrophil appear to exert either chemotactic or inhibitory effects on leukocyte migration. The lymphocytes release a variety of peptides called lymphokines that can inhibit migration of macrophages; chemotactically affect macrophages, neutrophils, basophils, or eosinophils; exert cytotoxic actions; induce lymphocyte proliferation; or induce vascular permeability. These peptide agents include interleukins (IL-1, IL-2, IL-3) and interferons (e.g., IFN_γ). Adding to the above network of effector molecules, three different systems in plasma provide more mediators that influence inflammation: the kinin system, the complement system, and the clotting and fibrinolytic system. These mediators enhance the vascular symptoms of erythema, edema, and hyperthermia as well as that of hyperalgesia. A brief overview of some of the interactions of these mediator systems with the effector cells is shown in Fig. 1. Interaction of these systems is intricate because stimulation of factor XII (Hageman factor) in the clotting system will cause it to activate prekallikrein to kallikrein which then converts kininogen to bradykinin in the kinin system as well as activating more factor XII. The factor XII also converts the plasminogen proactivator to plasminogen activator that converts plasminogen to plasmin, which in turn activates the complement system that mediates cytolytic action and provides a series of peptides that are chemotactic for neutrophils and increase vascular permeability. The action of the peptide mediators produced by the three plasma systems noted above can be enhanced by prostaglandins. For example, the sense of pain induced by bradykinin (or histamine from mast cells) can be increased by prostaglandins (Ferreira *et al.*, 1978); the presence of vasodilation caused by prostaglandins makes more severe the edema that is induced by bradykinin, histamine, C_{5a} of complement (Williams *et al.*, 1983) or LTB_4 (Bray *et al.*, 1981b).

The release of degradative, hydrolytic enzymes by effector cells presents a basis for another significant aspect of inflammatory events, namely loss of function (Weissman *et al.*, 1971). The degradative enzymes can promote injury of tissue and the destruction of structural materials to the extent that irreversible

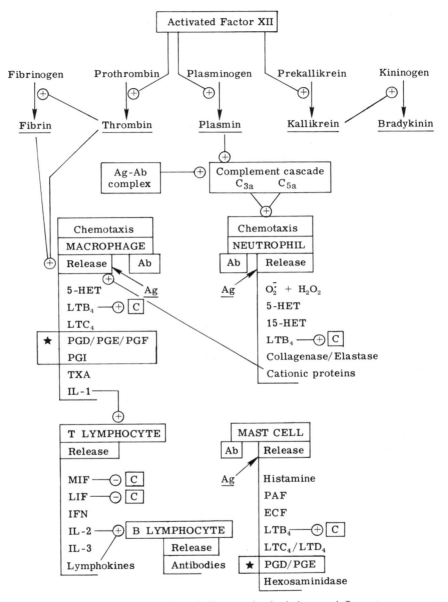

Fig. 1. Interactions of effector cells and effector molecules in immune-inflammatory responses. Ab, Antibodies; Ag, antigens; C, chemotaxis. For further explanations, see text.

damage may occur. The hydrolytic and destructive events occur in the presence of other inflammatory symptoms, but are not mediated by the same effector molecules. Ironically, added prostaglandins, by elevating cellular cAMP levels, can inhibit the release of acid hydrolases from granulocytes and diminish this aspect of inflammation (Weissmann *et al.*, 1971). Thus, attention to the vascular-oriented symptoms of edema and erythema will not adequately account for other severe pathological events that often occur, and the prevention of one symptom may not be sufficient to prevent other symptoms of great importance from occurring. This situation again emphasizes the importance of an appropriate choice of an experimental model in examining the mechanism and efficacy of an antiinflammatory agent at a specific rate-limiting step. Several examples will be presented in this article to illustrate the difficulty of using *in vitro* results for inhibition of a single specific step to predict antiinflammatory actions *in vivo*.

With so many alternate mediator events involved, it is surprising that blocking any single step could diminish the overall inflammation. The fact that anti-cyclooxygenase agents *do* serve as useful antiinflammatory agents indicates that cyclooxygenase action is often one of the important rate-limiting reactions mediating the eventual expression of the symptoms of inflammation. The commonly used anticyclooxygenase agents seem to be more useful in acute inflammation conditions than in chronic immune-mediated inflammation. Thus we can regard the enzymatic formation of prostaglandins as one significant rate-limiting aspect of acute inflammatory models. Blocking that step remains the most successful strategy of all attempted so far to reduce undesired symptoms of inflammation, but new initiatives in reducing more proximal events associated with earlier rate-limiting steps in immune responses may be developed in the future. More research on how inhibiting cyclooxygenase action can be so important in the overall symptoms of inflammation should help determine whether it is due to the enzyme's ability to amplify hydroperoxide concentrations (see Section 2 of this article) or to a unique role of prostanoids in creating the detectable symptoms. Figure 1 illustrates some prostanoid origins in two of the effector cells of inflammatory processes. It is not yet clear how prostanoid biosynthesis in macrophages and mast cells can affect the overall process as it does or whether it is only involved in the readily detected symptoms of hyperalgesia, erythema, and edema associated with the overall process.

1.3 EICOSANOIDS IN CELL–CELL SIGNALING

John Vane's recognition in 1971 that the commonly used antiinflammatory agents, aspirin and indomethacin, have their principal mode of action in blocking prostaglandin biosynthesis, gave us a convenient strategy for indicating the participation of prostaglandins in complex cellular processes. Since his discovery, the nonsteroidal antiinflammatory (or ''antiprostaglandin'') drugs have been used successfully to implicate prostaglandins in a wide variety of physiological and pathophysiological processes. Nevertheless, the past decade has also generated an awareness that although prostaglandins are potent agents in modulating and amplifying inflammatory cellular signals, they frequently are not the primary carriers of those signals. This means that blocking prostaglandin biosynthesis in many cases does not prevent the signal from occurring, but merely reduces the amplitude of the response that the signal elicits. Even in situations clearly mediated by prostaglandin biosynthesis, a challenge remains in interpreting the way by which that biosynthesis facilitates the symptoms observed. We still have insufficient evidence of the facilitative roles of prostaglandins to be able to designate which actions are due to the presence of prostaglandins per se, and which actions are due to the process of forming prostaglandins *in situ*.

The release of prostaglandins during cell–cell signaling events apparently entails a stimulated hydrolytic process at the cellular membrane to release arachidonic acid, an oxidative conversion of arachidonic acid to PGG_2, a subsequent conversion of the PGG_2 to PGH_2, and then into one of the various prostaglandin-derived mediators, such as PGE_2, thromboxane A_2, or prostacyclin (PGI_2).

Lipoxygenation is a parallel oxidative event for arachidonate which produces the 5-hydroperoxy-arachidonate that is then cyclized to the epoxide, leukotriene A_4. Leukotriene A_4, in turn, serves as the parent compound for a variety of active derivatives, LTB_4, LTC_4, LTD_4, and LTE_4. Altogether the prostaglandins, thromboxanes, prostacyclins, and leukotrienes represent a potent complex set of modulators called eicosanoids. These 20 carbon autacoids are derived from nonesterified fatty acid (Lands and Samuelsson, 1968), which can be released upon stimulation of cellular phospholipases. The released autacoids can influence cellular responses to hydroxy acids, thrombotic and chemotactic agents, and apparently alter calcium availability in a way that amplifies or aggravates the normal cellular response. This hyperreactivity, or hypersensitivity, induced by the eicosanoids is an important feature in understanding the complex cellular interactions during inflammatory processes.

Again, inhibition at the earliest committed step of eicosanoid biosynthesis (lipid hydrolysis) seems likely to lead to successful suppression of eicosanoid levels, and there is currently a vigorous search for inhibitors of the hydrolytic release of arachidonate. Antiinflammatory steroids have been reported to act at this point by inducing the formation of a polypeptide inhibitor of the phospholipid hydrolase(s) (Flower and Blackwell, 1979; Hirata *et al.*, 1980).

Subsequent reports by Blackwell *et al.* (1980, 1983) have emphasized that the release of preformed polypeptide (macrocortin) was induced by steroids, although RNA and protein synthesis were also needed for optimal release. The size of the effective peptide may differ as evidenced by two active fractions, MW = 15,000 and 40,000. The smaller size was routinely noted in Blackwell's reports (macrocortin), and the larger, named lipomodulin was routinely described by

Hirata (1983). Unfortunately, the induction of these small proteins is accompanied by the induction of too many side effects, and the use of corticoids over a long time period is not desirable. No selective inducer of lipomodulin/macrocortin release or synthesis has yet been recognized, but its discovery would have great importance.

Many signaling steps are involved in the very early phases of an inflammatory condition prior to the hydrolytic release of arachidonate. These include complex immunologic cell signaling between macrophages and lymphocytes which precede the T-cell modulation of the proliferation of antibody-producing B cells. This complex network of signals includes lymphokines whose function is modulated by both prostaglandins and leukotrienes. Altering the early immunologic signals with antiprostaglandin agents may give effects paradoxically opposite from the results of the same agents acting on the later signals emitted by the terminal effector cells. Thus a model system for chronic inflammation that has early immune-suppressive prostaglandin-mediated responses limiting the eventual inflammatory state may actually produce a greater overall response when prostaglandin synthesis is inhibited. On the other hand, the eicosanoid-enhanced mobilization of effector cells with their released mediators that occurs later in the immune-inflammatory sequence provides the commonly recognized symptoms of acute inflammation that are used to screen antiinflammatory agents.

Eicosanoids formed by both fatty acid oxygenases (cyclooxygenase and lipoxygenase) have proinflammatory actions, and there is considerable uncertainty at this time about whether PGH_2- or LTA_4-derived eicosanoids are the major types of inflammatory mediator. The quantitative evaluation of the effectiveness of agents in biological screening systems requires a detailed understanding of how the agent affects eicosanoid biosynthesis and how eicosanoids affect the inflammatory model being studied. Unfortunately some planned therapeutic strategies may eliminate certain symptoms with little effect on the overall cause of the disease that remains. Our current mastery of antiinflammatory strategies is more precise for the acute symptoms than for the chronic aspects of inflammation because of the more quantitatively developed understanding of acute model systems. To help review this understanding, the remainder of this article focuses primarily on the fatty acid oxygenases, their reaction mechanisms, and the manner in which anticyclooxygenase and antilipoxygenase agents can to some degree decrease acute immune-inflammatory processes.

2 Fatty Acid Oxygenase Mechanisms

An unusual accelerative feature of the kinetics of catalysis by fatty acid oxygenases arises from the fact that the lipid peroxide product of the enzymes can initiate a more rapid oxygenation reaction (Haining and Axelrod, 1958; Hemler *et al.*, 1979). This aspect of a hydroperoxide-initiated free-radical chain reaction (Hemler and Lands, 1980) appears to influence the overall rate of reaction for all fatty acid oxygenases, both cyclooxygenase and lipoxygenase. Chain termination events appear to be quite rapid relative to chain initiation processes, and a continual presence of lipid hydroperoxide is needed to sustain the oxygenase activity (Lands *et al.*, 1971, 1973). When the peroxide scavenger, glutathione peroxidase, is added to a reacting system, oxygen consumption rapidly ceases, and the enzyme remains inert until the level of lipid peroxide is once again increased, and then the reaction resumes (see Lands *et al.*, 1976, for cyclooxygenase, and Smith and Lands, 1972a, for soy lipoxygenase). Even with large amounts of fatty acid oxygenase present with substrate fatty acid, little eicosanoid biosynthesis will occur without sufficient lipid peroxide activator. This phenomenon also occurs with the 12-lipoxygenase from rat lung (Yokoyama *et al.*, 1983) or human platelets (Siegel *et al.*, 1979) and the 5-lipoxygenase of RBL-1 cells (Egan *et al.*, 1983). The prostaglandin-forming cyclooxygenase activity appears to need about 0.02 μM lipid hydroperoxide to act at a significant rate (Kulmacz and Lands, 1983). Thus, in catalyzing oxygenation of arachidonate to form PGG_2, the cyclooxygenase may transiently amplify the hydroperoxide concentration to higher levels (ca. 0.1 to 1 μM) that could stimulate other oxygenases within the activated cell. This amplification may present an important rate-limiting event in the overall inflammatory condition as noted earlier.

   Continuous removal of lipid peroxides by cellular peroxidases tends to ensure that only limited eicosanoid biosynthesis occurs under most normal tissue conditions (Cook and Lands, 1976). Inflammatory disorders with their associated production of eicosanoids have increased levels of lipid peroxides. The fact that inflammation is associated with the recruitment of phagocytic cells to the inflammatory site has particular significance in terms of the ability of those cells to produce peroxides and overwhelm the local capacity for peroxide removal. We recently found that the concentration of hydrogen peroxide and lipid peroxides produced by neutrophils (5×10^6 cells/ml) are 100 and 0.2 μM, respectively (Marshall and Lands, unpublished results). This oxidative stress can create an environment in which the glutathione/glutathione peroxidase system is under pressure, and the eicosanoid biosynthesis will be greater than that in normal tissue of lower peroxide tone. The greater the degree of infiltration of phagocytic cells into an inflammatory site, the greater will be the oxidative loss of glutathione and the probability of eicosanoid biosynthesis.

   The unusual kinetic and mechanistic features of the fatty acid oxygenases include not only the accelerative self-activation due to product activation (Hemler *et al.*, 1978), but also include self-catalyzed inactivation during reaction (sometimes noted as "suicide substrate" action) (Smith and Lands, 1972a,b). This suicide process is apparently dependent upon the substrate forming a reactive intermediate in the presence of oxygen that destroys the catalytic competence rather than forming product. The rate constant for this destruction varies for different substrate analogs for lipoxygenase (Smith and Lands, 1972a) and cyclooxygenase (Lands *et al.*, 1971, 1973). The complex mechanisms of oxygenases provide many points in which inhibitors could act to produce an eventual antiinflammatory response, as discussed below.

3 Types of Oxygenase Inhibitors

The inhibitors of cyclooxygenase currently available can be classified in three categories (Lands, 1981), depending on whether they produce (A) a rapid reversible competitive inhibition, (B) a time-dependent inactivation, or (C) a rapid reversible noncompetitive inhibition (free-radical trapping) (Fig. 2).

3.1 REVERSIBLE COMPETITIVE INHIBITORS

The competitive inhibitors represent an easily understood interaction at the substrate site in which a substrate analog such as a closely related polyunsaturated fatty acid can bind at the site but cannot form a product. Several polyunsaturated fatty acids have inhibition binding constants of $2-20 \times 10^{-6}$ M (Rome and Lands, 1975; Lands *et al.*, 1973) that are similar to the affinity of the substrate, arachidonate. Stronger binding and inhibition occur with the more highly unsaturated acids (Lands *et al.*, 1973; Ziboh *et al.*, 1974). Competitive inhibition at the substrate site can also occur with substituted carboxylic acids such as arylpropionate derivatives. Ibuprofen, which has a binding constant of approximately 5×10^{-6} M (Rome and Lands, 1975), is a major commercial success, and it is used

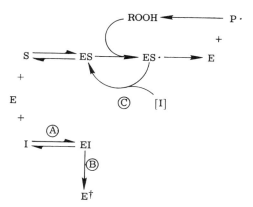

FIG. 2. Categories of inhibitors of cyclooxygenase. A and C are reversible inhibitions, B is a time-dependent inactivation.

for a wide range of inflammatory conditions. Binding of this type of inhibitor to the cyclooxygenase appears to depend more on hydrophobic features than on its ionic character since binding of these agents was not appreciably influenced by converting the carboxylate function to the methyl ester (Rome and Lands, 1975). Nevertheless, formation of the methyl ester prevented the time-dependent inactivation of aspirin, indomethacin, and all time-dependent agents tested, and left these agents as simple reversible competitive inhibitors. In cases where the inhibitor has an asymmetric center next to the carboxyl group, the more active stereoisomer tends to have the S configuration (Juby *et al.*, 1972). This chiral influence is variable, with a 6-fold preference for dextrorotatory pirprofen and a 130-fold one for dextrorotatory naproxen (Ku and Wasvary, 1975). Reviews of the optimal structural characteristics (Shen *et al.*, 1974; Gryglewski, 1974) emphasized a biplanar array for the substrate site following the earlier suggestions of Shen (1967). Recent computer-assisted modeling studies led Gund and Shen (1977) to reaffirm some of the prior concepts while emphasizing a probable carboxyl binding locus below the plane of the "ring binding region." Another computer study produced a different concept; that the inhibitors may more closely resemble the geometry of the peroxy radical (Appleton and Brown, 1979) that forms during the reaction. These heuristic treatments of structure–activity relationships are useful adjuncts to model studies in trying to develop clearer alternatives for the dimensions of new drugs able to fit the hypothetical active site that complements the substrate (see the chapter by Cohen in this volume).

The requirement for hydroperoxide concentrations to activate the cyclooxygenation of the *n*-3 class of polyunsaturated fatty acids is greater than that for the *n*-6 acids (Culp *et al.*, 1979; Lands and Byrnes, 1981). Thus the *n*-3 analogs are ineffective substrates in conditions of low hydroperoxide contents in which the *n*-6 acids are readily oxidized, as reported earlier by Lands *et al.* (1973). In this situation, which may prevail normally in intact normal tissues, the *n*-3 acids would be competitive inhibitors of eicosanoid biosynthesis from arachidonate. Feeding supplements of *n*-3 fatty acids (as fish oil) reduced the severity of eicosanoid-mediated cerebral stroke in cats (Black *et al.*, 1979), myocardial infarction in dogs (Culp *et al.*, 1980), and leukotriene formation in mice (Murphy *et al.*, 1981). It seems possible that this phenomenon may be the basis for the low incidence of immune-inflammatory disorders in Eskimos and Japanese ingesting a maritime diet. Individuals living in fishing villages may be under a continuous form of antiinflammatory regimen from *in utero* to old age.

Acetylenic analogs of unsaturated fatty acids can also serve as competitive inhibitors. These acids, like the *n*-3 analogs, can bind the substrate site of the oxygenases competitively, and all of the 18- and 20-carbon acetylenic analogs examined exhibited a reversible interaction (K_I = 2 to 20 μM) at the substrate site competitive with arachidonate (Downing *et al.*, 1972; Vanderhoek and Lands, 1973a). When sufficient hydroperoxide activator is present aerobically, the acetylenic analogs can serve as suicide substrates although they form no detectable eicosanoid products. Thus these analogs may inhibit the formation of eicosanoids by either a reversible, competitive process or a time-dependent inactivation. These two inhibitory mechanisms have very different pharmacodynamic features, and the latter type is also found with the most widely used agents, aspirin and indomethacin.

3.2 TIME-DEPENDENT INACTIVATION

The tetrayne analog of arachidonate irreversibly inhibited prostaglandin formation (Downing et al., 1970) and a 9,12-dinoic analog of linoleate was effective against both cyclooxygenase and lipoxygenase activity (Downing et al., 1972). Although none of the 15 isomers of octadecynoic acid was reported by Downing et al. (1972) to be effective, a detailed examination of the inhibitory characteristics of the monoynoic substrate analogs by Vanderhoek and Lands (1973a) indicated that a time-dependent inactivation of the cyclooxygenase activity occurred for two isomers: the 10- and 13-octadecynoic acids. Several different acetylenic analogs had first-order rate constants for the inactivation of cyclooxygenase that ranged from 0.08 to 0.26 min^{-1}. Apparently, certain acetylenic analogs begin to react as substrate, but form a metastable intermediate with oxygen that leads efficiently to destructive side reactions which inactivate the catalytic site. The resulting oxygen consumption may be stoichiometric with the enzyme inactivated and too small to be conveniently measured.

The inactivation of cyclooxygenase by only the 10- and 13-isomers of octadecynoic acid is compatible with a highly selective removal of the hydrogen at carbon-12 to form a reactive (perhaps allenic) destructive intermediate. On the other hand, inhibition by the 9,12-octadecadiynoic acid suggests removal of the hydrogen at carbon 8, 11, or 14 and inhibition by 5,8,11,14-eicosatetraynoic acid is compatible with H removal at either carbon-7, -10, -13, or -16. Thus the uncertain selectivity of this event questions the strict orientational arrangement of the radical-generating part of the catalytic site with certain positions of the acyl chain. A similar approach to inhibiting lipoxygenase activity by analogs that may form abortive intermediates is found in recent reports by Corey and Park (1982), Corey and Munroe (1982), and Pfister and Murthy (1983). The utility of these inhibitors as antiinflammatory agents may also depend upon their ability to inactivate in the conditions of the low hydroperoxide content that prevails in vivo. If the conditions do not favor the inactivation reaction, then the agents may be little better than oleate in inhibiting competitively.

Several commercially successful antiinflammatory agents inactivate cyclooxygenase activity in a time-dependent manner (Smith and Lands, 1971; Lands et al., 1974; Rome and Lands, 1975). No subsequent treatment has so far been able to restore activity, and the cyclooxygenase appears to be irreversibly inactivated.

A consequence of this type of inactivation is that once the enzyme is inactivated, removal of the drug will not permit synthesis of prostaglandins until new enzyme is formed by protein synthesis in the tissue. The irreversible mechanism provides a vastly different pharmacodynamic phenomenon with its effect extending beyond the time needed to clear the drug from the tissue. Thus, the action of a single dose of this type of agent can be greatly different than that of a competitive inhibitor that must be present continuously to inhibit prostaglandin formation. Aspirin, which is the most commonly used member of the class of irreversible inhibitors, forms a covalent acetylated derivative of the enzyme (Roth and Majerus, 1975) which is widely regarded as the basis of the irreversible inactivation. Such a covalent modification is not readily evident, however, for the other time-dependent inhibitory agents, and the selectivity and rapidity of their inactivation make it apparent that some further mechanisms must be discerned for these agents. Although the binding constants of these agents for competitive inhibition with arachidonic acid were unaltered by esterifying the carboxyl group, the time-dependent inactivation did not occur with the corresponding methyl esters (Rome and Lands, 1975). This result clearly indicates the importance of the carboxylic acid group in the time-dependent inactivation process of cyclooxygenase. The presence of an aryl halogen at selected sites in the molecules that were effective in exhibiting time-dependent inactivation points the way to understanding a cooperative role between the carboxylate function and the halogen atom. Two mechanisms were considered for this cooperative time-dependent action: either a chemical modification through halogenation or arylation, or an allosteric intramolecular rearrangement (Rome and Lands, 1975). The initial binding of indomethacin and aspirin to the substrate site is not very strong relative to arachidonate. Thus, the inhibitory potency of these drugs appears more dependent upon their rate of inactivation (k') of the cyclooxygenase and the length of exposure (t) than upon their binding affinity (K_I) for the active site (Rome and Lands, 1975). Due to the progressive inactivation of the enzyme, the apparent K_I value obtained for these agents can be appreciably lower than that due to the actual affinity of the agent of the active site. Thus, 0.3 μM of the irreversible inactivator, flurbiprofen, can rapidly become more inhibitory than 50 μM ibuprofen, although ibuprofen, which is fully reversible, has a similar binding constant at the substrate site (e.g., see Fig. 1 in Rome and Lands, 1975). Inactivation thus creates an unusual behavior that depends upon the degree of exposure of the enzyme to the antiinflammatory drug prior to assaying the catalytic activity.

Compounds that appear to bind to the substrate site can prevent the action of the time-dependent drugs like aspirin and indomethacin (Lands et al., 1974). Furthermore, since arachidonate binds more tightly than aspirin or indomethacin, little inhibition was observed when the drug was added to the enzyme at the same time as substrate (Lands et al., 1972; Rome and Lands, 1975). On the other hand, a brief exposure of the enzyme to low levels of an irreversible agent prior to adding substrate can give extensive inhibition of prostaglandin formation. Thus, incubation of seminal vesicle microsomes for 2 min with a very low level (0.16 μM) of the time-dependent agent, indomethacin, gave 53% inhibition, which was reduced to 24% in the presence of 330 μM of salicylic acid and prevented completely by 660 μM salicylate (Humes *et al.*, 1981). These results confirm the previously detailed ability of *o*-phenanthroline to block the irreversible action of indomethacin that was described earlier by Lands *et al.* (1974).

3.3 REVERSIBLE NONCOMPETITIVE INHIBITORS (ANTIOXIDANTS)

All of the experimental results on fatty acid oxygenases appear to be consistent with the assignment of a vital role for tissue peroxides in facilitating eicosanoid biosynthesis. Thus, an increased ratio of peroxide-removing to peroxide-forming activity is a significant factor in suppressing eicosanoid formation and in enhancing the effectiveness of those antiinflammatory agents which act by antagonizing hydroperoxide activations (Hanel and Lands, 1982). These considerations can help improve predictions of drug action that Robak *et al.* (1980) regarded as impossible. Also, they help clarify how stereoselective effects can be observed with the inhibition of cyclooxygenase and with *in vivo* antiinflammatory effectiveness in spite of the nonselective stimulation of cyclooxygenase activity that phenolic compounds exhibit in the presence of high peroxide levels *in vitro*. Those *in vitro* conditions probably are unrealistic in relation to those pertaining *in vivo*. Phenolic compounds are clearly inhibitors of prostaglandin biosynthesis when the cyclooxygenase reaction is operating under conditions resembling those in normal tissues (Lands and Hanel, 1982). The stereoselective inhibition of inflammation that was reported by Payne *et al.* (1982) does not seem dependent upon the process that nonselectively stimulates prostaglandin formation *in vitro*, but it does agree with a selective inhibition of prostaglandin formation. These results agree with our results on the importance of peroxide levels in affecting the effectiveness of antioxidant inhibitors (Lands and Hanel, 1982; Hanel and Lands, 1982).

In the case of severe inflammatory conditions in which phagocytic leukocytes generate appreciable amounts of peroxides, we might expect the phenolic agents to be less effective inhibitors of prostaglandin formation. This rationale may underlie the ineffectiveness of paracetamol as an antiinflammatory agent even though it is relatively effective as an analgesic agent (Lands, 1981; Lands and Hanel, 1982). The antioxidant radical-trapping type of noncompetitive reversible agent is very sensitive to the steady-state levels of hydroperoxide in the vicinity of the enzyme active site. Thus, phenolic agents such as acetamidophenol become increasingly potent inhibitors of the prostaglandin-forming cyclooxygenase action when the level of hydroperoxide is lowered. A number of hyperalgesic conditions may have only slightly elevated hydroperoxide levels that still permit phenolic agents such as paracetamol to inhibit effectively the prostaglandin bio-synthesis. Understanding how hydroperoxide levels alter the effectiveness of certain anticyclooxygenase agents might help in the development of useful analgesic agents that would not have the ulcerogenic property displayed by irreversible inhibitors such as aspirin or indomethacin.

The antioxidant, radical-trapping agents can inhibit all types of fatty acid oxygenase (cyclooxygenase or lipoxygenase) and they might seem, on that basis, to be well suited to general antiinflammatory use. However, their inability to block cyclooxygenase activity in the presence of moderate amounts of lipid hydroperoxides may be an important constraint in their success *in vivo*. Clearly some aspect of the severe inflammatory condition makes the radical trapping by these agents no longer a rate-limiting feature.

An extensive study of the chemical structures of effective phenolic radical-trapping inhibitors by Dewhirst (1980) indicated that the most effective inhibitors had two aromatic rings connected by a short bridge. Dewhirst noted the frequent occurrence of such compounds in over-the-counter remedies including counterirritants, analgesic rubs, and ointments. Many phenolic antioxidant compounds inhibit lipoxygenase as well as cyclooxygenase activities, although some compounds are more inhibitory with one enzyme than the other (Vanderhoek and Lands, 1973b). Flavonoids that were reported to have antiallergenic actions can inhibit the 5-lipoxygenase activity that forms leukotrienes (Yoshimoto *et al.*, 1983). Agents like phenidone and nordihydroguaiaretic acid effectively inhibit both types of enzymes although these agents have not been applied successfully to therapeutic regimens. A summary of the types of inhibition observed with several common antiinflammatory agents is given in Table 1.

4 Quantitation of Inhibitor Action

Quantitative assessments of the antiinflammatory action of an agent will depend greatly upon the complexity of the model selected to evaluate its effectiveness. Unfortunately, the use of relatively pure fatty acid oxygenases can give misleading insights at times. Some of the needed quantitative kinetic considerations in a proper evaluation have been discussed in detail in earlier reviews (Lands and Rome, 1976; Lands and Hanel, 1983). We will examine some quantitative aspects that influence interpretations of the effectiveness of each of the three types of cyclooxygenase inhibitor outlined in this article. For example, the general property of reversible, competitive inhibitors always makes the assignment of an I_{50} value for an oxygenase inhibitor dependent upon the amount of substrate arachidonate available. Thus the I_{50} value is not a stable criterion, and its value easily changes from model to model—or even among different investigators. For example, varying arachidonate concentrations from 1 to 300 μM can

TABLE 1

Types of inhibition by antiinflammatory drugs[a]

Agent	Type of inhibition		
	A	B	C
Aspirin	+	−	−
Indomethacin	+	+	−
Ibuprofen	+	−	−
Flurbiprofen	+	+	−
BL-2365	+	−	−
BL-2338	+	+	−
Mefenamic acid	+	−	+
Flufenamic acid	+	−	+
Meclofenamic acid	+	+	+
Paracetamol	+	−	+
Phenylbutazone	+	−	+

[a]The three types of inhibition are (A) reversible competitive interactions at the substrate site; (B) time-dependent inactivation that generally follows binding at the substrate site; (C) reversible noncompetitive inhibition that is especially characteristic of radical trapping or antioxidant compounds (see also Fig. 2).

cause the observed I_{50} of an inhibitor with a $K_I = 1$ μM to vary from 1.2 to 31 μM. This feature is especially significant when comparing results from different investigators using slightly different model systems or conditions. The variability is due to the competitive nature of the interactions of the substrate and agent at the substrate site, and it does not occur with noncompetitive agents (Lands and Rome, 1976). However, both types of reversible agent require a continued exposure of the oxygenase to the agent for inhibition to be maintained. Any factors that remove the agent after inhibition has been established would reverse the inhibitory effect.

A different problem is associated with the inactivation caused by time-dependent inhibitors that have an initial competitive interaction at the substrate site. Other agents that reversibly block the substrate site will protect the enzyme from the irreversible agent (Lands et al., 1974). This situation creates complex time-dependent effects on oxygenase activity in vitro that are certain to be further complicated by pharmacodynamic aspects in vivo. A continued presence in the tissue of this type of inhibitor is not needed to cause sustained inhibitory effects, and oxygenase activity may remain inactive long after the drug has diffused from the tissue. This inactivation phenomenon provides much lower I_{50} values for these agents with correspondingly lower doses needed for antiinflammatory effectiveness. Some recognition of this type of inhibition is also necessary to interpret properly the I_{50} values obtained in some model systems *in vivo*, because reversal of that inhibition may depend on protein synthesis to replace the inactivated enzyme. Thus aspirin treatment will tend to inhibit the cyclooxygenase of both endothelial cells and platelets. After a brief period of time, however, the endothelial cells produce more of the specific mRNA that leads to synthesis of new PGH synthetase proteins. The nonnucleated platelets do not form mRNA and thus cannot replace their damaged cyclooxygenase. This phenomenon provides an important rationale for a convenient antithrombotic regimen employing small, alternate-day doses of aspirin. In this situation, the rate-limiting events in thrombosis differ significantly from those regulating inflammation, but the rationale for differential effects may be applied to other cell–cell signaling situations.

The paradoxical kinetic behavior of the "antioxidant" agents can be ascribed to their effects on the two separate catalytic activities exhibited by PGH synthetase, namely cyclooxygenase and peroxidase. Hemler and Lands (1980) suggested that the radical-trapping capacity of phenolic agents is the basis for the inhibition of the cyclooxygenase that occurs in low ambient peroxide conditions. In an alternate hypothesis, Kuehl *et al.* (1977, 1980) proposed that the principal inflammatory mediator is a radical generated by the hydroperoxidase when acting on the PGG_2 intermediate in prostaglandin biosynthesis. This hypothesis shifted attention away from the inflammatory action of prostaglandins and proposed new mediators for inflammatory events. Although one cannot disprove the additional putative role for radicals produced during peroxidase catalysis or deny the existence of alternate mediators in inflammation, the primary driving force for that hypothesis was to reconcile the lack of inhibition of prostaglandin biosynthesis by the agent *in vitro* with its observed effectiveness *in vivo*. Our demonstration that all of these phenolic agents can be effective inhibitors *in vitro* under conditions of moderate ambient hydroperoxide (Hanel and Lands, 1982; Lands and Hanel, 1982) eliminates the need for an alternate hypothesis and places attention once again on the proinflammatory activity of the cyclooxygenase in synthesizing prostaglandins and on the inhibitory action of the phenolic agents in preventing prostaglandin biosynthesis *in vivo*. Future studies will yield more information about the relative desirability of inhibiting lipoxygenase and cyclooxygenase in developing effective antiinflammatory drugs.

References

Appleton, R. A., and Brown, K. (1979). *Prostaglandins* **18**, 29–34.
Black, K. L., Culp, B., Madison, D., Randall, O. S., and Lands, W. E. M. (1979). *Prostaglandins Med.* **3**, 257–268.
Blackwell, G. J., Carnuccio, R., Di Rosa, M., Flower, R. J., Parente, L., and Persico, P. (1980). *Nature (London)* **287**, 147–149.

Blackwell, G. J., Carnuccio, R., Di Rosa, M., Flower, R. J., Ivanyi, J., Langham, C. S. J., Parente, L., Persico, P., and Woods, J. (1983). *Adv. Prostaglandin, Thromboxane Leukotriene Res.* **11**, 65–71.

Bray, M. A., Ford-Hutchinson, A. W., and Smith, M. J. H. (1981a). *Prostaglandins* **22**, 213–222.

Bray, M. A., Cunningham, F. M., Ford-Hutchinson, A. W., and Smith, M. J. H. (1981b). *J. Pharmacol.* **72**, 483–486.

Cook, H. W., and Lands, W. E. M. (1976). *Nature (London)* **260**, 630–632.

Corey, E. J., and Munroe, J. E. (1982). *J. Am. Chem. Soc.* **104**, 1752–1754.

Corey, E. J., and Park, H. (1982). *J. Am. Chem. Soc.* **104**, 1750–1752.

Culp, B. R., Titus, B. G., and Lands, W. E. M. (1979). *Prostaglandins Med.* **3**, 269–278.

Culp, B. R., Lands, W. E. M., Lucchesi, B. R., Pitt, B., and Romson, J. (1980). *Prostaglandins* **20**, 1021–1031.

Dewhirst, F. (1980). *Prostaglandins* **20**, 209–222.

Di Rosa, M., Papdimitrou, J. M., and Willoughby, D. A. (1971). *J. Pathol.* **105**, 239–256.

Downing, D. T., Ahern, D. G., and Bachta, M. (1970). *Biochem. Biophys. Res. Commun.* **40**, 218–223.

Downing, D. T., Barve, J. A., Gunstone, F. D., Jacobsberg, F. R., and Lie Ken Jie, M. (1972). *Biochim. Biophys. Acta* **280**, 343–347.

Egan, R. W., Tischler, A. N., Baptista, E. M., Ham, E. A., Soderman, D. D., and Gale, P. H. (1983). *Adv. Prostaglandin, Thromboxane Leukotriene Res.* **11**, 151–157.

Ferreira, S. H., Nakamura, M., and Castro, M. S. A. (1978). *Prostaglandins* **16**, 31–37.

Flower, R. J., and Blackwell, G. J. (1979). *Nature (London)* **278**, 456–459.

Gryglewski, R. J. (1974). In "Prostaglandin Synthetase Inhibitors" (H. J. Robinson and J. R. Vane, eds.), pp. 33–52. Raven, New York.

Gund, P., and Shen, T. Y. (1977). *J. Med. Chem.* **20**, 1146–1152.

Haining, J. L., and Axelrod, B. (1958). *J. Biol. Chem.* **232**, 193–202.

Hanel, A. M., and Lands, W. E. M. (1982). *Biochem. Pharmacol.* **31**, 3307–3311.

Hemler, M. E., and Lands, W. E. M. (1980). *J. Biol. Chem.* **255**, 6253–6261.

Hemler, M. E., Graff, G., and Lands, W. E. M. (1978). *Biochem. Biophys. Res. Commun.* **85**, 1325–1331.

Hemler, M. E., Cook, H. W., and Lands, W. E. M. (1979). *Arch. Biochem. Biophys.* **193**, 340–345.

Hirata, F. (1983). *Adv. Prostaglandin, Thromboxane Leukotriene Res.* **11**, 73–74.

Hirata, F., Schiffmann, E., Venkatasubramanian, K., Salomon, D., and Axelrod, J. (1980). *Proc. Natl. Acad. Sci. U.S.A.* **77**, 2533–2536.

Humes, J. L., Winter, C. A., Sadowski, S. J., and Kuehl, F. A. (1981). *Proc. Natl. Acad. Sci. U.S.A.* **78**, 2053–2056.

Juby, P. F., Goodwin, W. R., Hudyma, T. W., and Partyka, R. A. (1972). *J. Med. Chem.* **15**, 1297–1306.

Ku, E. C., and Wasvary, J. M. (1975). *Biochim. Biophys. Acta* **384**, 360–368.

Kuehl, F. A., Jr., Humes, J. L., Egan, R. W., Ham, E. A., Beveride, G. C., and Van Arman, C. G. (1977). *Nature (London)* **265**, 170–173.

Kuehl, F. A., Jr., Humes, J. L., Ham, E. A., Egan, R. W., and Dougherty, H. W. (1980). *Adv. Prostaglandin Thromboxane Res.* **6**, 77–86.

Kulmacz, R. J., and Lands, W. E. M. (1983). *Prostaglandins* **25**, 531–540.

Lands, W. E. M. (1981). *Trends Pharmacol. Sci.* **2**, 78–80.

Lands, W. E. M., and Byrnes, M. J. (1981). *Prog. Lipid Res.* **20**, 287–290.

Lands, W. E. M., and Hanel, A. M. (1982). *Prostaglandins* **24**, 271–277.

Lands, W. E. M., and Hanel, A. M. (1983). In Prostaglandins and Related Substances" (C. R. Pace-Asciak and E. Granström, eds.), pp. 203–223. Elsevier, Amsterdam.

Lands, W. E. M., and Rome, L. H. (1976). In "Prostaglandins: Chemical and Biochemical Aspects" (S. S. M. Karim, ed.), pp. 87–137. Univ. Park Press, Baltimore.

Lands, W. E. M., and Samuelsson, B. (1968). Biochim. Biophys. Acta 164, 426–429.

Lands, W. E. M., Lee, R., and Smith, W. (1971). Ann. N.Y. Acad. Sci. 180, 107–122.

Lands, W. E. M., LeTellier, P., Rome, L., and Vanderhoek, J. (1972). Fed. Proc., Fed. Am. Soc. Exp. Biol. 31, 476.

Lands, W. E. M., LeTellier, P. R., Rome, L. H., and Vanderhoek, J. Y. (1973). Adv. Biosci. 9, 15–28.

Lands, W. E. M., LeTellier, P. R., Rome, L. H., and Vanderhoek, J. Y. (1974). In "Prostaglandins Synthetase Inhibitors" (H. J. Robinson and J. R. Vane, eds.), pp. 1–7. Raven, New York.

Lands, W. E. M., Cook, H. W., and Rome, L. H. (1976). Adv. Prostaglandin Thromboxane Res. 1, 7–17.

Murphy, R. C., Pickett, W. C., Culp, B. R., and Lands, W. E. M. (1981). Prostaglandins 22, 613–622.

Payne, T. G., Dewald, B., Siegl, H., Gubler, H. U., Ott, H., and Baggiolini, M. (1982). Nature (London) 296, 160–162.

Pfister, J. R., and Murthy, D. V. K. (1983). J. Med. Chem. 26, 1099–1103.

Robak, J., Kostka-Trabka, E., and Duniec, Z. (1980). Biochem. Pharmacol. 29, 1863–1865.

Rome, L. H., and Lands, W. E. M. (1975). Proc. Natl. Acad. Sci. U.S.A. 72, 4863–4865.

Roth, G. J., and Majerus, P. W. (1975). J. Clin. Invest. 56, 624–632.

Shen, T. Y. (1967). Top. Med. Chem. 1, 29–78.

Shen, T. Y., Ham, E. A., Cirillo, V. J., and Zanetti, M. (1974). In "Prostaglandin Synthetase Inhibitors" (H. J. Robinson and J. R. Vane, eds.), pp. 19–31. Raven, New York.

Siegel, M. I., McConnell, R. T., Abrahams, S. L., Porter, N. A., and Cuatrecasas, P. (1979). Biochem. Biophys. Res. Commun. 89, 1273–1280.

Smith, W. L., and Lands, W. E. M. (1971). J. Biol. Chem. 246, 6700–6702.

Smith, W. L., and Lands, W. E. M. (1972a). J. Biol. Chem. 247, 1038–1047.

Smith, W. L., and Lands, W. E. M. (1972b). Biochemistry 11, 3276–3285.

Vanderhoek, J. Y., and Lands, W. E. M. (1973a). Biochim. Biophys. Acta 296, 374–381.

Vanderhoek, J. Y., and Lands, W. E. M. (1973b). Biochim. Biophys. Acta 296, 382–385.

Vane, J. R. (1971). Nature (London) New Biol. 231, 232–235.

Weissmann, G., Dukor, P., and Zurier, R. B. (1971). Nature (London) New Biol. 231, 131–135.

Williams, T. J., Jose, P. J., Wedmore, C. V., Peck, M. J., and Forrest, M. J. (1983). Adv. Prostaglandin, Thromboxane Leukotriene Res. 11, 33–37.

Yokoyama, C., Mizuno, K., Mitachi, H., Yoshimoto, T., Yamamoto, S., and Pace-Asciak, C. R. (1983). Biochim. Biophys. Acta 750, 237–243.

Yoshimoto, T., Furukawa, M., Yamamoto, S., Horie, T., and Watanabe-Kohno, S. (1983). Biochem. Biophys. Res. Commun. 116, 612–618.

Ziboh, V. A., Vanderhoek, J. Y., and Lands, W. E. M. (1974). Prostaglandins 5, 233–240.

Recent Advances in the Molecular Pharmacology of Benzodiazepine Receptors and in the Structure–Activity Relationships of Their Agonists and Antagonists[1]

WILLY HAEFELY, EMILIO KYBURZ, MAX GERECKE, and HANNS MÖHLER

Department of Pharmaceutical Research
F. Hoffmann-La Roche & Co. Ltd.
Basel, Switzerland

[1]Abbreviations used in this article include the following: BZ, Benzodiazepine; BZR, Benzodiazepine receptor; CNS, Central nervous system; β-CCE, Ethyl ester of β-carboline-3-carboxylate; β-CCM, Methyl ester of β-carboline-3-carboxylate; β-CCPr, *n*-Propyl ester of β-carboline-3-carboxylate; CL 218,872, 6-[(3-Trifluoromethyl)phenyl]-3-methyl-1,2,4-triazolo[4,3-*b*]pyridazine; Clon, Clonazepam; DHP, Dihydropicrotoxinin; Diaz, Diazepam; DMCM, Methyl-6,7-dimethyl-4-ethyl-β-carboline-3-carboxylate; EPSP, Excitatory postsynaptic potential; Flu, Flunitrazepam; GABA, γ-Aminobutyric acid; IPSP, Inhibitory postsynaptic potential; PAGE, Polyacrylamide gel electrophoresis; QSAR, Quantitative structure–activity relationships; IBTBO, 4-Isopropyl-1-phospha-2,6,7-trioxabicyclo[2,2,2]octane-1-oxide; SAfR, Structure–affinity relationships; SAR, Structure–activity relationships; SDS, Sodium dodecyl sulfate; TBPS, *t*-Butylbicyclophosphorothionate; THIP, 4,5,6,7-Tetrahydroisoxazolo[5,4-*c*]pyridin-3-ol.

ADVANCES IN DRUG RESEARCH, VOL. 14
0-12-013314-8

1 Introduction

In the past few years, the investigation of benzodiazepine (BZ) actions has been one of the fastest, if not the fastest moving research field in molecular neuropsychopharmacology.

The early days of the BZ era have been reviewed by Haefely (1983b). In 1957 the pharmacologist Randall observed the interesting pharmacological profile of chlordiazepoxide, the first reasonably active derivative of a novel chemical class of compounds in which the chemist Sternbach had started explorative synthetic work about 3 years earlier. Already in 1960 chlordiazepoxide was launched under the trade name Librium, followed 2 years later by its derivative diazepam (trade name Valium). These two drugs, and congeners thereof, which appeared on the market in rapid succession, soon became the most frequently prescribed centrally active drugs and, by the end of 1983, about 35 BZ drugs were available for therapy (see Fig. 1). BZs are the drugs of choice in the pharmacotherapy of anxiety and related emotional disorders, in the treatment of sleep disorders, status epilepticus, and other convulsive states; they are used as centrally acting muscle relaxants, for premedication, and for inducing agents in anesthesiology.

Efforts to elucidate the mechanism(s) of action of these unusually well-tolerated and broadly effective drugs were not successful until about 10 years ago. Although Schmidt et al. had obtained first evidence in 1967 that BZs may affect one distinct inhibitory synaptic process, it was not until 1974 that sufficient convincing evidence from behavioral, electrophysiological, and biochemical experiments had been accumulated to indicate that BZs quite specifically act at synapses in which γ-aminobutyric acid (GABA) is used as transmitter (Costa et al., 1975; Haefely et al., 1975). This view was not readily accepted in spite of rapidly accumulating electrophysiological confirmation.

The hope of demonstrating the localization of benzodiazepine receptors (BZRs) in GABAergic synapses by autoradiography and the increasing number of tissue binding studies with radiolabeled neurotransmitters and drugs led to the identification of specific, saturable, low-capacity, high-affinity binding sites for tritiated Diaz ($[^3H]$Diaz) in homogenates of the mammalian brain tissue (Bosmann et al., 1977; Möhler and Okada, 1977a,b; Squires and Braestrup, 1977). This initiated an explosive interest in BZRs and led within a few years to the publication of hundreds of papers reporting BZ binding experiments. A great stimulus for these studies was the finding by several investigators in 1978 that GABA enhances high-affinity binding of BZs and the proposal that BZs increase GABA binding to its receptor. The stimulation of BZ binding by GABA and other GABA mimetics, in spite of its debatable relevance for BZ actions, convinced even the most sceptics that a close association exists between the actions of GABA and BZs. It was soon found that BZ binding was also modulated by other agents proposed to interact with the GABA-gated chloride channel. The existence of highly specific BZ binding sites immediately suggested the possibility that these sites may be receptors for endogenous modulators. Several more or less well-identified compounds with inhibitory activity on $[^3H]$BZ binding were extracted from the central nervous tissue. Great excitement was evoked when Braestrup et al. (1980b) reported the presence in human urine of a low-molecular-weight compound with extremely high affinity for BZ binding sites, namely the ethyl ester of β-carboline-3-carboxylic acid (β-CCE). It was soon

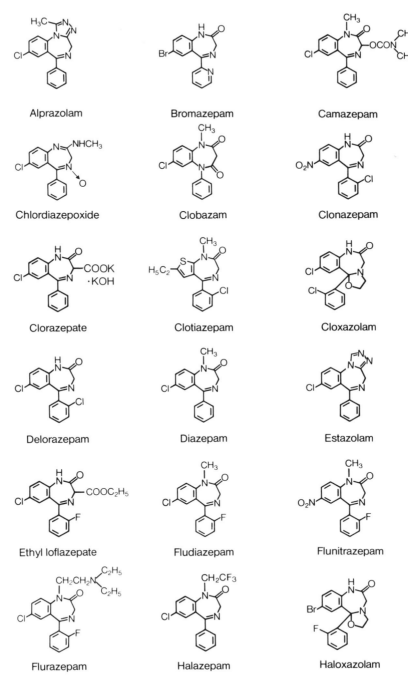

Alprazolam

Bromazepam

Camazepam

Chlordiazepoxide

Clobazam

Clonazepam

Clorazepate

Clotiazepam

Cloxazolam

Delorazepam

Diazepam

Estazolam

Ethyl loflazepate

Fludiazepam

Flunitrazepam

Flurazepam

Halazepam

Haloxazolam

FIG. 1. Commercially available benzodiazepines.

168

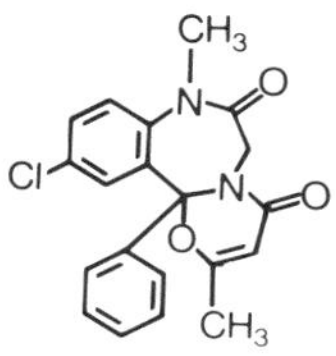

Ketazolam

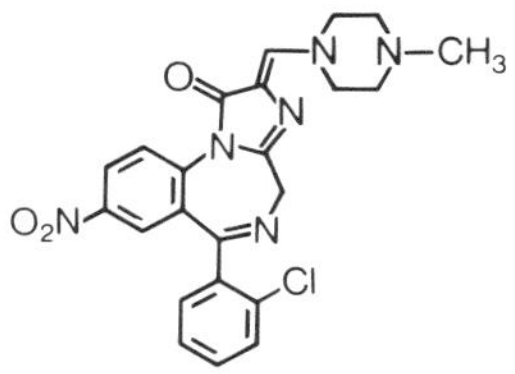

Loprazolam

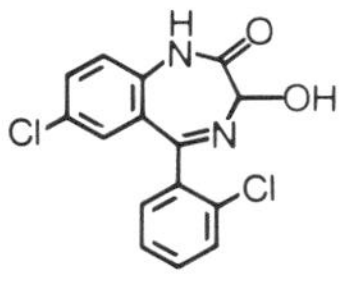

Lorazepam

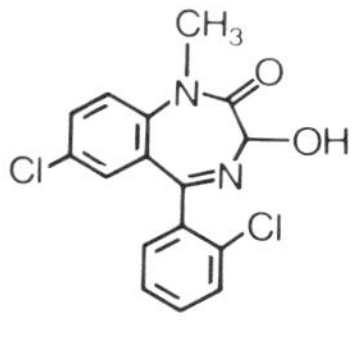

Lormetazepam

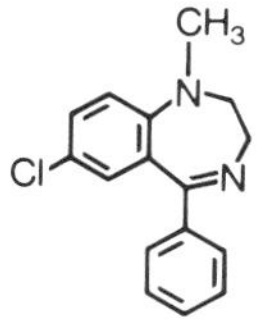

Medazepam

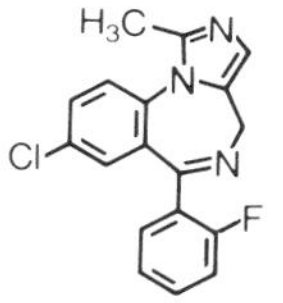

Midazolam

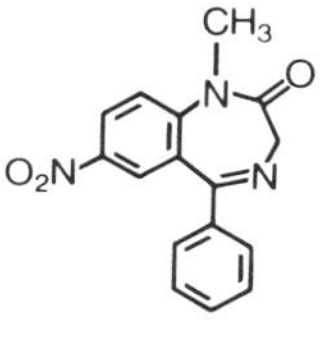

Nimetazepam

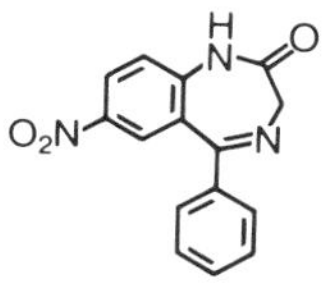

Nitrazepam

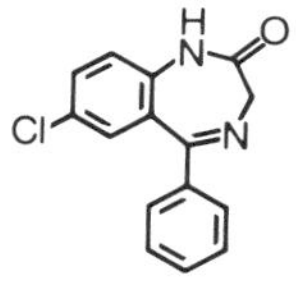

Nordazepam

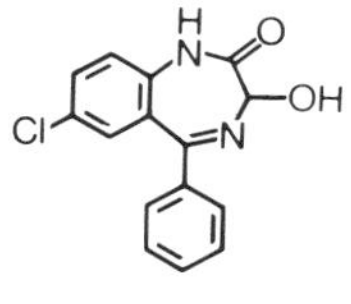

Oxazepam

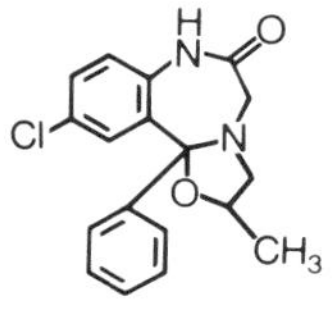

Oxazolam

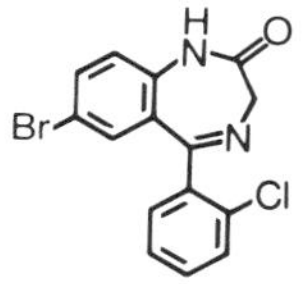

Phenazepam

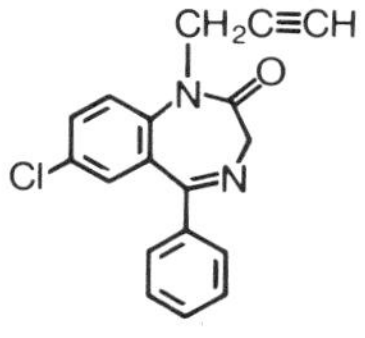

Pinazepam

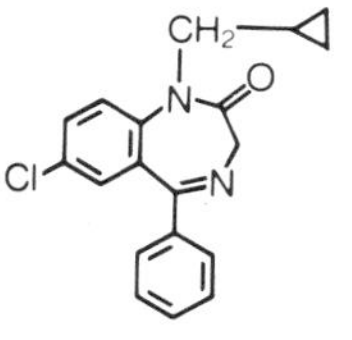

Prazepam

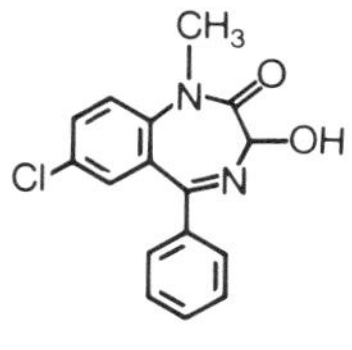

Temazepam

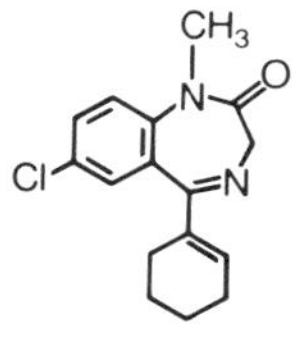

Tetrazepam

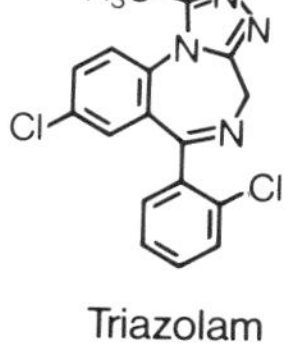

Triazolam

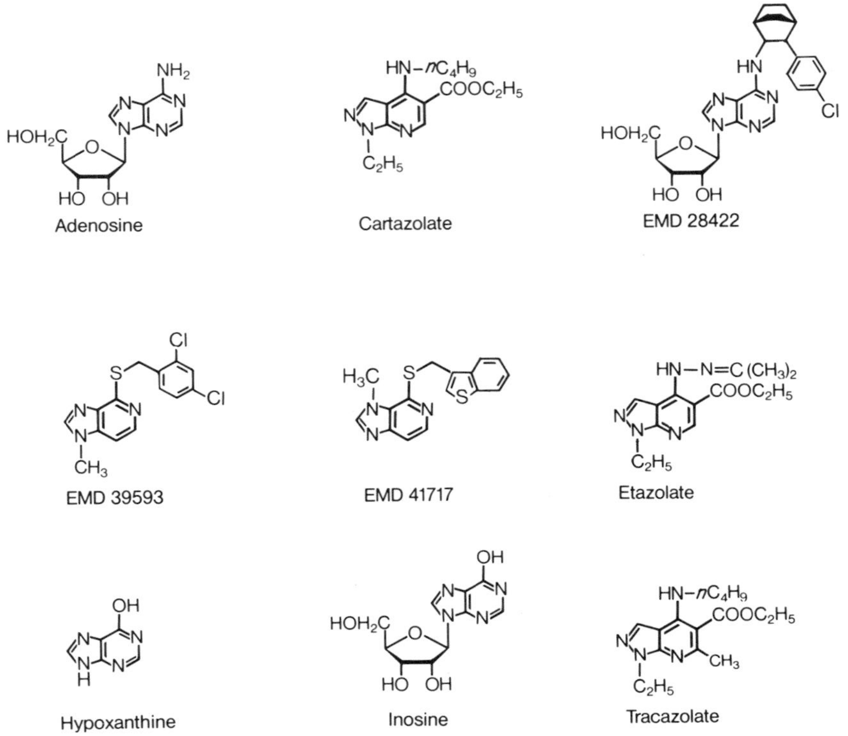

FIG. 2. Purines and analogs.

found that β-CCE had been formed during the extraction procedure. Although β-CCE was recognized to be an artifact, the systematic study of the pharmacology of β-carboline-3-carboxylic acid derivatives turned out to be a very important stimulus in the research on BZ receptorology.

In 1981 the first report on the imidazobenzodiazepinone derivative Ro 15-1788 was published (Hunkeler *et al.*, 1981); it showed that chemical variation of the BZ molecule could lead to substances whose only major property is to bind potently to BZRs and to block all pharmacological effects of the classic BZs. Soon afterward, BZ antagonistic activity was found in β-carbolines (Cowen *et al.*, 1981). These two classes of specific antagonists provided a further important argument for accepting the view that the high-affinity BZ binding sites (or at least part of them) are the recognition sites of specific pharmacological receptors that mediate the effects of BZs at doses used in therapy (Haefely, 1983c).

Equally exciting was the discovery that some β-carbolines did not only block the effects of classic BZs but, when given alone, produced effects exactly opposite to classic BZs, such as convulsions, anxiety, muscle rigidity, and sleep disturbances (see, e.g., Corda *et al.*, 1983a,b). These opposite effects were

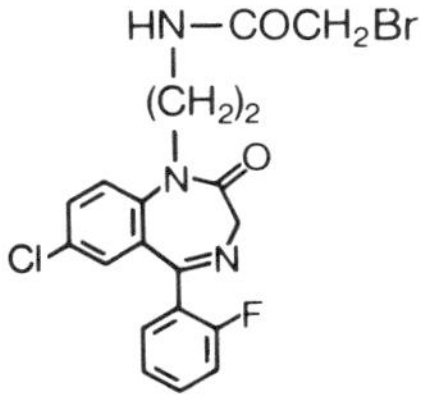

Kenazepine

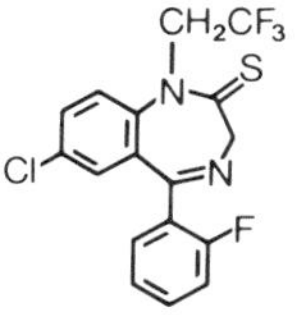

Quazepam

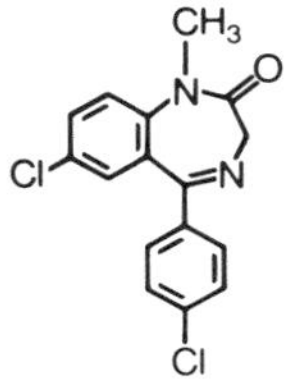

Ro 5-4864

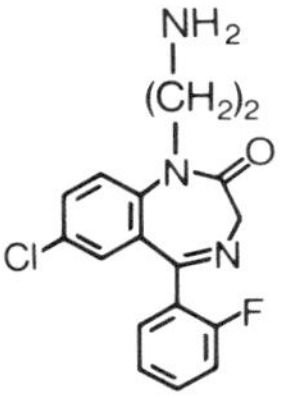

Ro 7-1986

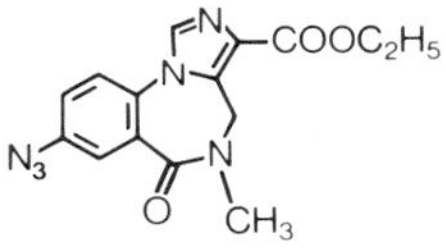

Ro 15-4513

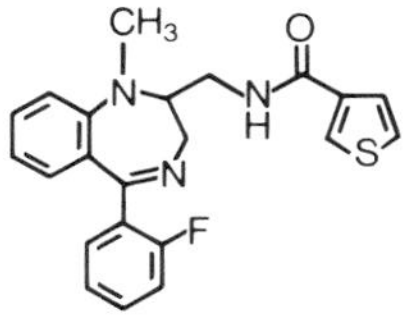

Tifluadom

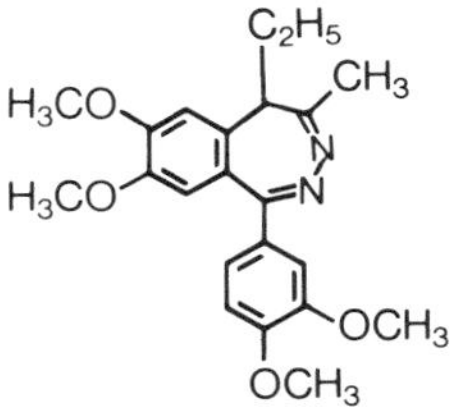

Tofisopam

FIG. 3. Various benzodiazepines.

blocked both by classic BZs and by drugs characterized as competitive antagonists, e.g., Ro 15-1788, β-CCE, and CGS 8216. The terms agonists, inverse agonists, and antagonists were proposed to account for the three types of GABA receptor (GABA-R) modulation which are mediated by BZRs (Polc *et al.*, 1982; Jensen *et al.*, 1983). Progress in solubilization and purification of BZRs, binding studies on solubilized BZ binding protein, *in situ* molecular mass determination of BZRs, and, quite recently, the translation and subsequent membrane incorporation of a functioning GABA-R/BZR/Cl^- channel complex in frog oocytes injected with a mixture of chicken brain mRNA (Smart *et al.*, 1983) strongly support the concept of an oligomeric protein complex consisting of a transmembrane anion conducting channel, a GABA-R which gates the channel and, at least, one allosteric regulatory binding site (the BZR). It seems that the complex contains four protomeric polypeptide subunits (Fig. 6), carrying a domain with one or several GABA recognition site(s), a domain acting as part of the transmembrane channel, and a domain with the binding site(s) for three prototypes of BZR ligands (see Fig. 7). There is also strong evidence that the channel-forming

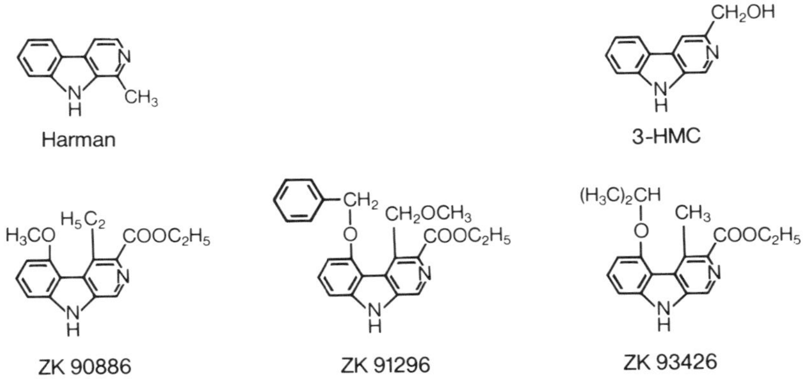

FIG. 4. Harman and β-carbolines.

moiety of the complex contains an area bearing recognition sites for barbiturates, many convulsants, and other agents (Olsen, 1981). Moreover, there is (at least under *in vitro* conditions) a bidirectional coupling between these various ligand binding sites.

The present article is an updating of the chapter "Benzodiazepine Receptors" in the handbook article of Haefely *et al.* (1981a) and an extension of other reviews (Möhler and Richards, 1983a,b); it deals with those studies, mainly obtained by radioligand binding techniques, that form the basis of the present concept of BZR location and function.

2 The Target Synapses and the Target Cells of BZs

2.1 THE GABAERGIC SYNAPSE AS THE PRIMARY SITE OF ACTION OF BZS

Though BZs have been found to affect the dynamics of virtually all known neurotransmitters in the CNS, at least at high doses, it was already obvious in the early 1970s that these changes could not be due to a direct action of BZs on neurons that use, e.g., catecholamines or acetylcholine as transmitter or to an action on their receptors. The proposal made by Haefely *et al.* (1975) and Costa *et al.* (1975) that BZs may produce their effects primarily by enhancing GABAergic transmission provided an explanation for the various secondary alterations induced by these drugs in other transmitter systems.

GABA acts on at least two different receptor types (Nistri and Constanti, 1978; Simmonds, 1983, 1984; Bowery *et al.*, 1983, 1984); the action of BZs seems to be restricted to synaptic effects of GABA that are mediated by so-called $GABA_A$-Rs. The direct consequence of $GABA_A$-R stimulation by GABA seems to be an increase of the permeability of neuronal membranes for anions, mainly for Cl^- anions. There is probably no direct alteration of biochemical parameters

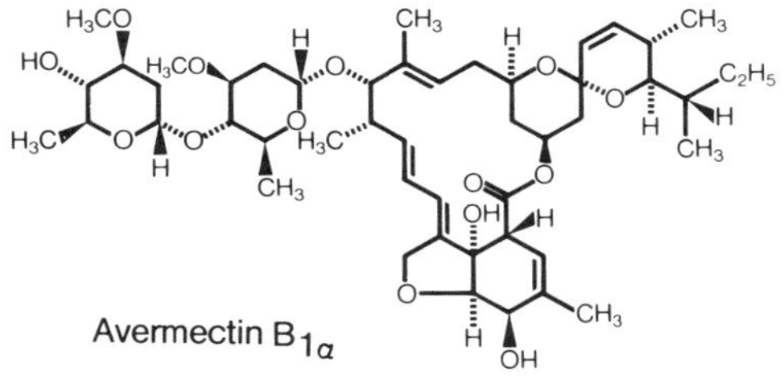

Avermectin B$_{1\alpha}$

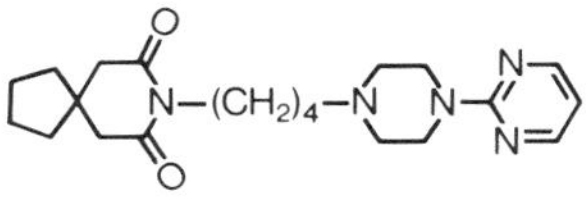

Buspirone

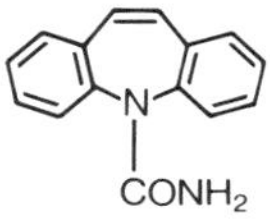

Carbamazepine

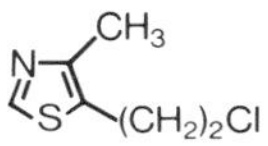

Clomethiazole

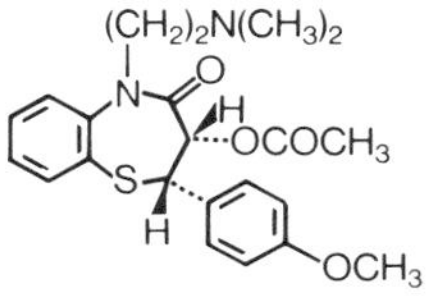

Diltiazem

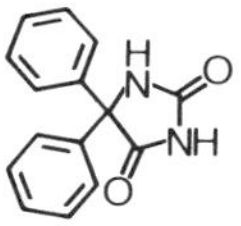

Diphenylhydantoin

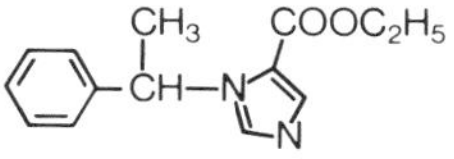

Etomidate

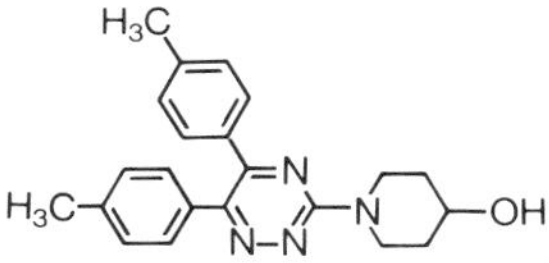

LY 81067

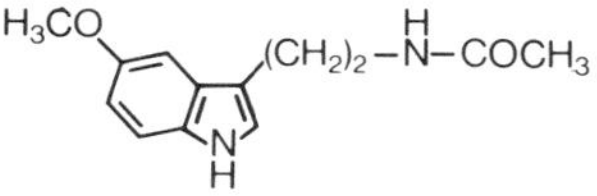

Melatonin

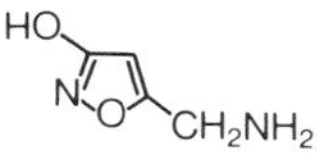

Muscimol

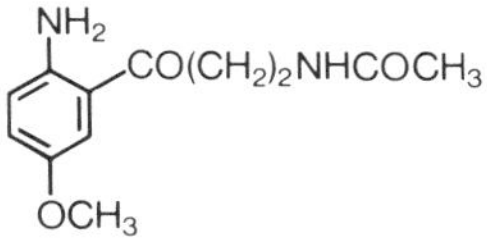

N$^\gamma$-Acetyl-5-methoxy-kynurenamine

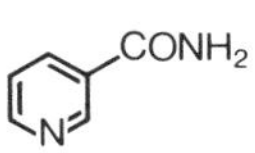

Nicotinamide

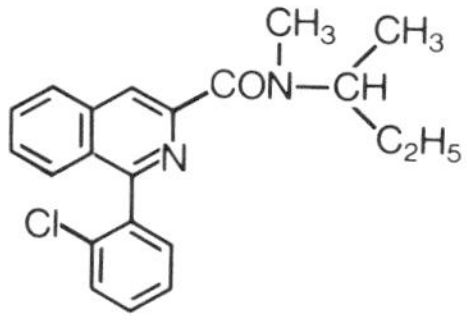

PK 11195

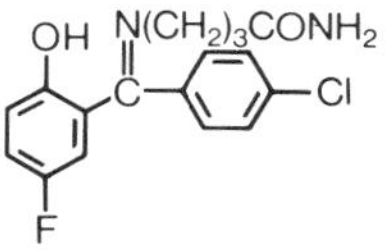

Progabide

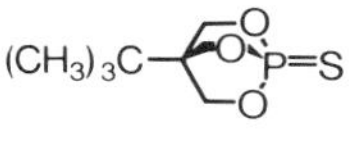

TBPS

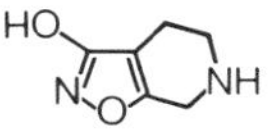

THIP

FIG. 5. Various other structures.

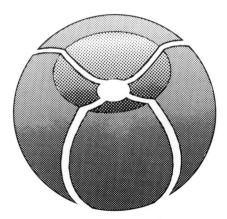

Fɪɢ. 6. Schematic hypothetical drawing of the tetrameric membrane protein complex acting as the GABA-R-gated Cl⁻ channel with a regulatory domain, called the BZR.

by GABA, such as, e.g., an increase or a decrease in the formation of cyclic nucleotides as second messengers (Smith *et al.*, 1982). The only function of the GABA-R seems to be the gating of transmembrane anion conducting channels (and, perhaps, a blockade of Ca^{2+} channels). Consequently, only electrophysiological methods can be used to study directly (on line) the physiological function of GABA in synaptic membranes, namely to increase net Cl^- ion translocation. Fortunately, distinct GABAergic synapses can be investigated by both extracellular recording of neuronal mass responses and intracellular recording of single cell responses *in situ* as well as *in vitro*. The modification of GABAergic synaptic transmission by BZs as revealed by electrophysiological responses has recently been reviewed (Haefely and Polc, 1983). The conclusion from these studies is that BZs, in principle, are able to enhance transmission at all GABAergic synapses in the mammalian CNS, in particular when normal GABAergic transmission is experimentally depressed. This should not be taken to mean that, in an individual treated with appropriate doses of BZ, transmission at all GABAergic synapses (estimated to constitute one-third of all synapses in the brain) is actually enhanced (Haefely, 1984). This seeming paradox follows from the finding (see Section 3.2) that BZs produce only a moderate shift to the left of the GABA dose–response curve without enhancing the maximum conductance increase by GABA. Whether or not this potentiating activity of BZs becomes manifest at a given GABAergic synapse depends on the concentration of GABA in this synapse and the fractional occupancy of GABA-Rs.

Not all effects of GABA (and, hence, of BZs) are strictly inhibitory, for two reasons. The axoaxonal GABAergic synapses on primary afferent endings in the spinal cord do not only inhibit transmitter release from the primary afferent endings by depolarization and short-circuiting of potentials, but they also induce

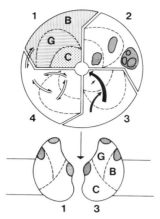

Fig. 7. Hypothetical anatomy and functions of the receptor–channel complex drawn in Fig. 6. A view from the extracellular space (above) shows the four monomers (1, 2, 3, 4). Four different functions and interactions are depicted. In (1) are shown the three domains: Cl⁻ channel part (C), GABA binding domain or GABA-R (G), and the regulatory domain with BZ binding site, the BZR (B). In (2) are indicated the ligand binding sites on the channel domain ("picrotoxin binding site," "barbiturate receptor," and "channel ligand site"), on the GABA-R (GABA binding site), and on the BZR (binding site for agonists, antagonists, and inverse agonists, composed of not entirely identical, but adjacent and probably partially overlapping subsites). No stoichiometry of binding sites (in particular of GABA-R to BZR) should be deduced from this model. In (3) is indicated the main function of the complex, namely the GABA-induced gating (opening) of the Cl⁻ channel (large arrow), with the regulation of this gating process by BZ agonists and inverse agonists (medium arrow), and the regulation of Cl⁻ channel properties by ligands of the picrotoxinin binding sites. In (4) are shown the four bidirectional coupling functions or domain–domain interactions (between GABA-R and Cl⁻ channel domain, between BZR and GABA-R, between BZR and channel ligands, and between the BZ binding sites of adjacent subunits). On a cross section through the membrane (see below) are shown the three domains of subunits 1 and 3.

the generation of action potentials in these sensory neurons, which can be recorded as the so-called dorsal root reflex. Another "excitatory" phenomenon induced by GABA is in fact disinhibition, i.e., with two GABAergic neurons arranged in series, activation of the first will inhibit the second, whose inhibitory influence, therefore, decreases. BZs increase dorsal root reflexes and are likely to produce disinhibition in more complex neuronal networks.

2.2 PRESYNAPTIC VERSUS POSTSYNAPTIC SITES OF ACTION OF BZS IN THE GABAERGIC SYNAPSE

The enhancement of GABAergic transmission could be the result of an action of BZs on the presynaptic side of the GABAergic synapse, i.e., on the GABAergic neuron itself. The agents could, for instance, improve electrosecretory coupling and, thereby, increase the amount of GABA released by an action potential.

Although such an action has not been definitely excluded (Mitchell and Martin, 1978), it seems less likely than a postsynaptic site of action, namely one close to the $GABA_A$-R in the subsynaptic membrane (that spot of a cell body, dendrite, or axon that is covered by a nerve ending and that is the receiving part in the signal transmission). This interaction of BZs with the $GABA_A$-R complex is the main topic of this article. The primary target cells of BZs, then, would be neurons that are innervated by GABAergic neurons and contain GABA-Rs on their cell bodies, dendrites, or axons. In view of the great number and wide distribution of GABAergic neurons, primary target cells for BZs are likely to be neurons using any type of transmitter substance. Even some GABAergic neurons receive inputs from other GABAergic cells; therefore such neurons, e.g., cerebellar Purkinje cells, have autoreceptors, i.e., receptors for the very transmitter they synthesize and secrete themselves. However, these receptors would be located postsynaptically with respect to the afferent GABAergic synapse. GABA-Rs on primary afferent endings in the spinal cord, which mediate part of the so-called presynaptic inhibition, are postsynaptic with respect to the axoaxonal GABAergic synapse.

2.3 THE SPECIFICITY OF BZS FOR GABA-MEDIATED RESPONSES

BZs in concentrations that are relevant for their pharmacological activity affect GABA-mediated responses with a high degree of selectivity. Responses to other inhibitory amino acids, such as glycine and β-alanine, or to excitatory neurotransmitters, are not altered by BZs (see Haefely and Polc, 1983, 1985).

3 Modification of GABA-R Function by BZR Ligands

3.1 ELECTROPHYSIOLOGICAL CHARACTERISTICS OF THE GABA-R-GATED Cl⁻ CHANNEL

As already mentioned, the immediate effects of BZR ligands on GABA-R function in neuronal membranes can, at present, be investigated only by electrophysiological techniques (measurement of $^{36}Cl^-$ uptake into neurons under the effect of a GABA mimetic is an alternative, albeit laborious and restricted to neuron populations, e.g., Thampy and Barnes, 1984). The role of $GABA_A$-Rs in cellular membranes is to activate an associated transmembrane ion-conducting channel which is selective for some anions, of which Cl^- is the biologically most relevant. We shall, therefore, refer to this channel as the Cl^- channel or Cl^- ionophore. It is very probable that some $GABA_A$-Rs are coupled to other channels with different ion selectivity. There seems to be a clear difference between $GABA_A$-Rs and $GABA_B$-Rs; the latter are characterized not only by a distinct ligand specificity (sharing with $GABA_A$-Rs only the affinity for GABA itself) but also by a coupling to other ion channels, among them probably a K^+ channel and a voltage-dependent Ca^{2+} channel. Activation of the $GABA_A$-R opens the Cl^- channel for Cl^- ions. The direction and the size of the Cl^- transmembrane flow depend on the number and conductance of Cl^- channels, the Cl^- equilibrium potential (E_{Cl^-}), which itself is determined by the concentration of Cl^- ions on both sides of the cellular membrane, and the resting membrane potential (E_M); the driving force for the Cl^- flux when Cl^- channels are open is the difference between E_M and E_{Cl^-} (the electrochemical potential gradient). The latter is not the same for all neurons even under physiological conditions, possibly because of different activities of Cl^- pumps. Thus, some types of neurons will be hyperpolarized by GABA (net influx of negatively charged Cl^- ions) and some others will be depolarized (net efflux of Cl^- ions). GABA may even produce opposite potential changes in the soma and in the dendrites of the same neuron. Since membrane potential changes in response to GABA may be small (depending on the resting membrane potential), investigators very often intentionally use intracellular pipettes filled with a chloride salt in order to increase, by leakage, the intracellular Cl^- concentration (thus reversing the electrochemical gradient for Cl^-) and thereby to obtain constant and large depolarization responses to GABA. Irrespective of the potential change, GABA produces a consistent increase in membrane conductance. The most accurate way to assess the membrane action of GABA on the cellular level is, therefore, the recording of membrane conductance (if possible under voltage clamp).

Consequently, analysis of BZ actions on the function of GABA-Rs requires the measurement of conductance changes induced by GABA in the absence and presence of a BZ. This analysis can be made on two levels of resolution. On a cellular level, conductance changes in a neuron (in a brain tissue slice or in cell culture) implanted with an intracellular recording electrode are monitored in response to GABA which is either added to the bathing fluid or applied by iontophoresis or pressure ejection into the vicinity of the recorded neuron. The ultimate goal of the electrophysiological approach is the study of single Cl^- channels. While results of single Cl^- channel studies with BZs have not yet been reported, indirect estimation of single channel function under the effect of BZs has been obtained by so-called fluctuation analysis of the GABA-induced synaptic noise, as will be shown below.

3.2 EFFECTS OF AGONISTS AT BZRS

Full dose–response curves for the depolarizing effect of GABA on dorsal root terminals in the frog hemisected spinal cord were shifted to the left by flurazepam (Nistri and Constanti, 1978) and midazolam (Nistri and Berti, 1983). Similar findings were obtained on the single cell level. In cultured chick and fetal mouse spinal cord cells chlordiazepoxide was found to shift to the left the dose–response curve for the conductance increase by GABA without change in its maximum (Choi et al., 1981a,b; MacDonald, 1978; MacDonald and Barker, 1979a,b). A fluctuation analysis of GABA-induced currents in cultured fetal mouse spinal cord cells by Study and Barker (1981) suggested that Diaz does not alter single channel conductance, has little, if any, effect on the mean open time, but clearly increases the probability of channel openings in response to GABA.

The lines of electrophysiological evidence can then be summarized as follows: BZ agonists shift the dose–response curve for the membrane conductance increase of GABA to the left (increase of the apparent potency of GABA). The shift is modest even after maximally effective BZ concentrations (approximately two- to threefold). The maximum effect of GABA is not altered. These results together with those from fluctuation analysis indicate that BZs do not alter single channel conductance, single channel ion specificity, single channel mean open time, number of channels, or driving force for Cl^- anions. However, they increase the frequency of channel openings or, in other terms, the probability of single channel openings in response to GABA. Two effects of BZs could account for this modulation of channel opening probability: either an increase in the affinity of GABA-Rs for GABA or an increase in the coupling between GABA-R activation and Cl^- channel opening.

These conclusions are the key for an understanding of the molecular mechanism of BZ action. Some questions, however, still remain open. One is whether all BZ agonists produce the same maximum shift of the GABA response curve or whether the magnitude of this shift represents the intrinsic activity of BZR ligands. A further important question to be answered in future studies is whether all BZRs have to be occupied for a maximal shift of the GABA dose–response curve or whether a receptor reserve exists.

3.3 EFFECTS OF ANTAGONISTS AT BZRS

BZ antagonists have so far been studied only on mass-evoked responses to GABA neuron stimulation, e.g., on presynaptic inhibition of primary afferents in the cat spinal cord (Polc et al., 1981b). In such studies, Ro 15-1788 had no effect by itself, but blocked specifically the enhancement of primary afferent depolarization by BZ agonists. In a few occasional qualitative studies on single cells, similar results were obtained (Bold et al., 1982; Barker et al., 1984).

3.4 EFFECTS OF INVERSE AGONISTS AT BZRS

Evidence that β-CCE (a weak convulsant) may actually depress the effect of GABA was obtained by Polc et al. (1981a) in the rat hippocampus. A "GABA antagonistic" effect was clearly apparent in the cat spinal cord, where β-CCE reduced primary afferent depolarization, an effect opposite to that of BZ ago-nists. This effect of β-CCE was blocked by Ro 15-1788 (Polc *et al.*, 1982). The convulsant inverse agonists β-CCM and DMCM reduced the effect of GABA on cultured chick (Chan *et al.*, 1983) and mouse (Jensen and Lambert, 1983) spinal cord neurons.

3.5 CONCLUSIONS

The study of the GABA-R/Cl$^-$ channel function in neuronal membranes clearly shows that BZ agonists enhance the function of this complex either by increasing the affinity of GABA-R to GABA and/or by improving the coupling between GABA-R and Cl$^-$ channel. The properties of single Cl$^-$ channels seem to be unaffected. Inverse agonists at BZRs reduce the effect of GABA. BZ antagonists are characterized by the absence of effects on the normal GABA-R/Cl$^-$ channel function and a selective blockade of the effect of agonists and inverse agonists.

4 General Aspects of Benzodiazepine Receptors (BZRs)

4.1 TERMINOLOGY

4.1.1 Receptor

The concept of specific receptors, responsible for the initiation of drug-induced changes in a biological target cell, is an old and central dogma of pharmacology. The molecular approach to pharmacological receptors, feasible on a large scale for little more than a decade, has essentially confirmed theoretical views pro-posed much earlier. The term receptor contains two absolutely necessary func-tions, namely that of recognition and binding of a ligand, and that of transduction or stimulus-forming function. An effector or amplification process is triggered by the isomerization of the initial ligand–receptor complex, i.e., by "receptor activation." It is now clear that specific receptor-mediated effects are initiated by the recognition and binding of a drug to a macromolecule; the binding of the drug to the receptor (or the formation of a ligand–receptor complex) induces a func-tional alteration in the receptor molecule (conformational change, isomerization) which acts as the pharmacological stimulus. Drugs that act in this way are called agonists. Drugs that produce an effect only in the presence of an agonist by inhibiting binding of an agonist and the ensuing stimulus formation, are called antagonists. The transducer function of the receptor may be distinguished, at least theoretically, from an effector or amplification function. A class of recep-tors exists, exemplified by the nicotinic cholinoceptor (see Conti-Tronconi and Rafteri, 1982), where the ligand binding monomeres are part of a cation channel-forming pentamer and where the ligand-induced conformational change of a ligand binding monomer or of another monomer seems to be the conformational perturbation that is identical with the transition of the channel from the closed to the open state. Another class of receptors (exemplified by purified β-adrenoceptors from red cells and lung tissue) uses more complex intermediate steps and more molecular species between isomerization of the ligand binding molecule and the effector function, namely the intracellular formation of cAMP. As shown by reconstitution experiments (Cerione *et al.*, 1983), the activated receptor interacts with and modifies a coupling protein; this results in the activation of the catalytic unit of the membrane-bound enzyme adenylate cyclase. The three elements, the ligand binding receptor, the (stimulatory) coupling or regulatory unit, and the catalytic unit of adenylate cyclase, may not even form a constant complex but may move independently in the membrane and make mutual random contacts (collision coupling).

These variable and complex compositions of receptors effectors lead to semantic confusion. Some authors use binding macromolecule as a synonym for receptor and do not care whether this molecule also has an effector function or not. Others maintain that for a drug-binding molecule to be called a receptor its active involvement in the generation of a pharmacological effect has to be proven, i.e., the receptor molecule must have a binding as well as a transducer function; the effector function may or may not be located on the receptor molecule.

A difficulty of using the terms binding site and receptor indiscriminately is that highly specific binding sites may be considered part of a receptor function when, in fact, no pharmacological effect at all is initiated by the ligand binding site complex. We prefer the term acceptor for such binding sites to differentiate them from receptors (Richards *et al.*, 1982). Acceptors may simply be sites of storage (reservoirs) or "sites of loss" (if the only consequence of binding to these sites is to reduce the amount of drug available for interacting with true receptors). Alternatively they may be sites relevant for the transport of ligands in the blood (ligand-binding sites on albumin) or for transmembrane translocation (internalization).

Pharmacological receptors are, according to present knowledge, macromolecules (proteins, glycoproteins, nucleic acids). Only a small part of the accessible surface of a macromolecule is actually involved in the binding of small-molecular-weight ligands. This area would appropriately be called ligand binding site. It is relatively complementary to the ligand, enabling a close apposition of the two and the formation of the weak intermolecular bonds which cause the reversible attachment of the ligand. The ligand site may be located on a larger (globular) part of the macromolecule whose main function is the ligand binding; this part may be called the ligand binding domain to distinguish it from other domains of the same molecule that assure other functions, e.g., binding to couplers or effectors. The analogy to antibodies is obvious, where (hypervariable) domains on the antigen binding arms carry the antigen binding sites and where domains on the (constant) Fc part are involved in functions, such as binding to cell surfaces or interaction with components of the complement system. We shall use the terms ligand (or BZ) binding molecule, ligand binding domain, or ligand binding site whenever we want to emphasize more precisely the various levels of resolution.

4.1.2 Benzodiazepines (BZs) and Benzodiazepine Receptors (BZRs)

The term BZ is a chemical one. In pharmacology and therapeutics the term BZs, however, has a more restricted meaning, designating drugs belonging (in a broad sense) to the chemical class of BZs and having a pharmacological activity similar or identical to that of the early "classical" BZs, such as Diaz. We shall not be able to completely avoid the use of the term BZs in the above-defined sense, although it is no longer correct since BZs with antagonistic activity have been found. The term BZR agonists will be used to include compounds of any chemical structure that interact in a similar way with the BZR as BZ agonists and, hence, have similar pharmacological activities. BZR antagonists shall denote agents that bind to the BZR, have no effect on GABA-R function, but block the effect of BZR agonists.

The term BZR, of course, no longer signifies a receptor that selectively interacts with ligands belonging to this chemical class. Cyclopyrrolones, triazolopyridazines, phenylquinolinones, and β-carbolines exist which have a pharmacological profile very similar to classical BZR agonists. On the other hand, there are BZ derivatives that interact highly specifically with a completely different receptor, such as, e.g., tifluadom with the opiate κ receptor (Römer et al., 1982a,b; Kley et al., 1983).

Should BZRs turn out to act as targets for an endogenous ligand (see Section 5.18), they will probably be given another name, related to the natural ligand. In the meantime, and in case an endogenous ligand should not be found, the term BZR will probably remain for historical reasons and for convenience.

4.1.3 Agonists, Antagonists, and Inverse Agonists at BZRs

These terms have evoked some controversy. They were coined when (1) a compound was found with Ro 15-1788 that had a high affinity to BZ binding sites, lacked relevant actions characteristic of classic BZ tranquillizers (zero or near zero efficacy or intrinsic activity), but blocked all these effects when given before or after a BZ or non-BZ tranquillizer acting through the BZ binding sites and (2) some β-carbolines were found to exert, through BZRs, effects diametrically opposite to those of BZ tranquillizers ("negative" efficacy or intrinsic activity). The terms are provisionally best considered as purely based on phenomenology. The potentiation of GABA effects and the ensuing behavioral and neurological actions by the classical BZs and similarly acting non-BZs are taken to reflect an agonistic interaction with the BZR ("positive" efficacy or intrinsic activity). Selective blockade of these effects is considered to reflect an antagonistic interaction with the BZR. The term inverse agonists was coined (Polc et al., 1982; Braestrup et al., 1983b) to emphasize the fact that these drugs, when given alone, are in fact receptor activators because they produce a marked effect on GABAergic transmission and behavior, in contrast to antagonists that are pharmacologically silent in the absence of an agonist. This allowed us to avoid complicated and too restricted terms such as "convulsant antagonists" or "anxiogenic antagonists." The situation (not necessarily the idea) that opposite effects can be evoked by the same receptor and that a third class of compounds blocks either of the opposite effects, is new in pharmacology. Ligands that evoke opposite effects through one receptor perhaps exist at the so-called picrotoxinin binding site (or barbiturate receptor), as convulsant ligands reduce GABA-modulated chloride conductance and anticonvulsant barbiturates enhance GABA action; however, ligands inactive by themselves but blocking convulsant and anticonvulsant activity at this site, have not been found to date. The greater complexity in the quality of ligand interactions in the case of the BZRs than in the case of the classical neurotransmitter and hormone receptors may be due to the fact that activation (in either direction) of the BZRs in the absence of GABA is without functional effect on the neuronal membrane, i.e., activation of the system by a GABA agonist has a permissive effect on the actions of BZs, and that the BZR acts as an allosteric regulatory site on the GABA-Rs. Recent patch clamp studies of single GABA-coupled chloride channels (Sakman et al., 1983) have shown that they are continuously closed in the absence of GABA. Conformational change into the open state requires stimulation by GABA or other GABA agonists. The BZR as an allosteric regulatory site of the GABA-R seems to mediate two opposing effects, one to amplify or facilitate the action of GABA, the other to reduce the action of GABA; by convention, agents facilitating GABA-R/Cl$^-$ channel function via the BZR (increasing the gain) are called agonists, and agents reducing the receptor/channel function (decreasing the gain) have been termed inverse agonists. These agents can be considered to act like positive and negative allosteric modulators (effectors), respectively, of the GABA-R/anion channel system. Antagonists at BZRs block the effect of both agonists and partial agonists by competitively inhibiting their binding to the BZR.

We shall come back to the problem of ligand–receptor interaction with opposite functional effect (see p. 189). Suffice it to say here that there seems to be no general rule that would help us to decide which of the BZR ligands is the agonist and which is the inverse agonist. Moreover, we have to wait for the eventual identification of a possible endogenous ligand of the BZR in order to know whether it acts as an agonist or inverse agonist in the terminology used here.

It is quite obvious that agents exist that cannot be classified as one of the three prototype ligands described (agonists, antagonists, inverse agonists), but which have properties combining agonistic with antagonistic (partial agonists, Haefely, 1984c; Haefely and Poli, 1985) or inverse agonistic with antagonistic features (partial inverse agonists).

4.2 METHODOLOGICAL PROBLEMS

This article is mainly concerned with studies of the BZR using the radioligand binding technique. Radioligands are probes for the ligand binding sites of receptors, but not for their transducer or effector functions. Receptor binding sites can be studied *in vivo* (*in situ*) or under various *in vitro* conditions. BZR binding *in vivo* will be treated in a special paragraph (Sections 5.15 and 5.16). Here we discuss a few technical aspects of *in vitro* binding studies.

4.2.1 In Vitro Binding

In vitro binding can be studied in subcellular fractions, in isolated intact cells or in intact cells in cell culture, as well as in tissue slices. Results of radioligand binding studies are greatly affected by (1) the preparation of the tissues used, (2) the conditions of the assay (temperature, ion composition, and ionic strength), (3) the radioligands used, and (4) the techniques used to separate bound from free radioligand (Schliebs *et al.*, 1983).

4.2.1.1 Preparation of tissue for binding assays. There are probably not two laboratories that use exactly the same tissue fractionation procedures for studies of BZ binding. It is important to attempt to find out differences in tissue preparation when attempting to understand divergent results reported by different authors.

Essentially, the numerous preparations used are modifications of either fractions of crude homogenates (''P_2'' fraction) obtained by differential centrifugation in an isotonic medium or membrane preparations treated i.a. with hypo-osmotic shock. Unless the membrane preparations are extensively washed, freeze-thawed, and/or treated with detergents, they contain considerable concentrations of endogenous GABA and, perhaps, several kinds of endogenous regulatory compounds that may affect the state of the receptors; an inhibitor of high-affinity GABA binding, gabamodulin, as well as an inhibitor of BZ binding, ''Diaz binding inhibitor'' (DBI), are examples. Several procedures are used to obtain ''thoroughly washed'' membrane preparations.

Cells in cell culture have recently been used to determine binding characteristics (Sher *et al.*, 1982; Chan *et al.*, 1983); the aim is to correlate interaction at binding sites with induced membrane conductance changes (Chan et al., 1983). The problem with intact cells is that ligands may be taken up into cells, making it difficult to measure exclusively membrane-bound radioligand. Moreover, growth in cell culture conditions may lead to quantitative and/or qualitative alterations in BZ binding sites. For instance, primary cultures from fetal mice had a high-affinity binding for [^{3}H]Diaz (K_D 5 nmol/liter) (Walker and Peacock, 1981); binding of [^{3}H]Diaz was completely inhibited by the "peripheral type" ligand Ro 5-4864 (20 nmol/liter) but only 26% with 20 nmol/liter lorazepam. GABA failed to enhance [^{3}H]Diaz binding; in fact, it even produced a small decrease. These results clearly indicate that the cultures contained by far more nonneuronal than neuronal type [^{3}H]Diaz binding sites as seen also, e.g., in cell line C_6, a rat glial tumor cell (Walker and Peacock, 1981). Mallorga et al. (1983) studied [^{3}H]clonazepam binding in chick neurons in primary culture.

Autoradiography of tissue sections has recently become an interesting extension of the radioligand approach. Since BZ binding sites are rather resistant to mild fixatives, equilibrium binding experiments can be performed on slide-mounted sections of formaldehyde-fixed brain tissue (Palacios et al., 1981a,b; Wamsley et al., 1981; Wamsley and Palacios, 1983). The great advantage of this method is that binding can be studied in distinct small regions, visible in the light microscope, and quantified (quantitative autoradiography).

4.2.1.2 Physical and chemical conditions of the assay. In order to reduce the rates of association and dissociation and the nonspecfic binding, most *in vitro* studies are still carried out at 0 to 4°C. The ionic compositions and strength used in published experiments vary enormously. At 37°C the binding kinetics of some, but not all, ligands are drastically different from those at low temperature, and some pronounced modifications by ions disappear at physiological temperature. It is being increasingly realized that binding at low temperature and in artificial media may poorly reflect the *in vivo* situation.

4.2.2 Radioligands for BZ binding sites

[^{3}H]Diaz is probably the most frequently used radioligand. Since it was the first BZ available with sufficiently high specific activity, those laboratories (e.g., in the industry) that have to rely on a large number of previous data for reasons of comparison still use [^{3}H]Diaz for screening purposes. [^{3}H]Flu (Speth et al., 1978) has the advantage of higher affinity; at low temperatures it dissociates more slowly from its binding sites, thus reducing possible loss in the washing procedure which may give rise to errors in B_{max} determinations. This is especially important for *in vivo* binding experiments. A further advantage of the higher affinity of [^{3}H]Flu is the lower nonspecific binding than with [^{3}H]Diaz at the concentrations required for the assay. Both [^{3}H]Diaz and [^{3}H]Flu also bind to the peripheral type of BZ binding sites; this has to be considered, notably at higher ligand concentrations, where both binding sites become labeled. [^{11}C]Flu, the positron-emitting radiolabel, is used for *in situ* visualization of BZR occupancy in the intact brain (positron emission tomography, PET) (Mazière *et al.*, 1983a,b). [^{3}H]Clonazepam and [^{3}H]meclonazepam (Table 7) are close analogs of Flu, [^{3}H]clonazepam has very low affinity for peripheral type binding sites. [^{3}H]Meclonazepam is a pure enantiomer with high biological activity and a stabilized conformation. The three 7-nitro derivatives [^{3}H]Flu, [^{3}H]clonazepam, and [^{3}H]meclonazepam are used for photoaffinity labeling. Some 1,4-BZs with either the positron-emitting ^{75}Br or the γ-emitting ^{77}Br in position 7 have been prepared (Scholl *et al.*, 1983). The 7-^{75}Br analog of Flu was found to have some advantages over [^{11}C]Flu as a radioligand for *in vivo* PET.

[^{3}H]Ro 5-4864 (Fig. 3) is the 4'-chloro derivative of Diaz. It lacks the typical central effects of BZ, but has a high affinity and selectivity for the peripheral type of BZ binding sites. This should not, however, detract from the fact that Ro 5-4864 may have actions related to other sites; the convulsant action of Ro 5-4864 could be mediated, e.g., by its interaction with the binding site for chloride channel convulsants (Ramanjaneyulu and Ticku, 1984).

[^{3}H]PK 11195 [1-(2-chlorophenyl)-N-methyl-N-(1-methylpropyl)-3-isoquinolinecarboxamide] (Fig. 5) is a potent ligand for the nonneuronal BZ binding site (Benavides *et al.*, 1983a,b). The compound was found to antagonize seizures induced by Ro 5-4864 by File and Mabutt (1983), who speculated that PK 11195 could be an antagonist at nonneuronal BZ binding sites.

[^{3}H]Zopiclone (Table 11) is a cyclopyrrolone with a K_D of 13 nmol/liter in rat hippocampus (Blanchard *et al.*, 1983); while the compound has a classic BZ-like neuropsychopharmacological profile, modulation of [^{3}H]zopiclone binding by various agents differs somewhat from that of [^{3}H]BZ ligands.

[^{3}H]CL 218,872 (Table 11) is a triazolopyridazine agonist (or partial agonist) ligand for the neuronal high-affinity binding sites. Its affinity is low; the only interest lies in its preference for a potential BZR subtype.

[^{3}H]Ro 15-1788 (Table 12) is an imidazobenzodiazepinone derivative and the most systematically used specific BZ antagonist. It does not bind to the peripheral type sites. ^{11}C-labeled Ro 15-1788 has been used for *in vivo* visualization of binding sites in the monkey brain (Mazière *et al.*, 1983b).

[^{3}H]Ro 15-4513 (Fig. 3) is a photosensitive azide analog of Ro 15-1788 with potent inhibitory effect on [^{3}H]Flu binding and marked BZ antagonistic activity *in vivo*. In contrast to Ro 15-1788, Ro 15-4513 is a partial inverse agonist. The ligand was used by Möhler *et al.* (1981a) for irreversible labeling of binding sites for BZ antagonists/inverse agonists.

[^{3}H]CGS 8216 (Table 13b) is a pyrazoloquinolinone derivative with BZ antagonistic and slight inverse agonistic activity (Petrack *et al.*, 1983). In addition, CGS 8216 binds to adenosine receptors.

The three β-carboline-3-carboxylate esters β-[³H]CCM, β-[³H]CCE, and β-[³H]CCPr (Nielsen et al., 1981) are interesting probes for the study of the sites to which non-BZ antagonists and inverse agonists bind.

4.3 A SHORT CHARACTERIZATION OF THE VARIOUS BZ BINDING SITES

At least five, more or less specific, binding sites for BZ are known. Three of them will be treated in detail in the following paragraphs.

4.3.1 Human Serum Albumin Binding Site

In the blood, most BZs are extensively bound to albumin (Wong and Sellers, 1979; Sellers et al., 1982). This binding reduces the free fraction of some BZs in the serum water to a very small ($<<5\%$) fraction of the total (pharmacological or therapeutic concentration) in the blood. Considerable species differences in plasma binding of BZs exist (Laznicek et al., 1982).

The area of the albumin molecule to which BZs bind with relative selectivity is called the "drug binding site II" or "indole binding site," because L-tryptophan is bound to the same site (Ball et al., 1979; Fehske et al., 1979; Müller and Wollert, 1979; Wong and Sellers, 1979). According to Kragh-Hansen (1983) the BZ binding region of albumin binds, in addition, D-tryptophan, L-thyroxine, octanoate, p-iodobenzoate, and Cl^- ions. The association constant for Diaz is reported as 4.7×10^{-5} liter/mol. The K_D for chlordiazepoxide binding to defatted human serum albumin was calculated to be 2.5×10^{-5} mol/liter (Sollenne and Means, 1979). Binding of [³H]Diaz (and L-tryptophan) to human serum albumin is saturable and Scatchard analysis gives a straight line (Fehske et al., 1979).

The primary structure of human serum albumin is known and secondary structures have been proposed. One of the 18 tyrosine residues of albumin seems to be critically involved in the specific binding of BZ and indoles, as indicated by a marked reduction of the affinity of Diaz and L-tryptophan to their common binding site when only one (the most reactive) tyrosine residue is modified by tetranitromethane (Fehske et al., 1979).

4.3.2 BZ Binding Sites in Schistosomes

Some BZ derivatives with a nitro group in position 7 (e.g., clonazepam and meclonazepam) are potent antischistosomal agents (Stohler, 1978). [¹⁴C]Meclonazepam was found by Bennett (1980) to bind specifically to membrane fragments of the dermis of male Schistosoma mansoni and to intact schistosomes. Binding is saturable and of low affinity; the K_D for meclonazepam is 2×10^{-6} mol/liter in S. mansoni and 3×10^{-5} mol/liter in S. japonicum, reflecting the different sensitivity of these parasites to the antischistosomal activity of meclonazepam. Various BZs displaced [^{14}C]meclonazepam according to their antischistosomal potency. Antischistosomal BZs seem to induce a rapid influx of Ca^{2+} into schistosomes and a depolarization; there is a rapid initial increase in the tension of the parasite's musculature (Pax *et al.*, 1978).

4.3.3 The Neuronal High-Affinity Binding Site(s)

These binding sites are quite obviously connected with the main pharmacological effects of BZs and are, therefore, often called central BZRs. This type of BZ binding site is the main subject of this article (Section 5).

4.3.4 The Nonneuronal (or Peripheral) Type of BZ Binding Site

This type of (relatively high-affinity) binding site was discovered during the pioneering studies of Braestrup and Squires (1977). It occurs in many peripheral organs and tissues, but is also present in the CNS, in the most concentrated form in nonneuronal elements. The term "peripheral" and "nonneuronal" type is used interchangeably. This binding site will be treated in Section 6.

4.3.5 The Low-Affinity (Micromolar) Type BZ Binding Site

This is a saturable binding site recently described in the brain that has a low (micromolar) affinity for BZ and a ligand specificity quite different from both the neuronal high-affinity and the peripheral binding sites (Bowling and De Lorenzo, 1982). This site will be discussed below (Section 7).

5 The Neuronal (Central) High-Affinity Binding Site(s)

5.1 DEFINITIONS

This binding site is defined by a high affinity for classical BZs (in the lower nanomolar range at low temperature) with a ligand specificity that reflects, on the whole, the relative *in vivo* potencies of the ligands in those tests used to screen for BZ-like activity (e.g., antagonism of pentetrazol-induced convulsions, anti-conflict tests, test for muscle relaxation and ataxia), most exceptions being readily explained by pharmacokinetic or metabolic peculiarities. Since, in addition, specific BZ antagonists inhibit the binding of agonists to these high-affinity states, the latter are undoubtedly those sites through which BZs produce their characteristic effects—provided they are coupled to the GABA-R/Cl$^-$ iono-phore. For convenience and clarity we shall use the term BZR when viewing the binding site as a physical and a functional component of the drug recognition–transducer–effector complex. We shall refer to the site as "BZR" or "site" when it is only identified by ligand binding and we are not sure whether it is a component of the GABA receptor complex or not.

The existence of subtypes of BZRs has been proposed (see Section 5.21). The term BZR_1 was coined for a binding site for which the triazolopyridazine CL 218,872 and some β-carbolines have a higher affinity than for the assumed BZR_2; according to this view, BZR_1 would be virtually the only type present in the cerebellar cortex, while in other regions of the CNS, such as in the cerebral cortex or hippocampus, BZR_2 would make up about one-half of the total BZ binding sites. Classical BZs do not differentiate these two proposed types. Gee et al. (1983a–c) have recently shown that the intraregional BZR_1/BZR_2 difference disappears when binding is performed at 37°C, whereas a (slightly) greater affinity of CL 218,872 remains for binding sites in the cerebellum than in the forebrain (interregional difference). It has therefore been proposed to distinguish between a cerebellar and noncerebellar type of neuronal high-affinity binding site. The above-mentioned terms will be used when unavoidable.

The three prototypes of ligands reflect the three ways we think ligands can alter the function of BZRs (see Section 4.1.3).

5.2 HYPOTHETICAL MODEL OF THE BZR/GABA-R/Cl⁻ CHANNEL COMPLEX

Although a hypothetical model of the $BZR/GABA-R/Cl^-$ channel complex is the result of the findings yet to be described in the next sections, we present it here (Fig. 8), so that it can be tested in the discussions that follow.

We assume that the complex is a tetrameric glycoprotein consisting of four identical or very similar protomers (subunits). The quaternary structure enables the formation of an ion pore that can close and open in response to small conformation changes in the subunits. The subunits are proposed to have at least three domains with different functions (Fig. 7). One domain forms the "anatomy" of the pore and by subtle conformational changes can hold the pore in an ion-impermeable or ion-permeable state. This "Cl^- ionophore" or, more correctly, the ionophore-forming domains of the four subunits, also have binding sites for ligands of very different chemical classes [see, however, the attempts of Ticku and Maksay (1983) to find common structural features]; according to their ligands, these binding sites on the ionophore domain have been coined "picrotoxinin site," "barbiturate receptor," "convulsant receptors," or site for "chloride channel agents." Each subunit also has a GABA binding domain; when GABA is bound, the GABA binding domain is thought to undergo a conformational change, which is transmitted intramolecularly to the adjacent ionophore and BZ binding domains, such that the pore is forced into or stabilized in an open state. Binding of a BZ agonist is assumed to produce a conformational

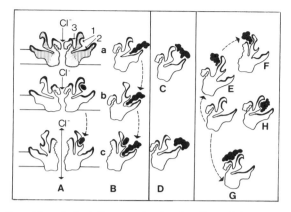

FIG. 8. Schematic and hypothetical diagrams showing the effects of the prototype ligands of the complex on the receptor complex. (Aa) is a section through the complex showing the inactive (closed) receptor–channel complex in its resting state with binding sites for GABA (1), BZR ligands (2), and ligands of the picrotoxinin binding site (3). In (Ab) GABA is recognized by the GABA-R. This induces (in Ac) a conformational change in the GABA-R domain, which is transmitted intra-molecularly to the channel domain (opening) and the BZR (shift toward a state of higher affinity for agonists and lower affinity for inverse agonists). In (B) is shown the recognition of a BZR agonist by the BZR (Ba), resulting in a perturbation of the BZR conformation, the GABA-R conformation (higher affinity state for GABA), and, perhaps, a conformational change of the channel domain favoring the opening. In the absence of GABA, the presence of a BZR agonist does not induce Cl^- conductance. However, if GABA now reaches the GABA-R, it will be bound with higher affinity and the opening of the channel domain is facilitated; this is illustrated as the facilitated Cl^- channel gating action of GABA in the presence of a BZR agonist (Bc). (C) suggests how an inverse agonist interacts with the complex: the induced conformation is unfavorable for the gating function of GABA, hence, GABA transmission is decreased. In (D) is indicated the interaction of a competitive antagonist; it lacks intrinsic activity, inhibits binding of an agonist or inverse agonist, but does not alter the normal gating function of GABA. In (E) and (F) are proposed two ways in which depressant barbiturates can interact with the complex, in (E) by shifting the GABA-R and BZR into a state of higher affinity and, in (F), by opening "directly" the Cl^- channel. (G) Picrotoxinin or another channel convulsant inhibits the gating mechanism initiated by the GABA–GABA-R complex forma-tion. In (H) is shown a possible way by which GABA-R blockers could inhibit the binding of GABA.

change of its own domain, which is transmitted to the GABA binding domain, with the result that the GABA binding site shifts to a higher affinity state and/or that the transmission of its GABA-induced conformational change to the ionophore domain is increased, i.e., the efficiency or the gain of coupling be-tween GABA-R and Cl^- channel is improved.

While all central type high-affinity binding sites for BZs seem to be coupled with GABA-R/Cl^- channel complexes, not all GABA-Rs are coupled to BZRs. At least in the cerebellum, the microscopic distribution of binding sites for BZs, GABA, and the convulsant TBPS (Wamsley et al., 1983) is not entirely con-gruent. Terminal GABA autoreceptors are not coupled to BZR according to

Brennan (1982); muscimol inhibition of [^{3}H]GABA release from brain slices induced by K^+ depolarization was unaffected by Flu (1 and 10 μM).

5.3 BASIC ASPECTS OF LIGAND–BZR INTERACTIONS

5.3.1 Affinity

The affinity of ligands for BZ binding sites is determined either by studying the binding of the radiolabeled ligands themselves or by displacement experiments. With the radiolabeled ligand, the equilibrium dissociation constant (K_D) is determined from equilibrium binding data (saturation isotherm) as the concentration that results in half-saturation of specific binding; K_D is obtained from the saturation isotherm directly or from Scatchard analysis of isotherms. Alternatively, K_D can be calculated from kinetic studies of radioligand binding which yield the association (k_{+1}) and dissociation rate constants (k_{-1}). With unlabeled ligands, displacement curves using various concentrations of the unlabeled ligand and a predetermined (nonsaturating) concentration of the radioligand are constructed. The IC_{50}, the concentration of the unlabeled ligand that inhibits specific binding of the radioligand by 50%, is easily obtained from displacement curves and is a useful parameter for comparison of agents studied under the same experimental conditions. The inhibitory constant K_i can be calculated from the IC_{50} value and the K_D of the radioligand, and is the value of choice for comparing data obtained in different laboratories.

   Relative affinities of BZ agonists have already been shown in the first papers on BZ binding (Squires and Braestrup, 1977; Möhler and Okada, 1977a,b; Braestrup *et al.*, 1977) to be correlated more or less accurately with therapeutic potencies and with pharmacological potencies in animal tests. This immediately raises two questions: do the K_D and K_i values obtained *in vitro* reflect affinities *in vivo*, and what are the pharmacologically and therapeutically effective concentrations of BZs in the brain?

   Apparent affinities of ligands determined *in vitro* at the usual temperatures of 0 to 4°C are mostly very different from the values obtained at physiological temperature. Apparent affinity may decrease by a factor of 10 or more at 37°C (Dudai, 1979; Speth *et al.*, 1979b,c; Möhler and Richards, 1981a; Quast *et al.*, 1982; Gee and Yamamura, 1982a–c; Gee *et al.*, 1982b). Whether or not temperature affects the affinity of all BZ agonists to the same degree has not been studied systematically. Dissociation of [^{3}H]Flu at 37°C is so rapid that its k_{-1}) could not be determined and compared to that of [^{3}H] Diaz (Möhler, unpublished). At 37°C both the association (k_{+1}) and dissociation (k_{-1}) rate constants are increased (k_{-1} more than k_{+1}), thus causing an elevation of K_D. The marked effect of temperature on K_D (elevated k_{-1}) is a source of errors in determinations of specifically bound radioligands (rapid loss of specifically bound ligand during washing procedures) (Fujimoto *et al.*, 1982a; Lloyd *et al.*, 1981). A further important finding is the loss at 37°C of intraregional brain differences in the apparent affinity of CL 218,872, and, hence, of one important argument for receptor multiplicity (Gee *et al.*, 1982b).

The concentration of BZs in the blood of animals or man after oral pharmacological and therapeutic doses is in the range of 10^{-8} to 10^{-6} M (Kaplan and Jack, 1981; Dorow *et al.*, 1982; Jochemsen *et al.*, 1983b). Concentrations of 10^{-6} M or even higher occur only with the less potent compounds and/or shortly after iv doses that produce marked depression of consciousness. These concentrations are total blood concentrations, and since most BZs are strongly bound to albumin, the free fraction of some BZs is not higher than 5% at the therapeutically relevant concentrations. Although the concentration of free BZs in tissues, and of most importance in the brain, is not known accurately, there is little reason to doubt that it is in the range of 10^{-8} to 10^{-7} M for the more potent BZs. Thus, the concentration of free BZ is in the same order of magnitude as the K_D values determined in radioligand binding *in vitro* at 37°C. Mennini and Garattini (1983) have determined total, totally membrane-bound, and specifically membrane-bound BZs in various brain areas and peripheral tissues. The free concentration of ligands appears to be about one-third of the total concentration. A good correlation was found between brain levels of six benzodiazepines determined by radioreceptor assay and pharmacological activity (Fujimoto and Okabayashi, 1982). The concentrations of BZs in the various brain areas differ considerably; the total concentration of Diaz in the rat brain was found to be highest in the hypothalamus, where it was five times that in the cerebral cortex and cerebellum (Hariton *et al.*, 1983). A more even distribution in rat brain was reported for six benzodiazepines by Fujimoto and Okabayashi (1982) and for diazepam by Hironaka *et al.* (1983). After ip administration of 0.5 and 1 mg/kg lorazepam to rats the peak drug levels in the brain were approximately 10^{-6} mol/g; sedative effects did not correlate with total brain levels (Lister *et al.*, 1983).

The apparent affinity of BZ ligands is affected by several other factors that will be described later (effects of GABA agonists, ions, Cl^- channel agents). Modulation of BZR affinity by any of these factors may account for the influence of the membrane washing procedures which may remove endogenous GABA, but also possible endogenous inhibitors.

5.3.2 Density (B_{max} Values)

Varying B_{max} values obtained by different authors with apparently similar techniques are probably due on most occasions to differences in the assay conditions. Again, the effect of washing the tissue preparations should not be underestimated, as BZRs themselves or endogenous inhibitors may be extracted from membranes to different degrees. An interesting finding is the elevated B_{max} for [^{3}H]Flu found in thoroughly washed membranes of animals that had been injected with Diaz 1 hr before sacrifice (Korneyev and Factor, 1981, 1983); Diaz present during the washing procedure may have removed an endogenous inhibitor or protected the liganded BZR from solubilization.

5.3.3 Association and Dissociation Kinetics

There are several reasons to study carefully the kinetics of association and dissociation of ligands at BZ binding sites. One important question is how fast BZR occupation would reflect the concentration of ligands in the biophase both during the rising phase after drug administration and during the falling phase after peak values have been achieved. Kinetic studies can also help to solve the problems of receptor heterogeneity; indeed, the presence of different binding sites is likely to be revealed by a polyphasic association and dissociation phase. Multiple steps in the ligand–receptor complex formation may also be reflected in the kinetics.

Kinetics at physiological temperature are too fast to be monitored precisely enough with the normally available techniques. Therefore, the studies to be discussed were performed at 0 to 4°C. Chiu and Rosenberg (1982) used well-washed, frozen-thawed membranes of rat cerebral cortex and [^{3}H]Diaz and [^{3}H]Flu. Equilibrium was reached more rapidly the higher the ligand concentrations (within 3 to 5 min at 20 nM). Association was not linear, but showed a slow and a fast component. The rate of complex formation was faster with [^{3}H]Diaz than with [^{3}H]Flu. The two components of association were not as conspicuous with [^{3}H]Diaz as with [^{3}H]Flu. Dissociation curves were also curvilinear, consisting of two exponential phases. The lower the ligand concentration used for equilibrium binding, the longer was the time for dissociation of the ligand binding site complex. When membranes were preincubated at 37°C before washing at 0°C, the dissociation was faster than after preincubation at 0°C. Prolonged binding of the ligand at equilibrium slowed down the dissociation; this was due to an increase of the fraction of the slow exponential phase. Dissociation was faster when it started at preequilibrium (before full equilibrium binding had been attained). Dissociation of [^{3}H]Diaz was faster than that of [^{3}H]Flu and the two dissociation components were less pronounced with the former; the fraction of the slow component was smaller with [^{3}H]Diaz than with [^{3}H]Flu. However, the two components of dissociation became more marked when dissociation was made with Ro 15-1788, Flu, or Clon instead of Diaz. GABA decreased the dissociation rate both for the fast and the slow component, and this effect was more pronounced at higher than at lower concentrations of [^{3}H]Flu. The proportion of the slow component for dissociation of [^{3}H]Flu was slightly increased by

NaCl, more markedly increased by GABA, and most markedly increased (up to 80%) by the combination of NaCl and GABA. Qualitatively similar results were obtained with [^{3}H]Diaz; however, binding of [^{3}H]Diaz was more markedly enhanced by NaCl and GABA than was that of [^{3}H]Flu. Pentobarbitone did not affect the dissociation of [^{3}H]Flu. Chiu and Rosenberg (1982) and Chiu et al. (1982) concluded that their results could best be explained by assuming that binding of the BZ ligands occurred to a homogeneous population of molecules that could, however, exist in two interconvertible conformations or binding states. Binding to the lower affinity state would result in an initial, readily reversible complex that would isomerize to a more stable one, in which the binding molecule is in a higher affinity conformation. This cyclic model of binding shows some analogy to that proposed for the nicotinic cholinoceptor, except that for the BZ binding a dissociation of the ligand from both the initial highly reversible and the isomerized, more stable complex was proposed. The rate of formation of the initial low-affinity complex was assumed to be faster than the isomerization to the more stable high-affinity complex. The percentage of the fast and the slow dissociation complexes at equilibrium would be influenced by temperature (percentage of BZ binding molecules in the low-affinity state increased), duration of binding, and by GABA (both increasing the percentage of the slowly dissociating isomerized complex). The dissociation from pre-equilibrium would be faster because the fraction of the stable high-affinity complex would be smaller than at equilibrium. The effect of GABA was proposed to consist of a change in the conformation of the BZ binding molecule or merely a stabilization of the ligand–receptor complex. Because the effect of GABA was more marked on [^{3}H]Diaz than on [^{3}H]Flu binding, the complex with the former was suggested to be more labile. Although Diaz binds more rapidly than Flu, the fast on-and-off kinetics of Diaz indicate that it may be less effective than Flu in inducing isomerization after initial binding.

Very similar results were reported by Doble (1982) and Doble et al. (1982a,b). They found, in addition, that the dissociation rates of both the fast and slow component were faster when β-CCE was used as displacer instead of cold Diaz. The latter difference was no longer seen in the presence of GABA, which slowed down the dissociation rate. Doble (1982) suggested that the biphasic dissociation was due to a cooperative effect between ligand-bound and ligand-free binding sites, that cooperativity between the sites may represent a functional correlate of the state of aggregation, and that GABA might uncouple these functional interactions between binding sites. It was furthermore speculated that one conformer of the uniform population of BZ binding sites is stabilized by agonists, the other conformer by antagonists.

Quast and Mählmann (1982) also proposed a two-step mechanism of BZ binding from kinetic studies, assuming the rapid formation of a precomplex with subsequent, slow isomerization.

5.3.4 Thermodynamics of BZ Ligand Binding

The strong temperature dependence of BZ binding (Braestrup and Squires, 1977) invited investigation of its thermodynamics. Studies of the thermodynamics of BZ binding are likely to give useful information or, at least, stimulate further investigations on the processes that determine ligand binding, receptor activation (isomerization), and the differences between agonists and antagonists.

Speth et al. (1979a) obtained a Van't Hoff plot indicating that the rate of change of K_D with increasing temperature was smaller between 0 and 16°C than between 16 and 37°C. Quast et al. (1982) found parallel Van't Hoff plots for Flu, Diaz, and nordazepam except for a deviation with Flu at temperatures below 10°C. They concluded that the overall changes in the binding process of agonists is driven by a large negative change in enthalpy (ΔH) of about -45 kJ/mol and that the contribution of entropy (ΔS) to the free energy of binding was negligible. The system was considered to be too complex to allow more than speculations to be made on the nature of the binding process, except that the ligand binding site interaction is unlikely to be a simple absorption of the ligand to a rigid recognition site. As discussed by Quast et al. (1982), the lipophilic properties of BZ suggest the initial step to be a hydrophobic association. The release of structured water, which one would expect to ensue, would lead to an increase of entropy. This initial association step might then be followed by events that are driven by a decrease in enthalpy to compensate for the loss of entropy found. Further events may be energetically more favorable noncovalent interactions within the receptor peptide itself (stimulus formation) and between the various components of the BZR/GABA-R channel complex (in the sense of the effector function). A comparison of the thermodynamics of interaction of agonists, competitive antagonists, and inverse agonists with BZ binding sites at 37°C was performed by Möhler and Richards (1981a). Binding of the agonist clonazepam was found to be an enthalpy-driven process ($\Delta H = -62$ kJ/mol) compensating for an unfavorable decrease in entropy. In contrast, the binding of the inverse agonist DMCM was an entropy-driven process ($\Delta S = +13.2$ EU). The binding reaction of the antagonist Ro 15-1788 was both entropy and enthalpy driven. It is not yet known whether the thermodynamic differences can be extended to other agonists, inverse agonists, and antagonists, and thus reflect basic aspects of this binding (Möhler, 1983; Doble, 1983). Interestingly, at temperatures below 21°C, the thermodynamic parameters of binding of [^{3}H]clonazepam and [^{3}H]Ro 15-1788 were identical. The agonist-induced change in the BZR conformation may not occur at these low temperatures (Möhler and Richards, 1981a).

5.4 NATURE OF THE BZ BINDING SITE

Virtually nothing is known about the chemical structure of the BZ binding site, i.e., the amino acid and sugar residues that come in direct contact with ligands.

It has been proposed that a tyrosinyl residue in or very close to the binding site plays a crucial part in recognition and binding of ligands (Sherman-Gold and Dudai, 1981). Indeed, nitration of the membrane-bound or solubilized BZ binding molecule with tetranitromethane or acetylation with N-acetylimidazole or treatment with diethyl pyrocarbonate (Sherman-Gold and Dudai, 1983a), which are known to affect tyrosine residues, led to a loss of [³H]Flu binding capacity. This loss was prevented by the presence of centrally active BZs, but not by GABA. It is noteworthy that binding of BZ to albumin was suggested to involve a tyrosinyl residue, too (Fehske et al., 1979). Burch and Ticku (1981), on the basis of similar experiments, concluded that histidine might be involved as an essential contact residue.

Very recently, proteolytic degradation of [³H]Flu photoaffinity-labeled BZ binding sites from rat cerebral cortex membranes has been reported by Klotz et al. (1984). Small peptide fragments were released into the aqueous supernatant by pronase and trypsin. An endogenous trypsin-like activity was found to be present in membranes.

The glycoprotein nature of BZRs is strongly suggested by the interaction of solubilized binding sites with lectins, such as concanavalin A, wheat germ agglutinin, wax bean agglutinin, and phytohemagglutinin (Sherman-Gold and Dudai, 1983b). While lectins did not prevent photolabeling of BZ binding material with Flu, photolabeled material no longer reacted with lectins. Periodate treatment of the solubilized BZ binding material to oxidize sugar residues in the protein resulted in loss of the BZ binding capacity. It cannot be decided yet whether the carbohydrate moieties are involved in the binding of BZs or whether they have an influence on the conformation of the binding site.

5.5 STRUCTURE–ACTIVITY RELATIONSHIPS (SAR) OF BZR AGONISTS

5.5.1 Diazepine and Azepine Derivatives

5.5.1.1 "Classical" 1,4-BZs.
In their pioneering synthetic work, Sternbach and collaborators (Sternbach et al. 1964, 1968; Sternbach 1973, 1978) discovered the fundamental SAR of this series. They recognized very early that the presence of the seven-membered imino-lactam ring (ring B) was essential and that substitution was advantageous only in the positions 1, 3, 7, and 2'. In particular, electronegative substituents in 7 and 2' markedly increased activity (Fig. 9). It is surprising to see that following this simple qualitative substitution pattern, thousands of derivatives were synthesized all over the world and that more than a dozen of them have found their way into current therapy.

The high number of compounds and the wealth of information assembled during the scientific and therapeutic exploitation of the BZs are not appropriately

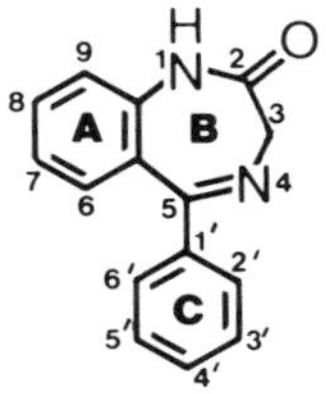

FIG. 9. 5-Phenyl-1,4-benzodiazepin-2-one: ring system of "classical" BZs.

reflected in quantitative structure–activity relationship (QSAR) studies, which appeared late and limited in number and scope. Graf and El-Menshawy (1977) published pK_a and P (distribution coefficient) values of 25 of the most common, commercial compounds, concluding that log P may vary widely over three orders of magnitude and, therefore, does not seem to be critical for CNS activity. Recently, Seiler and Zimmermann (1983) presented the same physicochemical parameters and the angle of twist of the 5-phenyl ring for 65 classical BZs. Blair and Webb (1977) attempted to correlate the activity of 59 BZs in pharmacological tests in mice (footshock-induced fighting, inclined screen, antipentetrazol) and in the cat (muscle relaxation) with calculated electronic parameters, such as the net charge on the carbonyl oxygen atom of the lactam ring, and the total dipole moment. Their CNDO/2 (complete neglect of differential orbital 2) calculations were based upon atomic coordinates obtained from the crystal structure of Diaz and thus could not take into account the influence of the varying substitution on the molecular geometry, thereby weakening the interpretation. This study also showed that it is impossible to explain the lack of activity of 4'-substituted compounds in terms of electronic effects.

A Free–Wilson QSAR analysis by Borea *et al.* (1979) using the data from 55 BZs in the above-mentioned tests in mice essentially confirmed the original, simple SAR. It underscores the importance of highly electron-withdrawing groups at the positions 7 and 2' for pharmacological potency and the generally negative effect of substitution at other positions. The individual group contributions to the antipentetrazol activity led to the following rank orders for position 7:

$$NO_2 > CF_3 > Br > CN > Cl > N(CH_3)_2 > SOCH_3 > SBu > SCH_3 > CH_3 > H > SO_2CH_3 > Ph > F$$

and for position 2':

$$Cl > F > Br > NO_2 > CF_3 > H > OCH_3 > CH_3$$

In a later study, Borea (1981) reported the application of the Hantsch method to a limited sample of 35 BZs and their antipentetrazol activity.

Biagi *et al.* (1980) showed that R_m values (chromatographically determined parameter for lipophilicity) obtained from a reversed-phase TLC system for 41 BZs correlated well with observed and calculated log P values and they attempted a further correlation with the activity in a conflict and an exploratory behavior test in rats. The authors came to the rather tenuous proposal that the anticonflict activity depends more upon the lipophilic character than does the general depressant effect, measured by the exploratory behavior.

A curious but apparently significant correlation was established by Ramanujam and Trieff (1978) between the rate constants for the reduction by sodium borohydride of the lactam keto group and the antipentetrazol ED_{50} in mice of a small group of 11 BZs.

The examples cited demonstrate the difficulty of finding a suitable basis for explaining the empirically established SAR of the classical BZs. In most cases, the biological evaluation was conducted in a whole battery of animal tests, carried out in different ways, at different research centers and covering different aspects of the activity spectrum. The interpretation and use of these *in vivo* results for QSAR analysis is considerably complicated by the frequent metabolic transformation into active (often common) metabolites and the particular pharmacokinetic properties of individual compounds.

In this situation, the discovery of high-affinity binding sites for BZs in 1977 and the introduction of a simple and reliable *in vitro* receptor binding assay were highly welcome. Great expectations were now attached to the study of structure–affinity relationship (SAfR). Together with *in vivo* tests, it became possible to detect compounds that act as prodrugs and exclude them from SAR studies. In addition, binding studies clearly showed that structures other than 1,4-BZs may act at the same receptor complex and have a similar mechanism of action (see Section 5.5.2).

Binding data for various compounds have been published. At the beginning, the authors stressed the good correlation between receptor activity *in vitro* and pharmacological activity in the animal tests most frequently used to screen for potential anxiolytic drugs (Squires and Braestrup, 1977; Möhler and Okada, 1977a,b). In the meantime, a large variety of structures have been screened; while the correlation more or less holds for BZ agonists, it cannot be extended to all receptor ligands. Indeed, binding to the receptor may lead to different biological effects (agonistic, inverse agonistic, antagonistic) (See Section 5.6).

Recently Braestrup and Nielsen (1983) published a compilation of binding data collected from different literature sources, containing also an impressive list of inactive agents.

In the following tables we present data collected in our laboratories with a view of assembling new SAR information.

Tables 1 to 11 contain (with few exceptions) agonists at the BZR. Table 1 shows the most "classical" type of 1,4-BZs and Tables 2 to 10 show different variations of this basic structure. Table 11 contains non-BZ ligands of the BZ receptor. Finally, antagonists, selective and inverse agonists are presented in Tables 12 and 13.

All IC_{50} values for [^{3}H]Diaz binding tabulated here have been determined in our laboratories over the last years by the method described by Möhler and Okada (1977). The antipentetrazol activities in the mouse, in contrast, have been investigated over more than two decades in different laboratories of Hoffmann-La Roche. Two fundamentally different methods were used: (1) Variants of the method of Everett and Richards (1944), where the dose necessary to prevent the convulsions produced by a fixed dose of pentetrazol in 50% of the animals was determined; (2) The method of Blum et al. (1973), where the preventive dose necessary for increasing by a factor of 2 the convulsive iv threshold dose of pentetrazol was established. With both methods, the compounds were administered orally to mice. Because these methods are not directly comparable and because they were slightly modified over the years, we prefer to present the results of the antipentetrazol tests only semiquantitatively: the signs + to + + + + indicate four orders of magnitude of potency, from slightly active to very active, for activities determined with the method of Everett and Richards (1944); the symbols × to × × × × refer to results obtained by the method of Blum et al. (1973).

Table 1 displays selected classical BZs with a hydrogen atom or a methyl

TABLE 1

"Classical" 7-substituted 1,4-BZs

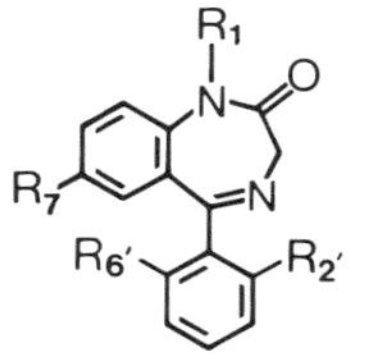

$R_1 = H$ or CH_3
$R_7 \neq H$

Name or code number	R_7	R_1	$R_{2'}$	$R_{6'}$	Inhibition of [^{3}H]Diaz binding [$IC_{50}(nM)$]	Antipentetrazol activity[a]
Ro 05-3061	F				40	0
Ro 05-4865	F	CH_3			17	+ + +
Ro 05-6820	F		F		7.4	+ + +
Ro 05-6822	F	CH_3	F		5.1	+ +
Nordazepam	Cl				9.4	+ + +
Diazepam	Cl	CH_3			8.1	+ + +
Ro 05-3367	Cl		F		2.0	+ + + +
Ro 07-3953	Cl		F	F	1.6	+ + + +

TABLE 1 (*Continued*)

Name or code number	R_7	R_1	$R_{2'}$	$R_{6'}$	Inhibition of [^{3}H]Diaz binding [$IC_{50}(nM)$]	Antipentetrazol activity[a]
Ro 07-4065	Cl	CH_3	F	F	4.1	+ + + +
Delorazepam	Cl		Cl		1.8	+ + + +
Ro 07-5193	Cl		Cl	F	3.0	+ + +
Ro 22-3294	Cl		Cl	Cl	7.0	+ + +
Ro 07-5220	Cl	CH_3	Cl	Cl	5.5	+ +
Ro 13-3780	Br	CH_3	F	F	2.4	× × × ×
Ro 07-9957	I	CH_3	F		2.9	+ + + +
Ro 05-2904	CF_3				13	+ + +
Ro 14-3074	N_3		F		5.3	× × × ×
Nitrazepam	NO_2				10	+ + + +
Ro 05-4435	NO_2		F		1.5	+ + + +
Flunitrazepam	NO_2	CH_3	F		3.8	+ + + +
Clonazepam	NO_2		Cl		1.8	+ + + +
Ro 05-4082	NO_2	CH_3	Cl		2.2	+ + + +
Ro 05-3590	NO_2		CF_3		3.5	+ + + +
Ro 20-7736	NHOH	CH_3	F		96	+ + +
Ro 05-3072	NH_2				386	0
Ro 05-4318	NH_2	CH_3			460	+ + +
Ro 20-1815	NH_2	CH_3	F		65	+ + +
Ro 05-4619	NH_2		Cl		75	0
Ro 05-3308	$NHCOCH_3$				> 1000	0
Ro 12-6377	$NHCONHCH_3$	CH_3	F		455	0
Ro 05-9090	CH_2NH_2	CH_3			> 1000	+
Ro 05-4528	CN	CH_3			380	+ + +
Ro 20-2541	CN	CH_3	F		30	+ + + +
Ro 20-2533	CH_2CH_3				36	+ +
Ro 20-5747	$CH{=}CH_2$				24	+
Ro 20-5397	CHO				43	0
Ro 20-3053	$COCH_3$		F		18	+ + +
Ro 05-3343	$SO_2N(CH_3)_2$				> 1000	

[a] In all the tables, the symbols + to + + + + indicate activities determined by the method of Everett and Richards (1944); the symbols × to × × × × refer to results obtained by the method of Blum *et al.* (1973).

group in position 1 (R_1) and different substituents in positions 7 (R_7) and 2' ($R_{2'}$). From these data, the following features may be pointed out:

Compounds bearing in position 7 electronegative substituents such as Cl, Br, I, NO_2, and also CF_3 or N_3, have a relatively high pharmacological potency *in vivo* compared to their binding affinity *in vitro*. This is particularly true for the group of the 7-nitro derivatives and their most potent representative, flunitrazepam. In most cases, the size of the substituent in position 7 does not seem to play a critical role, since Cl, Br, I, and N_3 derivatives have very similar binding affinities.

On the other hand, the strongly electronegative substituent fluorine is surprisingly weak (compare, e.g., Ro 05-3061 with nordazepam or Ro 05-6820 with Ro 05-3367). This fact is in evident contrast with the substitution in 2', where F and Cl provide very similar potency.

The high pharmacological *in vivo* potency of the 7-cyano derivative Ro 05-4528 contrasts with its low *in vitro* binding affinity, suggesting the formation of an active metabolite.

Table 2A shows unconventional substitutions at ring A. A striking observation is made with ring A-unsubstituted compounds: derivatives monosubstituted with F or Cl in position 2' afford compounds virtually as potent *in vitro* and *in vivo* as those with the same substitution in position 7 [compare, e.g., Ro 05-4520 with Ro 05-4865 (Table 1) or Ro 05-4608 with Diaz].

TABLE 2

A. "Classical" 1,4-BZs: Variations on ring A

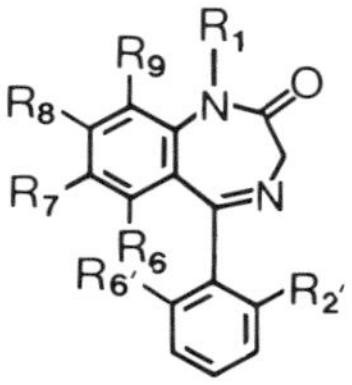

Code number	R_6	R_7	R_8	R_9	R_1	$R_{2'}$	$R_{6'}$	Inhibition of [³H]Diaz binding [$IC_{50}(nM)$]	Antipentetrazol activity
Ro 05-2921								350	‡
Ro 05-4336						F		21	+ +
Ro 07-4419						F	F	19	+
Ro 05-4520					CH_3	F		14	+ + +
Ro 05-4608					CH_3	Cl		3.8	+
Ro 05-3546	Cl							320	+
Ro 13-0699	Cl				CH_3	F		150	‡
Ro 07-6198			Cl			F	F	28	+
Ro 20-8895		Cl	CH_3			F		19	+
Ro 13-0593				Cl	CH_3	F		72	‡
Ro 13-0882	Cl		Cl		CH_3	F		300	‡

TABLE 2 (*Continued*)

Ro 22-6762	Cl	Cl		CH₃			40	++
Ro 20-8065	Cl	Cl			F		3.6	+++
Ro 20-8552	CH₃	Cl			F		14	0
Ro 05-2750	Cl		Cl				37	+++
Ro 07-3609	Cl		CH₃				52	++
Ro 14-2312	NH₂		Cl	CH₃	F		> 1000	0

B. 1,4-Diazepines condensed with a heterocycle

Name or code number	Structure	Inhibition of [³H]Diaz binding [IC₅₀(n*M*)]	Antipentetrazol activity

Thieno[2,3-*e*][1,4]diazepines

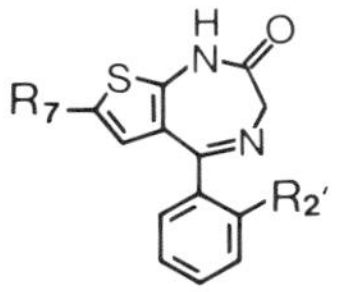

	R₇	R₂′		
Ro 11-8125		Cl	37	
Ro 08-6739	Cl		70	0
Ro 08-9212	Cl	Cl	3.9	×××

Thieno[3,2-*e*][1,4]diazepine

Ro 10-2643	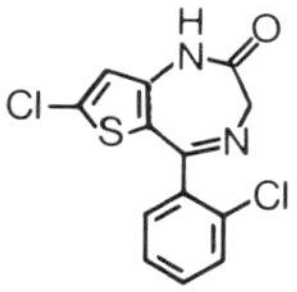 9.4	++

Pyrrolo[3,4-*e*][1,4]diazepine Premazepam	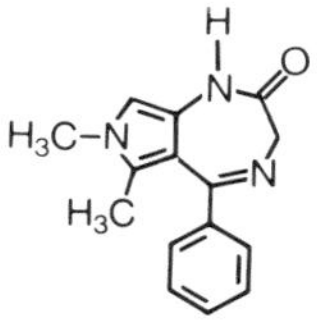 170	++

The monosubstitution with chlorine at the different positions of ring A gives rise to the following rank order for increasing affinity: 6 < 9 < 8 < 7. It is particularly important to note here the poor influence of a chlorine in position 6: Ro 05-3546 is only slightly more active than Ro 05-2921, but Ro 13-0699 is much weaker than Ro 05-4520.

Table 2B presents some 1,4-diazepine derivatives in which ring A has been replaced by a heterocycle. The monosubstituted thieno[2,3-*e*][1,4]diazepines, Ro 11-8125 and Ro 08-6739, have rather weak binding affinities *in vitro,* compared to the corresponding 1,4-BZs, Ro 05-4608 (Table 2A) and nordazepam. The difference is even more pronounced for pharmacological potency *in vivo:* Ro 08-6739 is inactive in the antipentetrazol test. In contrast, the disubstituted derivative, Ro 08-9212, as well as the isomeric thieno[3,2-*e*][1,4]diazepine, Ro 10-2643, are quite potent *in vitro* and *in vivo.* Premazepam is the prototype of pyrrolo[3,4-*e*][1,4]diazepines. Its affinity to the BZR and its anticonvulsant activity are rather low. Corsico *et al.* (1982) have proposed that premazepam is a potential antianxiety agent which antagonizes some sedative effects of diazepam in animals, thus behaving as a partial agonist.

Table 3 describes the influence of a variety of substituents R_1 larger than methyl in the classical 1,4-BZs. In all cases, the affinity of the derivatives carrying a side chain is smaller than that of the parent compound with R = H. However, even relatively long side chains on nitrogen 1 induce only a moderate decrease in affinity. This fact has been exploited for BZR purification by using Ro 07-1986, attached through a spacer chain to agarose, as a ligand in affinity chromatography (Tallman and Gallager, 1979; Sigel *et al.,* 1982).

In contrast, a bulky lipophilic substituent, such as *tert*-butyl, drastically reduces the affinity to the receptor and the activity *in vivo.* The same is the case for the acidic carboxymethyl substituent present in Ro 07-5096.

Most of the other compounds of this list are pharmacologically more potent *in vivo* than could be expected from their binding affinities: this points to the likely transformation into metabolites with higher affinity. Indeed, N-1-unsubstituted metabolites have been found, e.g., in the case of prazepam, pinazepam, and flurazepam and its metabolites, Ro 07-1986 and Ro 07-2750.

Table 4: The importance of the C=N double bond in position 4,5 in the classic series is demonstrated by the examples in Table 4A: all compounds with a C—N single bond are inactive *in vitro.* The activity found *in vivo* is probably due to a partial metabolic dehydrogenation to a C=N double bond. The *N*-oxides chlordiazepoxide, and its metabolite demoxepam, shown in Table 4B, have both a relatively low *in vitro* affinity compared to their *in vivo* activity. They have to be considered at least partially as prodrugs of nordazepam.

Table 5 shows 1,4-BZs in which the phenyl ring in position 5 has been replaced by other substituents. The first compound presented, Ro 05-3663, carries a methyl group instead of the phenyl ring. It is a particular case, since it is inactive in the [³H]Diaz binding test, displaces α-dihydropicrotoxinin (O'Brien

TABLE 3

"Classical" 1,4-BZs with large substituents on N-1

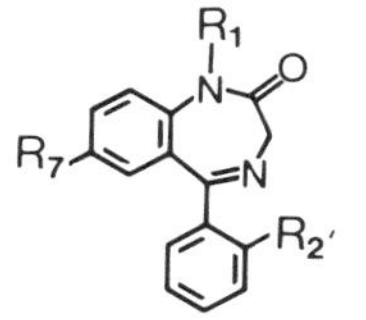

$R_1 \neq H$ or CH_3

Name or code number	R_1	R_7	$R_{2'}$	Inhibition of [^{3}H]Diaz binding [$IC_{50}(nM)$]	Antipentetrazol activity
Ro 17-2221	$CH_2CH_2NH_2$			260	
Ro 08-3026	$CH_2OCH_2CH_2NH_2$	Cl		63	0
Halazepam	CH_2CF_3	Cl		92	$\times\times\times$
Pinazepam	$CH_2C\equiv CH$	Cl		92.5	$\times\times\times$
Prazepam	CH_4-Cyclopropyl	Cl		110	$++$
Ro 06-9098	CH_2OCH_3	NO_2		430	$\times\times\times\times$
Ro 20-1310	$C(CH_3)_3$	Cl		620	0
Ro 05-7094	$CH(CH_3)CONHCH_3$	Cl		> 1000	$+$
Ro 07-1986	$CH_2CH_2NH_2$	Cl	F	8.3	$+++$
Flurazepam	$CH_2CH_2N(C_2H_5)_2$	Cl	F	14.8	$+++$
Ro 07-2750	CH_2CH_2OH	Cl	F	24.5	$++++$
Irazepine	CH_2CH_2NCS	Cl	F	33[a]	
Ro 08-9013	$CH_2CH_2OCH_2CONH_2$	Cl	F	42.5	$\times\times\times\times$
Ro 10-3580	$CH_2CH(OH)CH_2OH$	Cl	F	140	$\times\times\times$
Ro 07-9238	$CH_2CH_2OPO_3Na$	Cl	F	130	$\times\times\times\times$
Ro 22-4683	$C(CH_3)_3$	NO_2	Cl	300	0
Ro 07-5096	CH_2COOH	Cl	F	> 1000	$++$

[a]Irazepine is claimed to bind irreversibly to the receptor (Rice *et al.*, 1979; see Section 5.13.1).

and Spirt, 1980), and is a convulsant. Hence its activity is not mediated by the BZ receptor.

The binding values of tetrazepam, of its metabolite desmethyltetrazepam, and of compound Ro 05-3328 show that hydrogenation of ring C reduces the affinity to the receptor by a factor of 4 and 10, respectively. The reduction of anticonvulsant activity is even more marked: in the antipentetrazol test, Ro 05-3328 has only about one-seventieth the potency of nordazepam.

5.5.1.2 Medazepam, 4,5-annelated and ring B-open 1,4-BZ prodrugs.
Some characteristic prodrugs showing a low binding affinity *in vitro* but a high pharmacological activity *in vivo*, have already been encountered in Tables 3, 4,

TABLE 4

"Classical" 1,4-benzodiazepines: Variation of the 4,5-double bond
A. 4,5-Dihydro derivatives

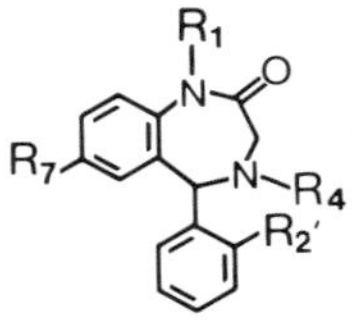

Code number	R_7	R_1	$R_{2'}$	R_4	Inhibition of [^{3}H]Diaz binding [$IC_{50}(nM)$]	Antipentetrazol activity
Ro 05-3395					> 1000	—
Ro 05-2181	Cl				> 5000	+ + +
Ro 05-2881	Cl	CH_3			> 1000	+ +
Ro 05-3636	Cl	CH_3	F	CH_3	> 1000	+ + +
Ro 15-8852	NO_2		Cl	CH_3	726	× × ×

B. N-Oxides

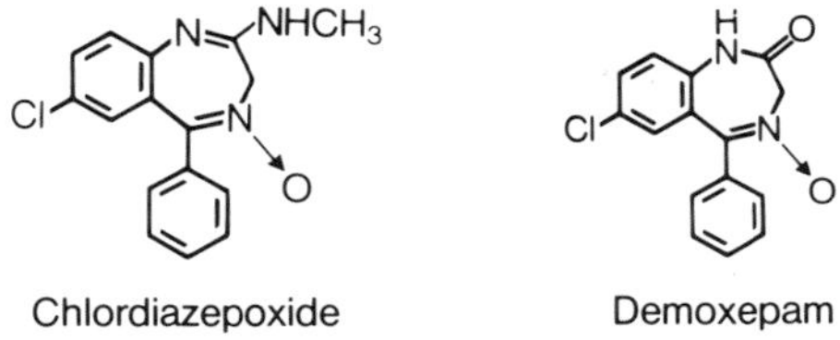

Chlordiazepoxide   Demoxepam

	Inhibition of [^{3}H]Diaz binding [$IC_{50}(nM)$]	Antipentetrazol activity
Chlordiazepoxide	352	+ +
Demoxepam	310	+ + +

and 5. In Table 6, further examples are presented. Medazepam has just about 1/100 the binding affinity of Diaz. This great difference demonstrates the important part played by a carbonyl group in position 2 of the classical BZs, which is present in Diaz but absent in medazepam. The pharmacological activity *in vivo* of medazepam is due to oxidative metabolism, resulting in the formation of diazepam and/or nordazepam.

The 4,5-annelated BZs, ketazolam, oxazolam, and cloxazolam, all have IC_{50} values in [^{3}H]Diaz binding higher than 1000 nM. This is in good accordance with the low affinity found for the 4,5-dihydro derivatives of Table 5A. It is known that the additional ring is rapidly removed *in vivo* by metabolic transformation:

TABLE 5

1,4-BZs: Replacement of the phenyl ring in position 5

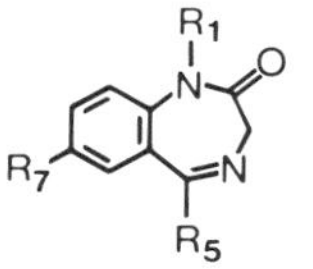

Name or code number	R_7	R_1	R_5	Inhibition of [³H]Diaz binding [$IC_{50}(nM)$]	Antipentetrazol activity
Ro 05-3663			CH_3	> 1000	Convulsive
Desmethyltetrazepam	Cl		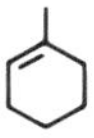 (cyclohexenyl)	34	+ +
Tetrazepam	Cl	CH_3	(cyclohexenyl)	34	+ +
Ro 05-3328	Cl		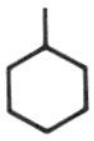 (cyclohexyl)	87	+
Bromazepam	Br		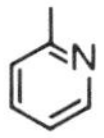 (2-pyridyl)	18	+ + + +
Ro 05-5605	Cl		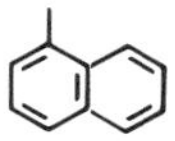 (naphthyl)	290	0
Ro 05-3580	Cl		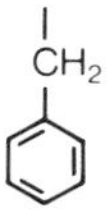 (CH_2-phenyl)	> 1000	+

ketazolam is transformed into diazepam and nordazepam (Eberts *et al.*, 1977), oxazolam into nordazepam, and cloxazolam into delorazepam (Murata *et al.*, 1973; Lavène *et al.*, 1980).

The derivatives with opened ring B, Ro 03-7355 and Ro 31-0214, have been deliberately designed as prodrugs: the peptide bond HN-R_4 is rapidly cleaved *in vivo* by peptidases, liberating the intermediates with a terminal NH_2 group, which rapidly cyclize to diazepam or bromazepam, respectively (Hassal *et al.*, 1977). The same principle has been applied for 45-0088 S, a prodrug of de-

TABLE 6

Prodrugs

A. Medazepam and 4,5-annelated 1,4-benzodiazepines

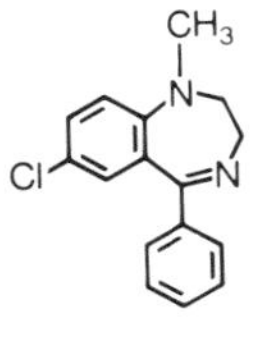

| Medazepam | Oxazolam   R = CH$_3$ Y = H | Ketazolam |
| | Cloxazolam R = H   Y = Cl | |

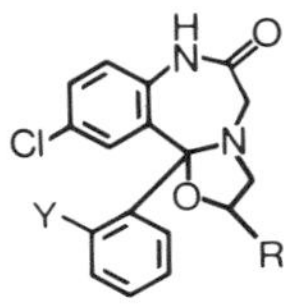

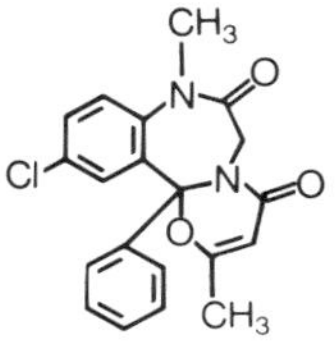

Name	Inhibition of [^{3}H]Diaz binding [IC$_{50}$(nM)]	Antipentetrazol activity
Medazepam	870	× × ×
Oxazolam	> 1000	× ×
Cloxazolam	> 1000	× × × ×
Ketazolam	> 1000	× × ×

B. Ring B-open 1,4 BZs

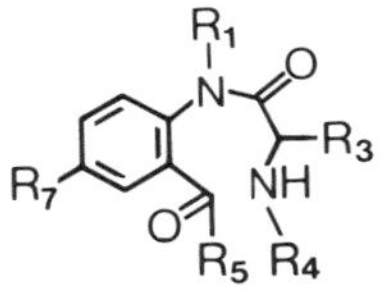

Code number	R$_7$	R$_1$	R$_3$	R$_4$	R$_5$	Inhibition of [^{3}H]Diaz binding [IC$_{50}$(nM)]	Antipentetrazol activity
Ro 07-4668	Cl			H	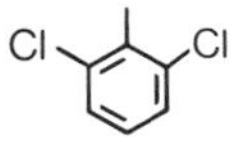 (2,6-dichlorophenyl)	> 1000	0
Ro 11-3129	NO$_2$		(S)-CH$_3$	H	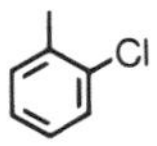 (2-chlorophenyl)	6.5	× × ×
Ro 03-7355	Cl	CH$_3$		COCH(CH$_2$)$_4$NH$_2$ NH$_2$	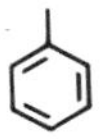 (phenyl)	420	× × ×

TABLE 6 (*Continued*)

Ro 31-0214	Br	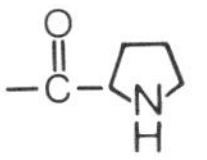 $-\overset{O}{\underset{}{C}}-\langle\underset{H}{N}\rangle$	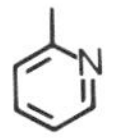 (pyridyl structure)	> 1000	× × ×
45-0088-S	Cl	$COCH_2NH_2$	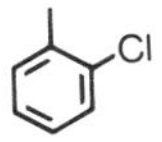 (o-chlorophenyl structure)	—	+ + + +[a]

[a]Value taken from Hirose *et al.* (1981).

lorazepam (Fujimoto *et al.*, 1980a,b; Hirose *et al.*, 1981). Whereas 45-0088 S is lacking receptor affinity *in vitro*, it is about four times more potent than diazepam in inhibiting [^{3}H]Flu binding *in vivo* (Wong and Bymaster, 1983).

Ro 11-3129 is not a true prodrug and Ro 07-4668 is an inactive compound. They are mentioned here to illustrate the importance of a closed 1,4-diazepine ring for activity: the ring open compound Ro 11-3129 is stable only as a salt; in neutral solution, it cyclizes rapidly to meclonazepam (Table 7). The IC_{50} value of 5.1 nM found here illustrates that this cyclization occurs even during the performance of the binding test *in vitro*. In contrast, the compound Ro 07-4668 cannot cyclize to the corresponding BZ, Ro 22-3294 (Table 1) because of steric hindrance by the *o,o*-dichloro substitution of R_5, and therefore is devoid of activity *in vitro* and *in vivo* (Fryer *et al.*, 1982; Fryer, 1983).

5.5.1.3 Stereochemical considerations. Most of the BZs in therapeutic use have no chirality center; however, their seven-membered ring B may adopt one of two possible, energetically preferred boat conformations, i.e., *a* and *b,* which are enantiomeric (mirror images) of each other (Fig. 10). NMR studies showed that, at room temperature, the two conformations easily interconvert (Linscheid and Lehn, 1967). It is therefore impossible to predict a priori which of the two will be present when bound to the receptor complex. In order to prove the stereospecificity of the interaction with the receptor, a few examples of enantiomeric pairs possessing a chirality center at position 3 have been tested, see, e.g., Table 7: (*S*)-Ro 11-6896/(*R*)-Ro 11-6893 and (*S*)-meclonazepam/(*R*)-Ro 11-3624. The *in vitro* and *in vivo* activity was restricted to the enantiomers possessing the S configuration.

The introduction of the methyl group in position 3 results in a stabilization of conformation *a* for ring B of the S-enantiomers and to that of the opposite conformation *b* for the R-enantiomers, the methyl group being preferentially located in a pseudoequatorial position.

This conformation is present in the crystalline state (Blount *et al.*, 1983), but also in solution as shown for the S-enantiomer of 3-methyl-diazepam by Sunjić *et*

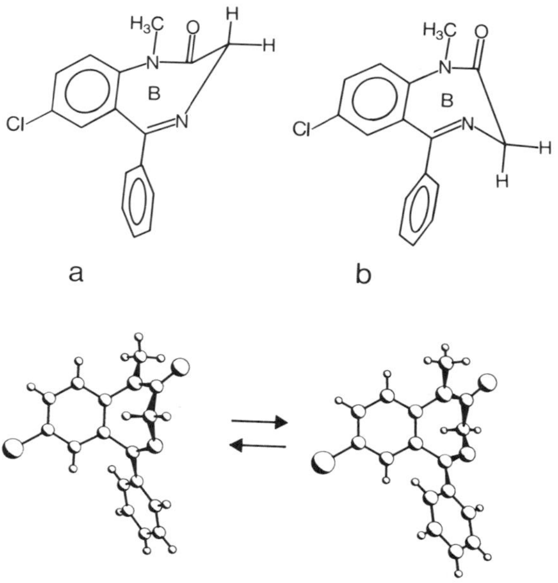

FIG. 10. The two enantiomeric conformations of diazepam.

al. (1979). The same authors could rule out a possible spontaneous conformational interconversion at 35°C, as observed, e.g., for the 3-unsubstituted compounds (see above).

These facts indicate that it is the conformation of ring B which is determinant for the affinity for the BZR and not the absolute configuration as such.

The study of conformationally rigid structure starting from BZ antagonists eventually provided conclusive evidence for the importance of the conformation for receptor affinity (see Section 5.6.1.2).

Table 7 assembles a number of 3-substituted, chiral 1,4-BZs, including six commercially available drugs.

Although it is generally well established that the affinity of BZs for the receptor is enantioselective (see above), none of the commercial drugs is available in enantiomerically pure form, but only as racemate. Of course, most of these drugs are 3-hydroxy derivatives (oxazepam, temazepam, and lorazepam), which are prone to racemize because of the easily occurring hydrolytic opening to a tautomeric intermediate achiral aldehyde. Reclosure of the intermediate leads to the racemic compound. The enantiomers are therefore difficult to isolate. The only successful optical resolution of oxazepam reported in the literature was achieved by chromatography on a chiral column (Blaschke and Markgraf, 1980). The ester oxazepam hemisuccinate has been resolved (Corbella *et al.*,

TABLE 7

"Classical" 1,4-BZs substituted in position 3

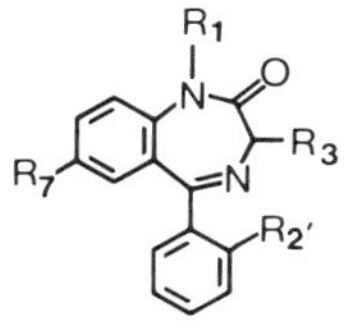

Name or code number	R_7	R_1	R_3	$R_{2'}$	Inhibition of [³H]Diaz binding [$IC_{50}(nM)$]	Antipen-tetrazol activity
Ro 11-4878	Cl		(S)-CH₃	F	3.5	××××
Meclonazepam	NO₂		(S)-CH₃	Cl	1.2	××××
Ro 11-6896	NO₂	CH₃	(S)-CH₃	F	7	××××
Ro 11-3624	NO₂		(R)-CH₃	Cl	> 1000	0
Ro 11-6893	NO₂	CH₃	(R)-CH₃	F	> 1000	0
Ro 07-4532	Cl	CH₃	(CH₃)₂		> 1000	0
Ro 06-7263	Cl	Cl	rac. CH₃ᵃ		49	+ +
Oxazepam	Cl		rac. OH		18	×××
Temazepam	Cl	CH₃	rac. OH		16	×××
Lorazepam	Cl		rac. OH	Cl	3.5	××××
Oxazepam hemisuccinate	Cl		rac.-OCOCH₂CH₂COONa		330	×××
Camazepam	Cl	CH₃	rac. OCON(CH₃)₂		900	
Ro 20-7078	Cl	CH₃	rac. Cl	F	5.3	+ + + +
Clorazepate	Cl		rac. COOK		59	×××

ᵃrac., Racemic.

1973) and the S-enantiomer was found to be more potent in different respects, i.e., in binding tests (Waddington and Owen, 1978), animal investigations (de Angelis *et al.*, 1972), and clinical investigations (Lescovelli *et al.*, 1976).

From these and other publications, the prodrug nature of oxazepam hemisuccinate becomes evident and complicates the interpretation, because of the already mentioned optical instability of the enantiomers. Camazepam as well as clorazepate have also to be regarded as prodrugs. In the latter case, the IC_{50} value of 59 nM in [³H]Diaz binding must be considered with caution, since chlorazepate is known to be easily decarboxylated into nordazepam, possibly even under the experimental conditions of the binding test.

5.5.1.4 1,5-BZs. *Table 8:* The 1,5-BZ derivative clobazam and its metabolite desmethylclobazam have an *in vivo* pharmacological profile similar to that of the 1,4-BZs. As shown in Table 8, they bind to the BZR. However, their *in vitro*

TABLE 8

1,5-Benzodiazepines

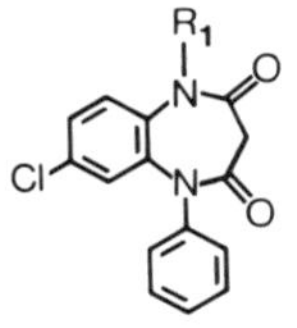

Name	R_1	Inhibition of [³H]Diaz binding [$IC_{50}(nM)$]	Antipentetrazol activity
Clobazam	CH_3	130	× × ×
Desmethylclobazam	H	210	× ×

affinity appears too low to account for the *in vivo* pharmacological properties. As an explanation, Schacht and Baecker (1982) postulated that the anxiolytic activity was mediated by the particular affinity to a subtype of the BZR, the thermostable BZ_3R (see Section 5.21.5).

5.5.1.5 1,2-Annelated 1,4-BZs. *Table 9:* The condensation of an additional ring on the 1,2-bond of the classical BZ nucleus resulted in very interesting new compounds, which stimulated new chemical and biological work on the BZs. Among the various heterocycles which have been fused in this position, *s*-triazole and imidazole are of prime interest: three triazolo- and two imidazo-BZs have been commercialized (estazolam, triazolam, alprazolam, midazolam, loprazolam), at least four others (adinazolam, U-43465 F, etizolam, brotizolam) are in clinical investigations.

Concerning the SAR and the SAfR of the 1,2-annelated compounds, the following observations can be made: The presence of electronegative substituents in the "classical" positions, i.e., of the substituents R_8 and R_2, in the triazolo- or the imidazo-BZ series, and of the substituents R_2 and $R_{2'}$ in the thienotriazolodiazepine series, is much less important for activity than in the "classical" series. In the triazolo-BZ series, the halogen-free U-31,957 is equipotent to Diaz and only about six times less active in the antipentetrazol test than the monohalogenated derivative alprazolam (Rudzik *et al.*, 1973), whereas in the "classical" series, the halogen-free Ro 05-2921 (Table 2A) has less than 1/130 the potency of nordazepam (Table 1) (Sternbach *et al.*, 1968). In the thienotriazolodiazepine series (Table 9B), the slight differences between the high

TABLE 9

1,2-Annelated 1,4-diazepines

A. s-Triazolo[4,3-a][1,4]benzodiazepines

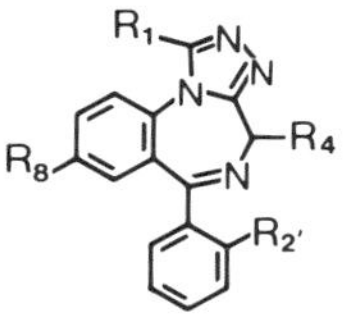

Name or code number	R_8	R_1	R_4	$R_{2'}$	Inhibition of [³H]Diaz binding [$IC_{50}(nM)$]	Antipen-tetrazol activity
-31957		CH_3				+++[a]
-35005		CH_3		Cl	4.3	++++
stazolam	Cl				8.5	++++
lprazolam	Cl	CH_3			20	++++
riazolam	Cl	CH_3		Cl	4.0	++++
-Hydroxytriazolam	Cl	$HOCH_2$			4.2	
dinazolam	Cl	$(CH_3)_2NCH_2$			135	××××
-43465 F	Cl	$(CH_3)_2N(CH_2)_2$			11.4	××
o 11-5073	Cl	CH_3	(S)-CH_3	F	3.3	××××
o 11-6679	NO_2	CH_3	(S)-CH_3	F	4.0	××××
o 11-5074	NO_2	CH_3	(S)-CH_3	Cl	3.4	××××
o 11-5242	NO_2	CH_3	(R)-CH_3	Cl	1500	0

B. Thieno[3,2-f]s-triazolo[4,3-a][1,4]diazepines

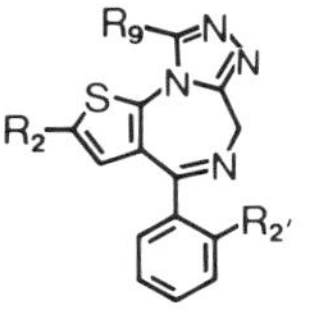

Name or ode number	R_2	R_9	$R_{2'}$	Inhibition of [³H]Diaz binding [$IC_{50}(nM)$]	Antipen-tetrazol activity
o 17-4582		CH_3	Cl	3.5	
tizolam	C_2H_5	CH_3	Cl	3.1	××××
o 11-1465	Cl	CH_3	Cl	1.4	××××

(continued)

TABLE 9 (*Continued*)

Name or code number	R_2	R_9	$R_{2'}$	Inhibition of $[^3H]$Diaz binding $[IC_{50}(nM)]$	Antipentetrazol activity
Brotizolam	Br	CH_3	Cl	1.2	××××
Ro 14-1636	I	CH_3	Cl	1.5	××××
Ro 11-7800	Cl	H_2NCH_2	Cl	2.9	××××

C. Imidazo[1,5-*a*][1,4]benzodiazepines

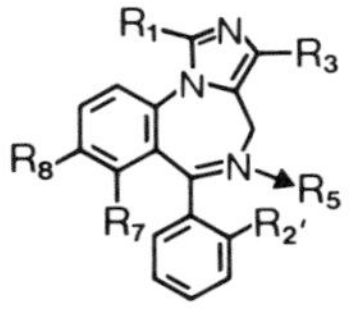

Name or code number	R_8	R_7	R_1	R_3	R_5	$R_{2'}$	Inhibition of $[^3H]$Diaz binding $[IC_{50}(nM)]$	Antipentetrazol activity
Midazolam	Cl		CH_3			F	4.8	×××
α-Hydroxymidazolam	Cl		$HOCH_2$			F	4.5	××
Ro 15-8670	Cl			$COOC_2H_5$			15	××
Ro 16-0529		Cl		$COOC(CH_3)_3$			14	0
Ro 21-5205	Cl			$COOCH_3$		F	7.4	+++
Ro 22-1892	Cl			$COOCH(CH_3)_2$	O	F	12	++
Ro 22-0992	Cl			COOH		Cl	13	0
Ro 21-8137	Cl			$CONH_2$		F	3.5	++++
Ro 21-8384	Cl			$CONH_2$		Cl	3.8	++++
Ro 21-8482	Cl		$(CH_3)_2NCH_2$	$CONH_2$		Cl	26	++++

D. Imidazo[1,2-*a*][1,4]benzodiazepine

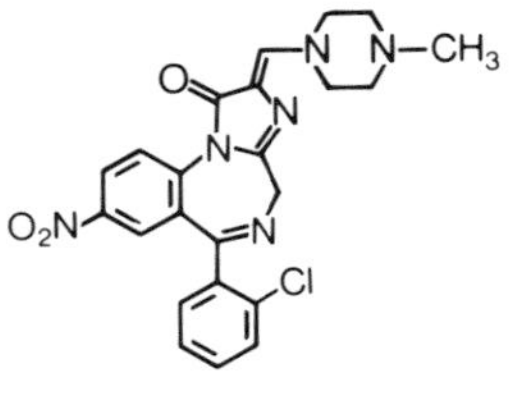

Loprazolam	6.3	××××

---

[a] Value taken form Rudzik *et al.* (1973).

in vitro affinities of the monochlorinated and the dihalogenated derivatives contrast with the marked differences in the nonannelated series (Table 2B). Similar comments apply to the imidazo[1,5-*a*][1,4]benzodiazepine series (Table 9C). As examples, Ro 16-0529 and Ro 21-5205 have binding values differing only by a factor of 2, whereas the IC_{50} of the corresponding nonannelated BZs, Ro 05-3546 (Table 2A) and Ro 05-3367 (Table 1), are 320 and 2, respectively. Of interest is also the good *in vitro* affinity of the *N*-oxide Ro 22-1892, which is only slightly less than that of related compounds unsubstituted at N-5.

From these examples the following trend becomes evident: annelation on position 1,2 with triazole or imidazole markedly increases the binding affinity to the BZR for compounds having a low affinity, whereas only slight increases in affinity are observed for already potent compounds.

Concerning the substitution on the additional ring, the following points may be noticed: in position 1 (respectively 9 for the thienotriazolodiazepine ring system), the substitution by rather small substituents like methyl, hydroxymethyl, or aminomethyl has only little influence, if any, on the affinity *in vitro*. In contrast, the introduction of a dimethylaminomethyl side chain reduces the affinity by a factor of 7 to 15, as exemplified by adinazolam and Ro 21-8482; however, the higher homolog of adinazolam, U-43,465 F, has again a substantial affinity to the BZR. The introduction of an ester, an amide, or a carboxylic acid group into position 3 of the imidazole ring has only a minimal influence on the binding values. Whereas the IC_{50} values of most of the compounds shown in Table 9A, B, and C are somewhat similar (from about 1.2 to about 15), the *in vivo* pharmacological activities differ much more. Some compounds, e.g., triazolam, brotizolam, Ro 11-1465, Ro 11-7800, and Ro 21-8384, are among the most potent known in the antipentetrazol test; others (e.g., U-43665 F, α-hydroxytriazolam, α-hydroxymidazolam, Ro 15-8670, Ro 16-0529) are markedly weaker or even inactive. The reason for these differences has not been elucidated: very rapid metabolic inactivation or difficulty to cross the blood–brain barrier may be involved in some cases, but probably do not explain all the discrepancies. Indeed, among the 1,2-annelated diazepines, quite different pharmacological profiles were found. Some compounds with very pronounced sedative properties have been commercialized or are in development as sleep inducers (estazolam, triazolam, brotizolam, midazolam, loprazolam). In comparison to the classical BZs, a particular and very interesting property of some of these compounds is their very short terminal elimination half-life in man, which is due to the proneness to metabolic oxidation of the 1-methyl group on the triazole or imidazole ring (Eberts *et al.*, 1981; Jochemsen *et al.*, 1983a,b; Heizmann *et al.*, 1983). Moreover, the imidazole ring of midazolam is sufficiently basic to form water-soluble salts, allowing for the preparation of a stable, aqueous injectable solution for use in anesthesiology. Loprazolam (Table 9D), a representative of the imidazo[1,2-*a*][1,4]BZs, another type of 1,2-annelated BZ, has recently reached the market as a hypnotic. Its affinity for the BZR is close to that of Diaz (Hunt *et al.*, 1979). For the two 8-deschloro-triazolo-BZs U-31,957 and U-35,005, striking changes in the activity profile as compared to the corresponding nonannelated BZ, have been described by Rudzik *et al.* (1973). In the anticonvulsant and anticonflict tests, these compounds were at least as active as Diaz; however, they were very weak in tests indicative of sedation. Among compounds selected for clinical use because of their potential anxiolytic properties, Ro 21-8384 is highly potent in the rat conflict test (Sepinwall and Cook, 1980). Alprazolam has an EEG profile in man more similar to that of an anxiolytic than that of a hypnotic (Itil *et al.*, 1973), but it has been claimed to have also antidepressant properties (review: Dawson *et al.*, 1984). Antidepressant activity has been claimed in particular for two compounds carrying a basic side chain in position 1, namely adinazolam and U-43465 F (Hester *et al.*, 1980; Thiébot *et al.*, 1982).

It is very likely that for the 1,2-annelated compounds the configuration of the seven-membered ring plays the same important role as in the nonannelated series. Indeed, among some chiral derivatives carrying a methyl group in position 4 (Table 9A), only those having an S configuration are biologically active.

5.5.1.6 1- and 2-Benzazepines. *Table 10A:* The 1-benzazepine lactams Ro 14-1359, Ro 15-8867, and the 2-benzazepine Ro 22-1274 have a relatively low affinity for the BZR when compared to the "classical" 1,4-BZs, such as Ro 05-3367 and clonazepam (Table 1).

As shown in Table 10, fusion of an additional ring in position 1,2 of 1-benzazepines or in the corresponding position 4,5 of 2-benzazepines, leads to compounds with markedly increased activity. In the series of annelated 1-benzazepines, the SAR and SAfR are somewhat more complex than for the corresponding 1,4-BZ. The additional triazole ring confers considerable *in vitro* binding and *in vivo* pharmacological activity to the compounds, provided they have two electronegative substituents R_8 and $R_{2'}$ (Borer *et al.*, 1983); surprisingly, the 5,6-dihydro derivative Ro 14-0609 is also quite active. In contrast, the unsubstituted triazolo-1-benzazepine, Ro 14-7187, is virtually inactive.

The annelation with an imidazole ring provides high binding affinity only when an ester or an amide group is present in position 3, e.g., Ro 14-5568 has an IC_{50} of only 232 nM, whereas the 3-substituted derivatives all have binding values below 20 nM. When R_3 is an ester group, electronegative substitutents R_8 and $R_{2'}$ become unnecessary: their absence even increases the affinity *in vitro*. *In vivo*, however, all these compounds are inactive in the antipentetrazol test. The unsubstituted derivatives Ro 15-2201 and Ro 15-0791 show a slight antagonistic activity.

Table 10B: Two types of annelated 2-benzazepines are presented in Table 10B: pyrimido[5,4-*d*][2]benzazepines and [1,2,3] triazolo-[4,5-*d*][2]benzazepines. The pyrimido-2-benzazepines shown have a high binding affinity *in vitro*

TABLE 10

1-Benzazepines and 2-benzazepines

Code number	Structure	Inhibition of [^{3}H]Diaz binding [IC_{50}(nM)]	Antipentetrazol activity

A. 1-Benzazepines

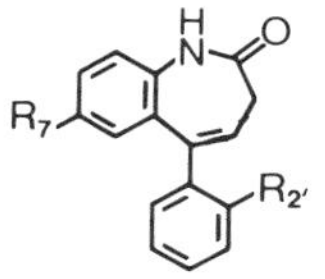

	R_7	$R_{2'}$		
Ro 14-1359	Cl	F	70	×
Ro 15-8867	NO$_2$	Cl	25	×

s-Triazolo[4,3-a][1]benzazepines

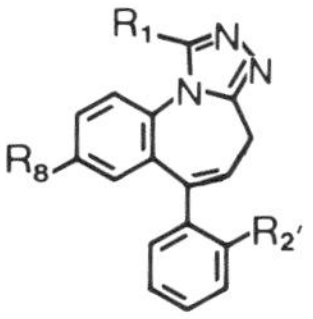

	R_8	R_1	$R_{2'}$		
Ro 14-7187		CH$_3$		410	0
Ro 13-9868	Cl	CH$_3$		42	× ×
Ro 14-5921	Cl		F	19	× × ×
Ro 14-0304	Cl	CH$_3$	F	6.5	× × ×
Ro 14-2652	Cl	H$_2$NCH$_2$	F	5.6	× × ×
Ro 15-9270	NO$_2$	CH$_3$	Cl	5	× × ×

Ro 14-0609	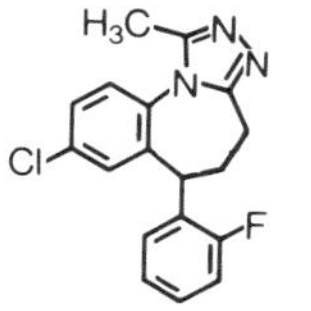	24.4	+ +

(*continued*)

TABLE 10 (*Continued*)

Imidazo[1,5-*a*][1]benzazepines

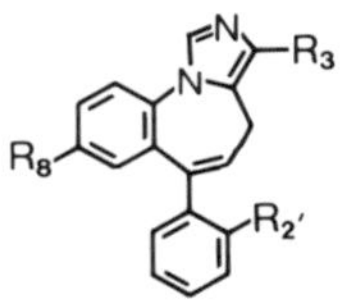

	R_8	R_3	$R_{2'}$		
Ro 15-2201		$COOCH_3$		1.5	0
Ro 15-0791		$COOC_2H_5$		2.5	0
Ro 15-2200		$COOC_2H_5$	F	4.2	0
Ro 14-3929	Cl	$COOC_2H_5$	F	16	0
Ro 14-3930	Cl	$CONH_2$	F	15	0
Ro 14-5568	Cl		F	230	0

B. 2-Benzazepines

Ro 22-1274   75

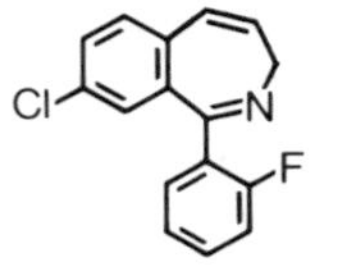

Pyrimido[5,4-*d*][2]benzazepines

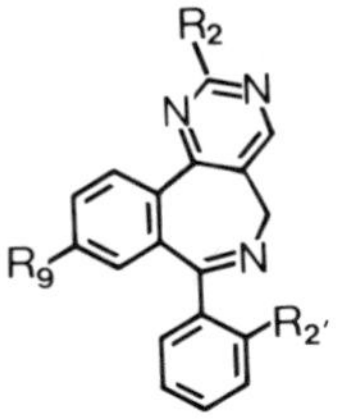

	R_9	R_2	$R_{2'}$		
Ro 22-1251	Cl	CH_3		11	
Ro 22-1366	Cl	CH_3	F	4.0	
Ro 22-2038	Cl	NH_2	F	2.8	+++
Ro 22-3245	Cl		Cl	2.8	++++

TABLE 10 (*Continued*)

[1,2,3]Triazolo[4,5-*d*][2]benzazepines

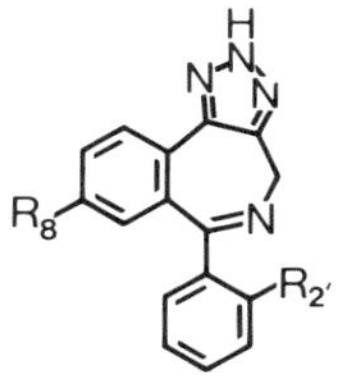

	R_8	$R_{2'}$		
Ro 22-3148			420^a	0
Ro 22-3147		Cl	5.2^a	0
Ro 22-0780	Cl		11	+++
Ro 22-2466	Cl	F	1.9	+++
Ro 22-2468	Cl	Cl	2.5	+++

[a]Values taken from Trybulski *et al.* (1983a).

as well as a high pharmacological activity *in vivo* (Trybulski *et al.*, 1983b). In the series of the triazolo-2-benzazepines, only the compounds substituted by at least one halogen have a substantial affinity for the BZR; the halogen-free Ro 22-3148 is a very weak inhibitor of Diaz binding. In this respect, the triazolo-2-benzazepine series resembles the series of "classical" BZs or of triazolo-1-benzazepines, but differs clearly from the triazolo-1,4-benzodiazepines (Table 9A) and the imidazo-1-benzazepine-3-carboxylates (Table 10A). *In vivo*, only the triazolo-2-benzazepines bearing an electronegative substituent in position 8 are active in the antipentetrazol test. An antagonistic profile has been ascribed to Ro 22-3147 (Trybulski *et al.*, 1983a).

5.5.2 Other Structures: Cyclopyrrolones, 2-Phenylquinolines, and Triazolopyridazines

The number of non-BZ structures displaying BZ agonistic properties *in vivo* and having a reasonable affinity for BZR is still rather small.

Of the compounds shown in *Table 11*, the representatives of the cyclopyrrolone series, zopiclone and suriclone, exhibit the highest affinity for BZRs. Suriclone in particular ranges among the most potent ligands. Their pharmacological profile is very similar to that of the agonistic BZs (see Section 5.8.1).

TABLE 11

Other structures: Cyclopyrrolones, 2-phenylquinolines, and triazolopyridazines

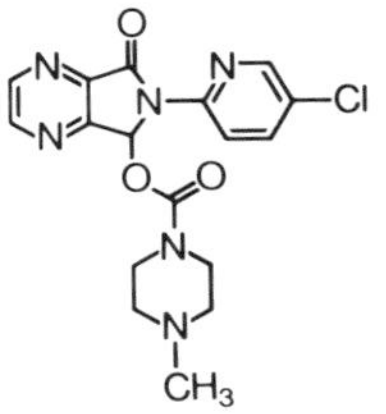

Zopiclone 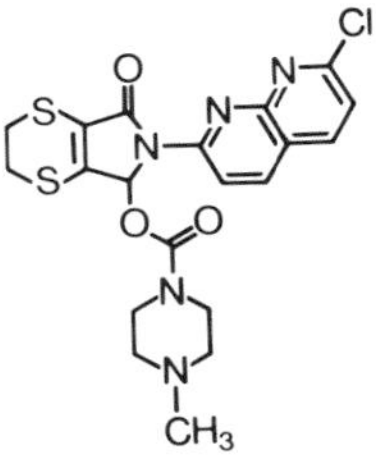   Suriclone

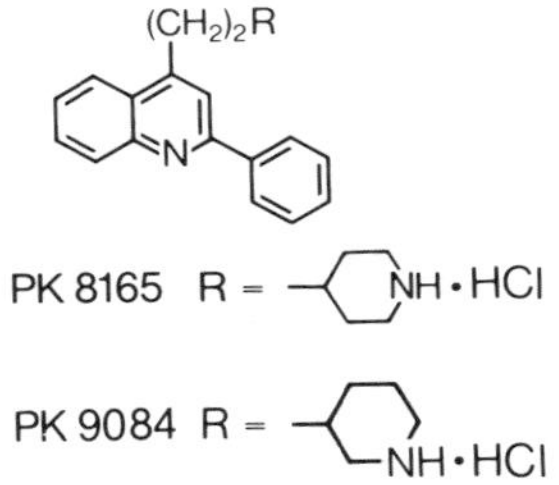

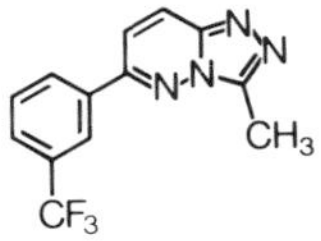

PK 8165   R = —⟨NH⟩·HCl   CL 218,872

PK 9084   R = —⟨NH⟩·HCl

Name or code number	Inhibition of [³H]Diaz binding [$IC_{50}(nM)$]	Antipentetrazol activity
Zopiclone	31	+ +
Suriclone	2.1	× × ×
PK 8165	100	0
PK 9084	380	0
CL 218,872	120	+ + +

The affinity for BZRs of the 2-phenylquinolines PK 8165 and PK 9084 is rather weak. These compounds lack most of the characteristic *in vivo* pharmacological effects of the BZs (see Section 5.10).

The triazolopyridazine derivative CL 218,872 also shows a rather weak affinity for BZRs; however, potentially interesting pharmacological activities have been found *in vivo* (see Section 5.8.2).

Common structural features of BZs and non-BZs, if present, are most likely to be found in the cyclopyrrolone series. Attempts to adapt the zopiclone molecule to a BZR model have indeed been reported (Fryer, 1983; Crippen, 1982) (see also Section 5.6.3). A remarkable difference appears to exist in the case of the 2-

phenylquinoline and triazolopyridazine series. Their bicyclic ring systems are planar and achiral, while the BZ system (boat conformation of ring B) shows specific steric requirements, as discussed in Section 5.5.1.3. It is therefore probable that, e.g., triazolopyridazines do not bind to, and interact with, the BZR in exactly the same way as BZs, but may achieve their *in vivo* activity by different mechanisms. For a discussion of the postulated involvement of receptor heterogeneity see Section 5.21.

5.6 SAR OF BZR ANTAGONISTS, MIXED AGONISTS, AND INVERSE AGONISTS

5.6.1 Tri- and Tetracyclic 1,4-BZ Derivatives

5.6.1.1 Discussion of structure–affinity relationships (SAfR). BZR antagonists were discovered in 1979 (Haefely *et al.*, 1981b) during the evaluation in a program aimed at the search for new anxiolytic structures (Hunkeler *et al.*, 1981). The strategy adopted was to reach substantial modifications in the structure of the well-established 1,4-BZs by a stepwise procedure, taking care to retain at least part of the affinity to the receptor and eventually to increase the latter again by further adaptations. As described by Hunkeler and Kyburz (1981), 7-fluoro-10-methyl-1,2,3,11a-tetrahydro-5H-pyrrolo[2,1-c][1,4]-benzodiazepine-5,11(10H)-dione (Ro 15-1695, Table 12A) was taken as starting point. According to Wright *et al.* (1978), this compound had antipentetrazol activity in mice of the order of chlordiazepoxide; however, we found it devoid of *in vitro* binding properties. In spite of this negative result, we synthesized some 1,2-annelated tetracyclic compounds in view of the strong affinity shown by some 1,2-annelated prototypes, such as triazolam, midazolam, and Ro 21-8384 (Table 9A and C) (see Section 5.5.1.5). Moreover, it had been observed, in the case of 2- and 1-benzazepines, that such annelations could markedly improve binding affinity (see Section 5.5.1.6).

While close analogs of the prototypes, i.e., the triazolo derivatives, Ro 14-5876 and Ro 14-7059 (Table 12A), or the imidazo carboxamide derivatives, Ro 14-7181 and Ro 16-4234 (Table 12B), failed to show any affinity for BZRs, some other more differing compounds, e.g, the imidazo ester Ro 14-5974 (Table 12B), or the tricyclic imidazo ester Ro 14-7437 (Table 12C), were surprisingly found to possess a high binding affinity.

Further variation of these leads confirmed that the new series obeys SAfRs different from those found with classical BZs. As shown in *Table 12B and C*, substitution with an electronegative substituent in ring A is not necessary for high affinity. A chlorine atom, if present, is best placed in position 8 for the tetracyclic compounds (Table 9B) and, correspondingly, in position 7 for the tricyclic analogs (Table 9C). Shifting the position of the chlorine atom to 7 or 8,

TABLE 12

A. Tri- and tetracyclic 1,4-BZ derivatives
(S)-7-fluoro-10-methyl-1,2,3,11a-tetrahydro-5H-pyrrolo[2,1-c][1,4]-benzodiazepine-5,11
(10H)-dione and (S)-3-methyl-9H-pyrrolo[2,1-c[-s-triazolo[4,3-a][1,4]benzodiazepine-9-
one derivatives

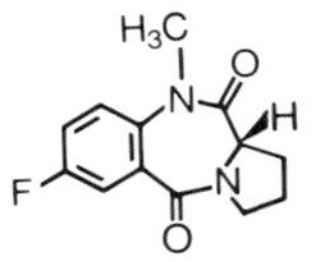

Ro 15-1695 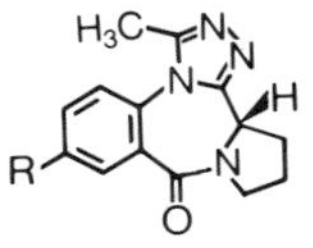   Ro 14-5876 R= Cl
                    Ro 14-7059 R= H

B. 9-Oxo-imidazo[1,5-a]pyrrolo[2,1-c][1,4]benzodiazepine-1-carboxylic
acid derivatives

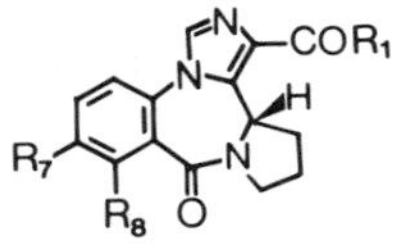

Code number	R_1	R_8	R_7	Inhibition of [^{3}H]Diaz binding [$IC_{50}(nM)$]
Ro 14-7181	NH$_2$			> 1000
Ro 16-4234	NH$_2$	Cl		3000
Ro 14-5974	O-Ethyl			6.4
Ro 15-4941	O-Ethyl	Cl		1.7
Ro 14-5975	O-Ethyl		Cl	62
Ro 16-3607	O-tert-Butyl	OCH$_3$		46
Ro 16-6624	O-tert-Butyl	Ethyl		10
Ro 16-3774	O-tert-Butyl	CH$_3$		3.2
Ro 16-0071	O-tert-Butyl			3.2
Ro 16-5824	O-tert-Butyl	SCH$_3$		3.4
Ro 16-8912	O-tert-Butyl	F		6.2
Ro 16-4261	O-tert-Butyl		F	7.7
Ro 16-0075	O-tert-Butyl	Cl		2.5
Ro 16-6127	O-tert-Butyl	Cl	F	3.1
Ro 16-3058	O-tert-Butyl		Cl	90
Ro 16-6028	O-tert-Butyl	Br		2.2
Ro 16-6605	O-tert-Butyl	I		2.1
Ro 16-6048	O-tert-Butyl	CF$_3$		3.3
Ro 16-6950	O-tert-Butyl	NO$_2$		2.8

TABLE 12 (*Continued*)

Code number	R_1	R_8	R_7	Inhibition of [^{3}H]Diaz binding [$IC_{50}(nM)$]
Ro 16-4019	O-*n*-Propyl	Cl		1.4
Ro 16-3031	O-*i*-Propyl	Cl		2.5
Ro 16-9906	O-Allyl	Cl		1.7
Ro 16-7081	O-*n*-Butyl	Cl		2.6
Ro 16-7082	O-*i*-Butyl	Cl		6.3
Ro 16-7083	O-*sec*-Butyl	Cl		2.9
Ro 16-9918	O-CH_2-cyclopropyl	Cl		2.3
Ro 16-4020	O-*n*-Hexyl	Cl		2.6
Ro 16-6654	O-Cyclohexyl	Cl		4
Ro 17-3206	O-Cycloheptyl	Cl		3.4
Ro 17-3207	O-Cyclooctyl	Cl		5.2
Ro 16-4021	O-Benzyl	Cl		1.5
Ro 17-1302	O-Phenyl	Cl		5.3

C. 5-Methyl-6-oxo-imidazo[1,5-*a*][1,4]benzodiazepine-3-carboxylic acid derivatives

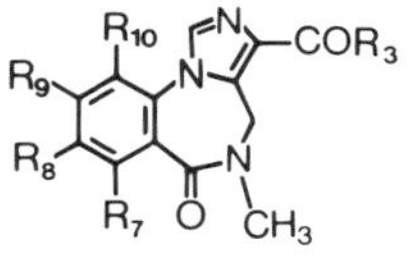

Code number	R_3	R_7	R_8	R_9	R_{10}	Inhibition of [^{3}H]Diaz binding [$IC_{50}(nM)$]
Ro 15-2427	NH_2					> 1000
Ro 14-7437	O-Ethyl					3
Ro 15-3505	O-Ethyl	Cl				2.7
Ro 15-1310	O-Ethyl		Cl			6.8
Ro 15-1746	O-Ethyl			Cl		> 1000
Ro 15-3237	O-Ethyl				Cl	> 1000
Ro 15-5623	O-Ethyl	F				2
Ro 15-1788	O-Ethyl		F			2.5
Ro 17-4896	O-Ethyl			F		> 1000

(*continued*)

TABLE 12 (*Continued*)

D. 9-Oxo-azeto[2,1-*c*]imidazo[1,5-*a*][1,4]benzodiazepine-1-carboxylic acid derivatives

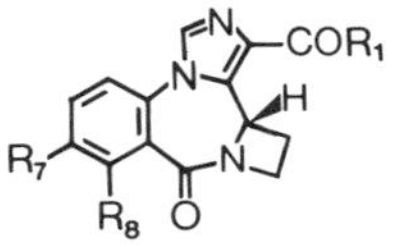

Code number	R_1	R_8	R_7	Inhibition of [³H]Diaz binding [$IC_{50}(nM)$]
Ro 17-9741	OCH₃	Cl		2.4
Ro 16-0858	O-Ethyl	Cl		1.3
Ro 16-0153	O-*tert*-Butyl	Cl		5.3
Ro 17-1812	OCH₂-cyclopropyl	Cl		1.3
Ro 17-3211	O-cyclohexyl	Cl		2.4
Ro 17-3401	O-benzyl	Cl		0.9
Ro 17-2620	O-*tert*-butyl		F	5.1
Ro 16-9351	O-*tert*-butyl	Cl	F	3.7
Ro 16-9905	O-*tert*-butyl	Br		1.2
Ro 17-1338	O-*tert*-butyl	I		1

Imidazo[1,5-*a*]pyrido[2,1-*c*][1,4]benzodiazepine derivative

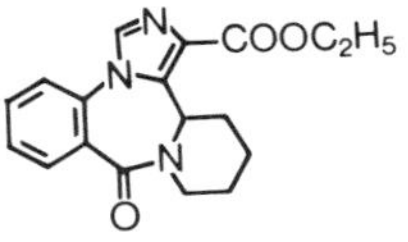

Ro 14-7462	1000

respectively, of the two systems reduces the affinity in clear contrast to the rules observed with the classical BZs. A fluorine atom at the same positions affects the binding properties much less, in particular in the tricyclic series.

As shown in Table 12B for the tetracyclics, a variety of other substituents in position 8 is compatible with a reasonable affinity, in particular if the substituent is electronegative. The same table assembles different esters, all showing high affinity.

Table 12D contains some esters of two further tetracyclic systems, i.e., the azeto derivatives, which all show high affinity and a piperido derivative which, on the contrary, is completely inactive.

5.6.1.2 Stereochemical aspects. The rigid tetracyclic compounds are excellent tools in identifying the ligand conformation accepted by the BZR. It is the conformation *a* (see Section 5.5.1.3), as established by X-ray analysis (Daly and Schönholzer, unpublished) of the S-enantiomer Ro 14-5974. The opposite R-enantiomer, Ro 14-7527, having a fixed *b* conformation, has no binding affinity (Fig. 11). Of special interest is the case of the achiral, flexible tricyclic compound Ro 14-7437 which, like the classical BZs, may assume either conformation with ease and indeed has high binding affinity. By introducing a methyl group in position 4 a chiral compound is obtained. At variance with the case of the classical BZs (compare Section 5.5.1.3), the S-enantiomer (Ro 15-2760) now prefers conformation *b* (Daly and Schönholzer, unpublished), evidently because of steric hindrance between the two methyl groups, and is inactive (Fig. 12). The R-enantiomer (Ro 15-3044), though having the "wrong" configuration, for steric reasons assumes the correct *a* conformation of ring B (Daly and Schönholzer, unpublished). Indeed, Ro 15-3044 has measurable binding affinity, in spite of the fact that the now semiaxial 4-methyl group reduces the affinity markedly.

Assuming that all compounds, agonists as well as antagonists, bind to the same receptor binding site, one may generalize that conformation *a* of ring B is a prerequisite for binding interaction with the BZR to occur.

5.6.2 Other Structures: β-Carbolines and Pyrazoloquinolines

Table 13A: The discovery of β-CCE and its properties (Nielsen *et al.*, 1979) resulted in a considerable interest in related structures and in the synthesis of numerous analogs. Ligands with the highest binding affinities were found among very closely related compounds: the methyl ester (β-CCM), the propyl ester (β-CCPr), and the amyl ester have IC_{50} values in Diaz binding very close to that of β-CCE; the phenyl ester is even seven times more potent *in vitro* (Braestrup and Nielsen, 1983).

Analogs bearing an acetyl or a formyl instead of an ester group in position 3 are also very active *in vitro*, whereas the replacement of the ester group by a hydroxymethyl (Cain *et al.*, 1982) or an amide group (Braestrup and Nielsen, 1980) lowers the activity markedly. However, the higher metabolic stability of these two groups leads to a longer duration of action *in vivo*. The alkylation of the amide nitrogen has been investigated by Locock *et al.* (1982) and the lowest IC_{50} value was found for the *N*-ethyl derivative; increasing the length of the alkyl group up to five carbon atoms resulted in a rapid decrease of affinity. Various esters of 1,2,3,4-tetrahydro-β-carboline-3-carboxylic acid (and analogs with substituents in positions 1, 6, and 9) were synthesized by Robertson *et al.* (1981) and by Cain *et al.* (1982). They display considerably lower affinity for the BZRs than the corresponding β-carboline derivatives. Harmane, harmaline, and some

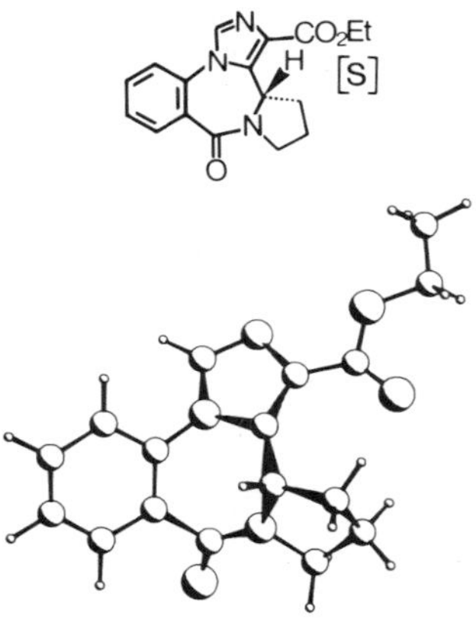

Ro 14-5974 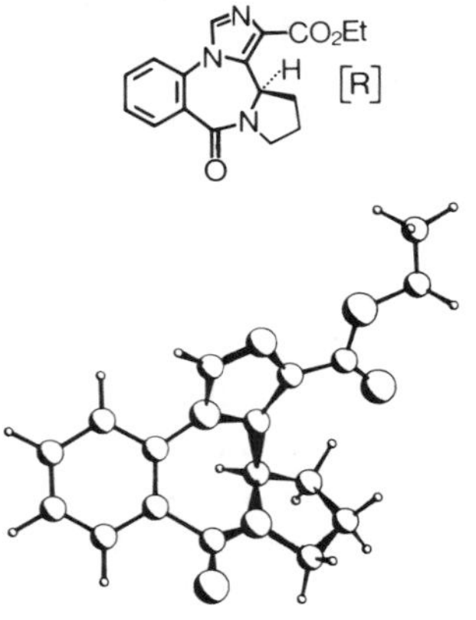   Ro 14-7527

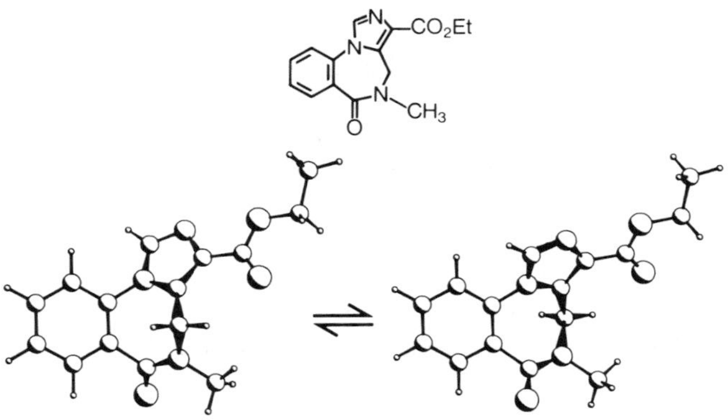

Ro 14-7437

FIG. 11. Stereochemistry and BZR affinity data of the enantiomeric tetracyclic 1,4-BZ derivatives Ro 14-5974 (IC_{50} = 6.4 nM) and Ro 14-7527 (IC_{50} > 1000 nM) and the tricyclic 1,4-BZ Ro 14-7437 (IC_{50} = 3 nM).

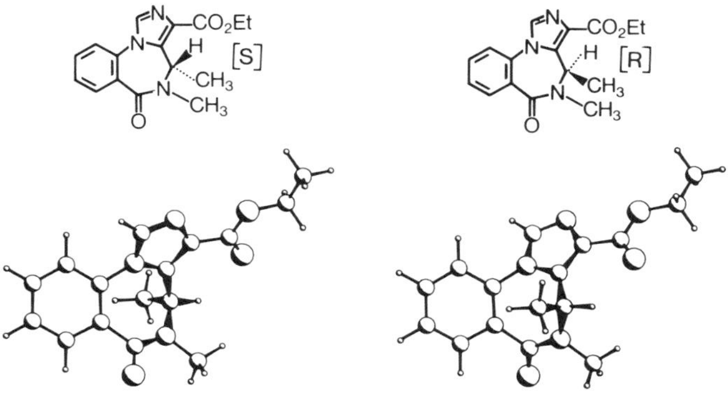

Ro 15-2760   Ro 15-3044

FIG. 12. Stereochemistry and BZR affinity data of the enantiomeric tricyclic 1,4-BZ derivatives Ro 15-2760 ($IC_{50} > 1000$ nM) and Ro 15-3044 ($IC_{50} = 280$ nM).

derivatives carrying no substituent in position 3 are very weak ligands for the BZR (Rommelspacher et al., 1980, 1981; Saano and Airaksinen, 1982).

A QSAfR analysis, using the method of Free and Wilson, was performed by Schauzu and Mager (1983) with a series of 12 β-carbolines described by Cain et al. (1982). Because of the limitation in number and variety, new aspects did not emerge from this study. The pharmacology of β-carbolines is discussed in Section 5.8.3.

The pyrazoloquinolines (Table 13B) represent another class of compounds with very high binding affinity to the BZR that was discovered by chance. Indeed, this series was aimed at diuretic activity. The first representative, CGS 8216, is a BZ antagonist (Czernik et al., 1982; Fong et al., 1982a). It was soon followed by two closely related analogs, the p-methoxy derivative, CGS 9895, which is a mixed agonist–antagonist, and the p-chloro derivative, CGS 9896, which is a potent anticonvulsant (Yokoyama et al., 1982; Gee and Yamamura, 1982b, see also Section 5.9).

No SAR studies have yet been published for this class of compounds. The striking facts are the marked differences in the pharmacological profile (efficiency) that are induced by slight structural variations, namely change of the p-substituent on the phenyl ring from H to OMe and Cl, the in vitro affinity to the BZR remaining virtually the same.

Both classes, the β-carbolines and the pyrazoloquinolines, possess a planar, tricyclic ring system and, therefore, differ markedly in shape from the tri- and tetracyclic 1,4-BZ antagonists and the BZ agonists. One may expect that the binding site of these non-BZ ligands will not be fully identical with that of the

TABLE 13

A. β-Carbolines

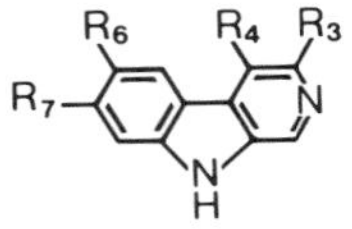

Compound	R_3	R_4	R_6	R_7	Inhibition of [³H]Diaz binding [IC_{50}(nM)]
β-CCM	$COOCH_3$				2.4
β-CCE	$COOC_2H_5$				0.9
β-CCPr	$COOCH_2CH_2CH_3$				1.8
β-CCtBu	$COOC(CH_3)_3$				3.8
β-CMA	$CONHCH_3$				250
DMCM	$COOCH_3$	C_2H_5	OCH_3	OCH_3	9.4

B. Pyrazoloquinolines

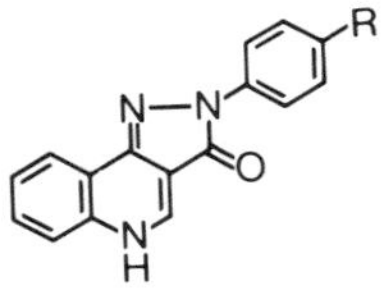

Code number	R	Inhibition of [³H]Diaz binding [IC_{50}(nM)]
CGS 8216		0.46
CGS 9895	OCH_3	0.34
CGS 9896	Cl	0.7

BZs and that their interactions with the BZR are different. A similar situation has already been discussed for the non-BZ agonists of the phenylquinoline and the triazolopyridazine series (see Section 5.5.2).

5.6.3 Conclusions on SAR and SAfR

Conventional SAR studies in the BZ series have not advanced our knowledge on the mechanism of action of BZs; however, they have contributed to increase the number of therapeutically useful drugs and have thus reached a practical goal. With the identification of specific high-affinity binding sites for BZs, the interest in the molecular mechanism of action of anxiolytic drugs increased considerably. The simple *in vitro* binding test is relatively well suited for the screening of large series of compounds and proved useful in detecting compounds acting directly on the receptor, distinguishing them from compounds requiring *in vivo* metabolic transformation in order to become active (prodrugs). It soon became clear that compounds from different structural classes may well act at the same receptor and have a similar mechanism of action as the BZs. However, among compounds with high affinity to the receptor, not only agonists, but also antagonists and inverse agonists, in other words ligands that differ dramatically in their intrinsive activity or efficacy, were found. All these facts pointed to a pivotal role of the BZR in mediating the biological effects of a variety of different structures and stimulated SAfR studies as an attempt to define the common structural features required for affinity to the BZR.

Fryer (1983) postulated a three-dimensional molecular model of ligands with five possible binding regions, of which at least three must be present in order for receptor interaction to occur. The model is based on crystallographic data of the active S-enantiomer of 3-methyl-Flu, Ro 11-6896, but is conceived in a way as to accommodate also non-BZ structures such as zopiclone, CL 218872, and β-carbolines.

In a more elaborated approach Crippen (1982) used published binding data from 29 drugs, comprising BZs and compounds from other structural classes, for determining the free energy of binding. The ligand molecules were described in terms of Cartesian coordinates for every atom, partly using published crystal data. In the cases where such were not available, the author assembled and used fragments of other published structures. Applying his distance geometry approach (Crippen, 1979, 1980, 1981), after some necessary simplifications, he deduced a binding site model for a subset of 18 compounds that consists of 15 site points and 5 adjustable energy parameters. He concluded that five atoms of each ligand can occupy corresponding points in the site and thus constitute a possible BZ pharmacophore.

There is an interesting, though less refined, precedent to these attempts to find common structural features between BZs and other structures. Camerman and

Camerman (1970, 1972), based on studies of the crystal structure of diazepam and diphenylhydantoin, postulated a common pharmacophore involving the two aromatic rings, the lactam oxygen and N-4 of diazepam.

This example illustrates well the danger inherent in such formalistic correlations. BZs and diphenylhydantoins produce quite different pharmacological effects, do not bind to the same receptor site, and are dissimilar in their interaction with GABAergic transmission. The common basis for a meaningful structural correlation is not given. Since the detection of common structural features is nowadays greatly facilitated by computer graphics, it is important to keep in mind that an essential prerequisite for SAR is to compare compounds with identical molecular mechanisms of action. Even when dealing with compounds having affinity to the same receptor, obvious limitations are set to approaches such as those described above by geometry and efficacy factors. Efforts directed at mapping the receptor by using X-ray data from ligands implicate, e.g., that a single receptor in a definite and constant shape interacts with all ligands in the same way, accepting them in the conformation which they adopt in the crystalline state. It seems very unlikely that such static conditions are fulfilled in nature. The other very serious limitations to the SAR studies performed to date is that ligands used for deducing common structural elements were often selected only on the basis of their affinity to the BZR, without differentiating them according to their intrinsic efficacy. The usual conditions of the binding test (see Section 4.2.1.2) do not allow a differentiation of the ligands according to their agonist, antagonist, and inverse agonist nature (see Section 5.3.4). Also, the pharmacological evaluation of BZs was until very recently restricted to the assessment of potency. Efforts to determine their efficacy are now being made. For the establishment of meaningful SAR, it is necessary to distinguish between the agonistic, antagonistic, and inverse agonistic activity of the ligands. Tentatively, it could be assumed that the different ligands exert their effect by interacting at the same sites, each influencing differently the conformation of the receptor glycoprotein environment, which modulates allosterically the supramolecular GABA-R, the BZR, and the chloride ionophore. Ligand structure and stereochemistry should correlate with the effector properties, but at present our understanding of these relationships is insufficient. We already mentioned that changes in ligand type may occur by simple interchange of a single substituent (see pyrazoloquinolines, Table 13B). Steric factors were shown to play an important role. In the BZ series of agonists and antagonists, the relevance of the conformation of ring B has been established. Interestingly, both types of compounds reach their highest affinity and *in vivo* potency with the same conformation. New molecular models are certainly needed; they should be shaped according to the particular SAR found for different types of ligands (effectors). Such refined models would reach a much greater predictive potential and usefulness than those based solely on affinity.

5.7 BASIC PHARMACOLOGY OF THE BZ ANTAGONISTS Ro 15-1788 AND Ro 15-3505

Two BZs have been selected to date for human pharmacology and clinical studies as BZ antagonists, Ro 15-1788 and Ro 15-3505.

The preclinical pharmacology of Ro 15-1788 has been described in several papers (Hunkeler *et al.*, 1981; Bonetti *et al.*, 1982; Möhler *et al.*, 1981c; Möhler and Richards, 1983b; Polc *et al.*, 1981b, 1982). In essence, Ro 15-1788 has a high affinity and selectivity for the high-affinity neuronal type of BZ binding sites *in vitro* and *in vivo*. It does not bind to the nonneuronal binding sites. In broad pharmacological testing, Ro 15-1788 was found to lack virtually any of the typical BZ-like actions and to be pharmacologically silent also in other respects in doses up to about 30 mg/kg iv. There are some observations of a marginal BZ agonistic activity such as a partial prevention of seizures induced by small, submaximal doses of pentetrazol (Kaijima *et al.*, 1983; Nutt, 1983; Prado de Carvalho *et al.*, 1983b), the retardation of occurrence of kindled seizures (Robertson, 1983; Robertson *et al.*, 1984), and the partial reduction of EEG paroxysmal activity in rats with a genetic form of absence epilepsy (Marescaux and Vergnes, unpublished). Several other borderline effects were observed that may be, but are not necessarily, due to a weak partial agonistic action at BZRs (Nutt, 1983).

The major effect of Ro 15-1788 and, for all practical purposes, the only relevant one at low doses is the selective prevention or reversal of all effects of BZ agonists that are mediated by BZRs. This specific antagonistic action at BZRs is also observed in man, e.g., reversal of sedation, muscle relaxation, sleep, and even coma induced by BZ agonists (Darragh *et al.*, 1982a,b, 1983a,b; O'Boyle *et al.*, 1983; Scollo-Lavizzari, 1983; Rapold *et al.*, 1984).

Ro 15-3505 is a close congener of Ro 15-1788. There are two relevant differences between these two compounds: Ro 15-3505 is 5 to 10 times more potent as a BZ antagonist than is Ro 15-1788. Moreover, in contrast to Ro 15-1788, Ro 15-3505 is a very weak partial inverse agonist (Haefely, 1983c). It has a marginal proconvulsant effect that can be blocked by Ro 15-1788. Initial human pharmacology studies confirm the more potent BZ antagonistic potency of Ro 15-3505. The inverse agonistic component of action has not yet been observed with certainty in man.

The binding of [^{3}H]Ro 15-1788 has been studied in various laboratories. It was found to interact with the same number of BZ binding sites as the agonist clonazepam (Möhler and Richards, 1981a). Evidence for only one population of binding sites was obtained. There were no major regional differences in the apparent affinity constant. Autoradiographically, density and distribution of [^{3}H]clonazepam and [^{3}H]Ro 15-1788 were very similar in various regions of the CNS. Inhibition of [^{3}H]Ro 15-1788 binding by various agonists was competitive. In heat inactivation experiments binding of [^{3}H]Ro 15-1788 and

[^{3}H]clonazepam was reduced in parallel; protection from heat inactivation was afforded by GABA, diazepam, and Ro 15-1788 in both radioligand binding assays. However, the mode of interaction of Ro 15-1788 with its binding sites differed from that of agonists. While binding of agonists was enhanced by GABA, pentobarbitone, SQ 20009, and several ions (see above), [^{3}H]Ro 15-1788 binding remained unaffected by these agents. It was speculated that the insensitivity of Ro 15-1788 binding to changes in the conformation of BZRs might reflect the inability of the antagonist to induce a conformational change of BZRs and, thereby, to trigger a biological response (Möhler and Richards, 1981a; Möher, 1984a).

5.8 NON-BZ LIGANDS OF BZRS

5.8.1 Cyclopyrrolones

The first non-BZ with a BZ-like pharmacological profile and with a high affinity for BZRs was zopiclone (Blanchard and Cotrel, 1983; Blanchard and Julou, 1983; Blanchard et al., 1979, 1983; Julou et al., 1983). In vitro zopiclone shows about one-half the affinity of diazepam. Zopiclone also inhibits [^{3}H]Flu binding in vivo after po administration. Its pharmacological effects are blocked by Ro 15-1788 (Hunkeler et al., 1981). Zopiclone is to be launched as a sleep inducer in France. The inhibitory effect of zopiclone on [^{3}H]Ro 15-1788 binding was affected in a manner intermediate between that of agonists and of antagonists by photoaffinity labeling with Flu (Möhler, 1982) and by the GABA shift (Möhler and Richards, 1981a).

Suriclone is the result of a structural variation of zopiclone. It was described by Blanchard and Julou (1983). Suriclone is a potent anticonvulsant, binds to the same number of sites as various BZs, and is about twice as potent as Flu. As with BZs, the affinity of suriclone is the same for BZ binding sites in the cerebellum and the forebrain. Unexpectedly, GABA was found not to enhance [^{3}H]suriclone binding. However, GABA protected suriclone binding sites from heat inactivation. Suriclone is presently undergoing clinical studies as an anxiolytic (Lapierre and Oyewumi, 1983).

5.8.2 Triazolopyridazines

CL 218,872 was described by Lippa et al. (1978b, 1979a,b, 1982a,b) as a non-BZ with relevant affinity for BZRs. The structural similarity of CL 218,872 to purines is obvious. CL 218,872 was reported to have an anticonflict activity in the shock-induced suppression of drinking paradigm with a strikingly flatter dose–response curve than Diaz or chlordiazepoxide. CL 218,872 is also anticonvulsant, particularly against pentetrazol-induced seizures; it was reported to be only about one-fourth as potent as chlordiazepoxide in producing motor deficit. The most interesting aspect of CL 218,872 is undoubtedly its hypothetical selective affinity for a putative subtype of BZR (Lippa *et al.*, 1978b; Klepner *et al.*, 1979) and the proposed "anxioselective" activity in the virtual absence of sedative and muscle relaxant effects (Lippa *et al.*, 1978b, 1979b). Not all investigators have been able to confirm such a marked separation between anticonflict and other actions. Most unfortunate, however, is the lack of clinical data on the effects of CL 218,872 in man, due to prohibitive hepatotoxic effects in animal toxicity studies. The availability of a nontoxic congener of CL 218,872 with a similar pharmacological profile would be very helpful in testing the various speculations initiated by experimental pharmacology, in particular, binding studies. CL 218,872 has a moderate affinity for BZ binding sites in membrane preparations of rat cortex, in the order of that of prazepam or about 30–50 times less than Flu. [³H]CL 218,872 binding to membranes of rat cerebral cortex suggested the presence of a high-affinity (K_D 10–30 nM) and a low-affinity site (K_D 200–600 nM) at ice temperature (Yamamura *et al.*, 1982). Nonspecific binding is higher than with the usual BZR radioligands. [³H]Cl 218,872 binding is inhibited by various BZs, β-carbolines, pyrazoloquinolinones, but not by the nonneuronal BZ binding site ligand, Ro 5-4864. Photoinactivation of BZ binding sites with [³H]Flu reduced binding of [³H]CL 218,872 and [³H]Flu to the same extent (Lippa *et al.*, 1982b). Binding was enhanced by GABA and the pyrazolopyridazine tracazolate (Fig. 2), but not by Cl⁻ ions and barbiturates. In the cerebellum (Niehoff *et al.*, 1982) the B_{max} for [³H]CL 218,872 and [³H]Flu were similar and the K_D for [³H]Cl 218,872 was 21 nM. Cartazolate (Fig. 2), barbiturates, and halide ions failed to stimulate [³H]Cl 218,872 binding. The inevitable conclusion is that CL 218,872 binds to BZ binding sites in a somewhat different manner than BZs: whereas the affinity for the GABA-occupied site is higher for both classes of compounds, possible conformational changes induced by "Cl⁻ channel agents" do not seem to affect the binding of CL 218,872. Photoaffinity labeling of membranes affected the inhibitory effect of CL 218,872 on [³H]Ro 15-1788 binding in a manner intermediate between that characteristic for agonists and that for antagonists (Möhler, 1982). The most striking finding, when CL 218,872 was studied as an inhibitor of [³H]BZ binding, was the shallow dose–response curve in membrane preparations of the forebrain (Lippa *et al.*, 1979a,b, 1980, 1982; Klepner, 1979; Young *et al.*, 1981). Hill coefficients for [³H]BZ displacement significantly below unity were found in the cerebral cortex and the hippocampus, indicating that binding of CL 218,872 in these structures did not obey the mass action law, in contrast to its interaction with cerebellar BZ binding sites, where the Hill coefficient was not different from 1. Not only the Hill coefficient for inhibition, but also the potency of CL 218,872 as a BZ binding inhibitor varied in various brain regions. These findings were interpreted as indication for the presence of two distinct molecular species of binding sites to which CL 218,872 binds with different affinity. In the cerebellum, about 90% of the BZ binding sites were calculated to be high-affinity binding sites for CL 218,872, termed BZ_1Rs. The low-affinity binding sites for the triazolopyridazine compound were termed BZ_2Rs; their density in the cerebral cortex was suggested to be about 40% and in the hippocampus about 60% of all [^{3}H]BZ binding sites. It was also proposed that CL 218,872 inhibited [^{3}H]BZ binding at BZ_1R competitively and, however, noncompetitively at BZ_2R. A regional difference in the proportion of BZ_1R and BZ_2R was also suggested by autoradiographic studies of [^{3}H]Flu binding in the presence of CL 218,872 in rat brain slices (Young et al., 1981; Niehoff and Kuhar, 1983). Also in vivo, CL 218,872 had a higher affinity for [^{3}H]BZ binding sites in the cerebellum than in other brain regions, while Diaz and chlordiazepoxide inhibited [^{3}H]Flu binding to the same extent in the cerebellum and in the cerebral cortex (Lippa et al., 1982b).

The significance of many of the binding results with CL 218,872 obtained at low temperature is questioned by more recent investigations (Gee and Yamamura, 1982a; Gee et al., 1982a,b, 1983a–c). They show that the intraregional heterogeneity of CL 218,872 (and β-CCPr) binding (Hill coefficient below unity) disappears at 37°C in unwashed and washed rat brain membranes. Only interregional differences remain, e.g., higher affinity of CL 218,872 in the cerebellum than in other regions, this difference being reduced also at physiological temperature. Rather than the BZ_1R and BZ_2R dichotomy, the above authors proposed a classification of cerebellar and noncerebellar binding sites. The association of hypothetical BZ_1R with anticonflict and anticonvulsant activity and of BZ_2R with sedative and muscle relaxant "side effects" was rejected; a partial agonistic property of CL 218,872 was proposed (Gee and Yamamura, 1983a; Gee et al., 1983a). Indeed, CL 218,872 attenuated the effect of Diaz on the righting reflex but enhanced its anticonvulsant action (Gee et al., 1983a). Chen et al. (1983a,b) confirmed the loss of BZ_1R and BZ_2R differentiation at 37°C also with solubilized BZ binding sites.

5.8.3 β-Carboline Derivatives

Interest in this chemical class of compounds was raised by the high affinity for BZ binding sites of β-CCE, a compound that was obtained by Nielsen et al. (1979) and Braestrup et al. (1980b) by heating (80°C) human urine extract with ethanol at pH 1, a condition favoring the formation of the ethyl ester from β-carboline-3-carboxylic acid, which itself derives from tryptophan. Numerous derivatives of β-carboline-3-carboxylic acid have since then been synthesized and investigated for their interaction with BZ binding sites.

β-Carboline derivatives with affinity for BZ binding sites are either agonists, competitive antagonists, inverse agonists, or mixed forms of agonists and inverse agonists (partial agonists and partial inverse agonists). SARs for β-carbolines are discussed in Section 5.6.2. In the following we discuss some representatives in more detail.

5.8.3.1 β-CCM. β-CCM potentiates convulsions induced by pentetrazol, maximum electroshock, nicotine, and picrotoxine in the mouse (Jones and Oakley, 1981). In addition to this proconvulsant activity, and in contrast to β-CCE, β-CCM also induces clonic–tonic seizures when given alone (Valin *et al.*, 1982; Prado de Carvalho *et al.*, 1983a). The dose–response curve for this convulsant action was found to be bell-shaped; the maximum effect (80–100% of mice convulsing, 30% of them showing tonic extension, the remainder generalized clonic seizures) was attained between 1 and 2 mg/kg iv. The effect decreases with higher doses; at about 50 mg/kg iv virtually no animal was found to convulse. In other experiments (Bonetti, unpublished) this bell-shaped dose–response curve was found for tonic extension only, all mice showing clonic convulsions up to the maximum dose (100 mg/kg iv) tested. The generation of seizures by β-CCM was prevented by β-CCE and β-CCPr. β-CCM has an "anxiogenic" effect in mice that is blocked by Ro 15-1788 (Prado de Carvalho *et al.*, 1983a,b). β-CCM blocks the effect of GABA on rat hippocampal pyramidal cells (Paterson and Roberts, 1983).

The number of sites that bound β-[^{3}H]CCM was only 20% smaller than the number of [^{3}H]Flu binding sites in the rat cerebellum (Braestrup and Nielsen, 1981b). In the hippocampus, however, the B_{max} for β-[^{3}H]CCM was 42% smaller than was the B_{max} for [^{3}H]Flu binding sites. GABA and muscimol reduced binding of β-[^{3}H]CCM in a bicuculline-sensitive manner; however, β-CCM failed to inhibit high-affinity [^{3}H]muscimol binding.

5.8.3.2 β-CCE. β-CCE was found to be proconvulsant in mice and rats (Oakley and Jones, 1980; Cowen *et al.*, 1981; Nutt, 1983) and in baboons with photosensitive epilepsy (Cepeda *et al.*, 1981). In contrast to β-CCM, β-CCE is not considered to be convulsant by itself in most species (except the squirrel monkey, Schweri *et al.*, 1983). β-CCE induces in rhesus monkeys a behavioral syndrome typical of an anxiety attack (Ninan *et al.*, 1982). In the rat, β-CCE has a proconflict activity (Petersen *et al.*, 1982). β-CCE blocks the convulsions induced by the strong convulsant β-carboline DMCM (Braestrup *et al.*, 1982) and blocks the antipentetrazole effect of Diaz (Oakley and Jones, 1980) as well as the Diaz-induced decrease of cerebellar cGMP (Fujimoto *et al.*, 1982b). β-CCE reduced the effect of exogenous GABA in the rat hippocampus (Polc *et al.*, 1981a) and depressed dorsal root potentials in the cat spinal cord, which reflect the depolarizing effect of endogenous GABA released at axoaxonal synapses on primary afferent endings (Polc *et al.*, 1982). The latter effect, as well as the antagonism of barbiturate effects, was abolished by Ro 15-1788, clearly demonstrating that the depressant effect of β-CCE on GABA-induced membrane phenomena is mediated by specific BZRs. β-CCE produced behavioral and biochemical signs of anxiety (Skolnick and Paul, 1983) and a seizure-type electroencephalographic pattern, which could be prevented by CGS 8216 (Skolnick *et al.*, 1983c).

Hofstee analysis of the inhibition by β-CCE of [^{3}H]Flu binding revealed a purely competitive type of inhibition in the cerebellum, but a mixed-type competitive inhibition in cerebral cortex and hippocampus (Braestrup and Nielsen, 1983). Binding of β-[^{3}H]CCE to rat whole brain membranes did not obey simple mass-action kinetics (Martin and Doble, 1983). The displacing potency of β-CCE was four to seven times higher in the cerebellum than in the hippocampus (Nielsen and Braestrup, 1980; Lippa *et al.*, 1980). *In vivo* [^{3}H]Flu binding is dose dependently reduced by β-CCE in mice (Hirsch and Lydigsen, 1981); when given 10 min (iv), 30 min (ip), or 45 min (po) before the radioligand, the 50% displacement doses were found to be 2.1 mg/kg (iv), 54 mg/kg (ip; 1/25 the potency of Diaz), and 450 mg/kg (po). At the maximally effective oral dose β-CCE was lethal for about 70% of the animals within 2 hr. After 2.1 mg/kg β-CCE iv [^{3}H]Flu was displaced by 37% in the hippocampus and 76% in the cerebellum, confirming the differential affinity found *in vitro*.

The affinity of β-CCE binding was unaffected by photoaffinity labeling of BZ binding sites with Flu (Möhler, 1982; Thomas and Tallman, 1983) or by GABA (Patel *et al.*, 1981; Möhler and Richards, 1981a). B_{max} for β-[^{3}H]CCE was about 20% smaller than B_{max} for [^{3}H]Diaz in the cerebral cortex, but not in the cerebellum (Skolnick *et al.*, 1982a,d). Regional differences in the binding affinity of β-[^{3}H]CCE *in vivo* were described by Minchin and Nutt (1983). B_{max} for β-[^{3}H]CCE was hardly affected by alkylation of BZ binding sites with irazepine, which reduced B_{max} for [^{3}H]Diaz by about one-third. Irazepine reduced the apparent affinity of [^{3}H]Diaz more markedly than that of β-[^{3}H]CCE. For a comparison of β-[^{3}H]CCE and β-[^{3}H]CCPr binding see the next section. Medina *et al.* (1983c) found the number of β-[^{3}H]CCE binding sites to be higher than that of [^{3}H]Flu sites in the main regions of rat brain.

5.8.3.3 β-CCPr. β-CCPr is neither proconvulsant, convulsant, nor anticonvulsant in doses up to 200 mg/kg iv (Braestrup and Nielsen, 1981b); very little of β-CCPr injected ip actually reaches the brain. In mice, β-CCPr blocks the proconvulsant effect of β-CCM (Oakley and Jones, 1982).

β-[^{3}H]CCPr binding has been recently intensively studied in the hope to have a probe for subtypes of BZ binding sites. Compared to other BZR ligands, β-[^{3}H]CCPr is a less ideal radioligand because of its high nonspecific binding (Hirsch *et al.*, 1982) and low stability in aqueous solutions.

β-[^{3}H]CCPr labels fewer sites than [^{3}H]Flu in the rat hippocampus (57%) and cerebral cortex (71%) (Braestrup and Nielsen, 1981a; Nielsen *et al.*, 1981). In the mouse forebrain the number of sites labeled by β-[³H]CCPr and [³H]Diaz was the same (Hirsch *et al.*, 1982). In contrast to the rat (Nielsen *et al.*, 1981), the affinity of β-[³H]CCPr in the mouse was not greater in the cerebellum than in the hippocampus. Furthermore, Ni^{2+} inhibited β-[³H]CCPr binding up to 70% over the same concentration range that increased [³H]Diaz binding up to 80%, Ni^{2+} greatly increased the nonspecific binding of β-[³H]CCPr. Also in the mouse forebrain, heat inactivation of β-[³H]CCPr and [³H]Diaz binding was identical (Hirsch *et al.*, 1982); kainic acid lesions led to a similar decrease in the binding of both ligands.

β-CCM and β-CCE inhibited β-[³H]CCPr binding in hippocampus and cerebral cortex monophasically, suggesting that β-carbolines bind to a single homogeneous class of sites (Braestrup and Nielsen, 1981a). In contrast, inhibition of [³H]Flu binding in the hippocampus by β-CCPr was biphasic (shallow inhibition curve, Hill coefficient below 1). In rat cerebral cortex, a small population of superhigh-affinity binding sites (K_D = 30–100 μ*M*) for β-[³H]CCPr was reported (Ehlert *et al.*, 1983a).

GABA did not affect the apparent affinity of β-[³H]CCPr in the cerebellum (Gee *et al.*, 1983c) nor the IC_{50} values of β-CCPr in [³H]Flu or [³H]Ro 15-1788 binding in rat cerebral cortex (Möhler and Richards, 1981a; Ehlert *et al.*, 1983a). A slight, dose-dependent stimulation was found in well-washed membranes of mouse forebrain (Hirsch *et al.*, 1982). Also in thoroughly washed synaptosomes of bovine brain β-[³H]CCPr binding was stimulated by GABA, but to a clearly smaller extent than [³H]Flu binding (Fehske *et al.*, 1982). The effect of GABA, pyrazolopyridines, barbiturates, and etomidate on β-[³H]CCPr binding was studied by Ehlert *et al.* (1981). Avermectin $B_{1\alpha}$ (Fig. 5) stimulated β-[³H]CCPr binding less than that of [³H]Diaz in mouse forebrain membranes (Hirsch *et al.*, 1982). Picrotoxin and pentobarbitone had no effect on β-[³H]CCPr binding. Photoaffinity labeling did not affect binding of β-CCPr (Gee and Yamamura, 1982d, 1983a; Hirsch, 1982).

β-CCPr was found to have no intrinsic activity on the binding of the cage convulsant [³⁵S]TBPS (Fig. 5) to rat cortex membranes, but was found to block the stimulant effect of BZ agonists as well as the inhibitory effect of inverse agonists on [³⁵S]TBPS binding (Supavilai and Karobath, 1983).

Comparing β-[³H]CCPr to β-[³H]CCE binding in thoroughly washed synaptosomal preparations of bovine brain and retina, Fehske *et al.* (1982) found a similar K_D for β-[³H]CCPr in all regions. However, in all regions less binding sites for β-[³H]CCPr were found than for [³H]Flu (60% in cortex, hippocampus, retina; 80% in the cerebellum); this difference was not found for β-[³H]CCE binding sites. The adenosine derivative EMD 28422 (Fig. 2) produced a profound increase in the nonspecific binding of β-[³H]CCPr, but had only a small, bicuculline-sensitive stimulating effect on [³H]Flu binding.

As found with CL 218,872, β-CCPr no longer differentiated between the assumed BZ_1R and BZ_2R in the hippocampus at 37°C (Gee et al., 1982b,c, 1983c).

5.8.3.4 DMCM (methyl 6,7-dimethoxy-β-carboline-3-carboxylate). DMCM (Table 13A) is a potent convulsant (Braestrup et al., 1982; Petersen, 1983). It produces clonic–tonic convulsions in mice and rats with an ED_{50} of about 3 mg/kg ip. At doses above 15 mg/kg all animals are killed. In the curarized rat, DMCM increased the spontaneous firing rate of neurons in the substantia nigra pars reticulata, an effect that was reduced by Diaz and antagonized by Ro 15-1788 (Mereu and Biggio, 1983). At convulsant doses, DMCM displaced [³H]Flu binding *in vivo*. Ro 15-1788 as well as β-CCE (in spite of its proconvulsant activity) completely prevented the occurrence of seizures. DMCM reduced the effect of GABA on cultured spinal cord neurons (Barker et al., 1984) by decreasing the frequency of Cl^- channel opening. In contrast to agonists, DMCM elevates cerebellar cGMP in rats (Serra et al., 1983).

The [³H]BZ displacing action of DMCM was reduced by GABA in contrast to the effect of agonists (Braestrup et al., 1980b). The displacing potency of DMCM was roughly the same in the hippocampus and cerebellum, in contrast to β-CCPr and β-CCM, which are more potent in the cerebellum.

[³H]DMCM binding was studied by Braestrup et al. (1983a). The ligand is not ideal due to marked absorption to many materials, e.g., filters, and the high nonspecific binding in tissues. This, together with a marked sensitivity to all kinds of modulatory influences, calls for caution when interpreting DMCM binding data. [³H]DMCM binding was less reduced by increase of the temperature than [³H]Flu binding, suggesting a high entropic component in the binding of the former. Association and dissociation were polyexponential. Scatchard analysis of [³H]DMCM saturation binding yielded a curvilinear plot, suggesting a high- and a low-affinity component. Surprisingly, photoaffinity labeling of BZ binding sites with Flu, which reduced [³H]Flu binding, markedly increased the specific binding of [³H]DMCM by affecting its affinity. The regional distribution of [³H]DMCM binding was similar to that of [³H]Flu with the exception of a high binding in the hippocampus and a lower binding in cerebellum and striatum; the regional distribution of [³H]DMCM is thus very different from that of [³H]CCPr. GABA and muscimol decreased [³H]DMCM binding only slightly at 0°C but very markedly (by 80%) at 37°C. Some "channel agents" likewise decreased the binding of [³H]DMCM, while picrotoxinin and bicuculline enhanced it. Specific binding of [³H]DMCM was dramatically increased (by 1000%) by silver ions. Braestrup et al. (1983a) concluded that DMCM binds to the same binding molecules as BZ agonists, however, in a different way. One possibility is that the two ligand classes bind to only partially overlapping recognition areas. The results clearly add new evidence for the fact that three fundamentally different interactions of agonists, antagonists, and inverse agonists occur at a regulatory (allosteric) site for GABA-R functions.

5.8.3.5 Other β-carbolines. FG 7142 (N-methyl-β-carboline-3-carbox-amide) is a proconvulsant in the baboon with photosensitive epilepsy and a mild convulsant in mice (Rossier *et al.*, 1983). FG 7142 induces in the cat a state of increased attention, restlessness, excessive response to stimuli, and fearful behavior (Ongini, 1983; Ongini *et al.*, 1983); no convulsions were observed. FG 7142 blocked the effects of Diaz and quazepam on behavior and EEGs, but also those induced by pentobarbitone. In the rat FG 7142 was reported to have a proconflict action (Petersen *et al.*, 1982). In a human volunteer attacks of severe anxiety, agitation, increased muscular tension, and increased muscle reflexes were evoked by the oral intake of 200 mg FG 7142. Seizures did not occur. The alarming syndrome had to be interrupted with the iv injection of a BZ agonist (Dorow *et al.*, 1983).

ZK 91296 (ethyl 5-benzyloxy-4-methoxymethyl-β-carboline-3-carboxylate) is a potent displacer of [^{3}H]BZ binding; it shows interesting anticonvulsant activity in the photosensitive baboon after iv doses of 0.25 to 16 mg/kg that failed to produce ataxia or visible impairment of arousal (Meldrum *et al.*, 1983; Petersen *et al.*, 1983; Meldrum and Braestrup, 1984).

ZK 90886 (ethyl 4-ethyl-5-methoxy-β-carboline-3-carboxylate) has proconvulsant activity (Jensen and Petersen, 1983).

ZK 93426 (ethyl 5-isopropoxy-4-methyl-β-carboline-3-carboxylate) is a rather pure BZ antagonist (Jensen and Petersen, 1983).

3-HMC [3-(hydroxymethyl)-β-carboline] is two orders of magnitude less potent than β-CCE as an [^{3}H]BZ displacer *in vitro*, but *in vivo* is as potent a BZ antagonist as β-CCE (Cain *et al.*, 1982). In doses of 15 mg/kg ip and higher, sleep latency in rats was increased and total sleep (primarily non-REM sleep) decreased (Mendelson *et al.*, 1983b,c). 3-HMC (7.5 mg/kg ip) given 5 min before flurazepam (40 mg/kg ip) attenuated the decrease in sleep latency observed with flurazepam alone (Mendelson *et al.*, 1983b).

Lippke *et al.* (1983) have synthesized and tested a series of β-carboline derivatives.

5.8.4 Pyrazoloquinolinones

CGS 8216 (2-phenyl-pyrazolo[3,4-c]quinolin-3[5H]-one). [^{3}H]CGS 8216 binds with high affinity and little nonspecific binding to central BZ binding sites (K_D = 0.44 nM at 0°C). At 37°C the K_D is only four times higher than at 0°C (Czernik *et al.*, 1982). Dissociation of CGS 8216 at 0°C was very slow ($t_{1/2}$ = 53 min), but very fast (complete within 1 min) at 37°C. The regional distribution of [^{3}H]CGS 8216 was similar to that of [^{3}H]Flu; however, CGS 8216 had little binding at nonneuronal BZ binding sites in the kidney. The affinity of [^{3}H]CGS 8216 binding and the displacing potency of CGS 8216 in [^{3}H]BZ binding were not enhanced by GABA (Möhler and Richards, 1981a; Morelli *et al.*, 1982; Skolnick *et al.*, 1982c) or even decreased (Morelli *et al.*, 1982), and unaffected by photoaffinity labeling with Flu (Möhler, 1982; Gee and Yamamura, 1983a). Inhibition of [^{3}H]Flu binding by CGS 8216 was of the mixed type (reduction of affinity as well as of B_{max}). When given orally before an iv tracer dose of [^{3}H]Flu, CGS 8216 inhibited specific [^{3}H]Flu binding in the brain with about the same potency as Diaz. In addition to its affinity for BZ binding sites, CGS 8216 blocked the stimulation by adenosine of cAMP formation in vesicles prepared from guinea pig brain (equivalent to theophylline) and inhibited cyclic AMP phosphodiesterase (potency between that of diazepam and theophylline). CGS 8216 was found to be more potent than theophylline as an inhibitor of [^{3}H] cyclo-hexyladenosine binding to adenosine A_1 binding sites (Williams and Risley, 1982b). CGS 8216 does not produce BZ-like effects, but blocks all major effects of BZ agonists (Boast *et al.*, 1983). In the thirsty rat conflict model CGS 8216 (2.5–10 mg/kg ip) reduced the number of punished responses and, in doses that were inactive by themselves, abolished the anticonflict action of pentobarbitone (Mendelson *et al.*, 1983a) and meprobamate (Petrack *et al.*, 1983); these results suggest that CGS 8216 might have an anxiogenic activity. This is also a conclusion drawn by File and Lister (1983), who found a reduction of the time rats spent in social interaction.

Among derivatives of CGS 8216, compounds with high affinity for [^{3}H]BZ binding sites were found which differed markedly from CGS 8216 in their *in vivo* pharmacological activity (Yokoyama *et al.*, 1982). For instance, the *p*-chloro-phenyl analog CGS 9896 seems to be a partial BZ agonist (Gee and Yamamu-ra, 1982a; Petrack *et al.*, 1983; Spencer and Lal, 1983) while the corresponding *p*-methoxyphenyl derivative CGS 9895 was characterized as a full agonist at low and as an antagonist at high doses. CGS 8216 antagonized the anticonflict effect of CGS 9896 in a drinking test (Patel *et al.*, 1983). CGS 9896 is a strong inhibitor of [^{3}H]Flu and β-[^{3}H]CCPr binding (Gee and Yamamura, 1982a–c; Gee *et al.*, 1982c). Its affinity for BZ binding sites is enhanced by GABA but not by Cl$^-$ ions, in contrast to that of CGS 8216 (Morelli *et al.*, 1982). The affinity of CGS 9896 is the same in cerebral cortex, hippocampus, and cerebellum, and the Hill coefficient for [^{3}H]BZ displacement is close to 1 except in the dorsal hippocampus. At 37°C the K_i values for CGS 9896 is 10 times higher than at 0°C. Shannon and Herling (1983) reported that none of the three pyrazolo-quinolinones produced Diaz-like discriminative effects in rats; CGS 8216 and CGS 9895, but not CGS 9896, blocked the discriminative stimulus effect of Diaz.

5.8.5 Phenylquinolines

Le Fur *et al.* (1981) and Le Fur (1982) described two phenylquinoline deriva-tives, PK 8165 and PK 9084 (Table 11), which have 1/20 to 1/200 the potency of Diaz in inhibiting [^{3}H]BZ binding in rat brain. They were considered to be less potent on the nonneuronal peripheral BZ binding site. In a punished drinking test in the rat, the dose–response curves for PK 8165 and PK 9084 were distinctly less steep than those for Diaz and chlordiazepoxide. The two phenylquinolines lacked anticonvulsant activity at 50 mg/kg ip and were less potent than chlordiazepoxide in depressing locomotor activity. The two compounds did not antagonize the increase of cerebellar cGMP induced by isoniazid and picrotoxin, which is a characteristic effect of BZ agonists. The drugs were proposed to be pure anxiolytics; clinical data are not available at present. In the social interaction model of anxiolytic activity, File and Lister (1983) found PK 8165 to be inactive and PK 9084 to have doubtful anticonflict activity. Gee *et al.* (1983a,b) reported that the two compounds attenuate the anticonvulsant and antipunishment effect of Diaz, suggesting a partial, at least, antagonistic property. GABA enhanced the affinity of PK 8165 moderately in the cerebellum (Morelli *et al.*, 1982) and slightly in the cerebral cortex (Morelli *et al.*, 1982; Skolnick *et al.*, 1982c).

5.8.6 *Imidazopyridines*

The two imidazopyridines EMD 39593 and EMD 41717 (Fig. 2) have a rather low potency as displacers of [^{3}H]BZ binding (K_i approximately 1 μM) and a Hill coefficient close to 1 (Skolnick *et al.*, 1983b); surprisingly, the two compounds rather selectively antagonized the anticonflict effect of BZs in rodents with no relevant antagonism of the anticonvulsant and muscle relaxant activity.

5.8.7 *Compounds without Relevant Affinity for BZRs*

A large number of compounds of very different chemical classes were studied for [^{3}H]BZ displacing activity. A list of such inactive compounds is presented by Braestrup and Nielsen (1983). Purine derivatives were tested, i.a. by Marangos *et al.* (1979b, 1981a), Davies *et al.* (1980), Boulenger *et al.* (1982), and Sung and Saneyoshi (1982). Some agents have such a low affinity for BZ binding sites, e.g., various penicillin derivatives and CNS depressants (Antoniadis *et al.*, 1979, 1980) or tetrazol derivatives (Rehavi *et al.*, 1982), that their proposed interaction with BZRs *in vivo* is very unlikely. Of various prostaglandins, PGA$_1$ and PGA$_2$ inhibited [^{3}H]Diaz binding with K_i of 7 and 15 μM (Asano and Ogasawara, 1982). L-Thyroxin and, more potently, D-thyroxin were reported to inhibit [^{3}H]Flu binding (Nagy and Lijtha, 1983).

5.9 COVALENT BINDING

Covalent binding of BZ binding sites was attempted early in the BZR era, because it was at that time thought to be the only way to prevent radioligand dissociation from binding sites during the processing of autoradiograms. In addition covalent labeling of BZ binding sites was, of course, felt to be necessary in later approaches to receptor isolation.

5.9.1 Irazepine and Kenazepine

First attempts to irreversibly label BZ binding sites led to the synthesis of irazepine (Table 3), a BZ bearing an isothiocyanate function attached by an ethyl chain to N_1 (Rice et al., 1979). Incubation of synaptosomes from rat brain with 20 nM irazepine resulted in a 21% reduction in B_{max} of [^{3}H]Diaz binding with no significant change in K_D. From model experiments with bionucleophiles irazepine was proposed to form covalent bonds by reacting with free amino or sulfydryl groups. Under conditions, where irazepine reduced the number of [^{3}H]Diaz binding sites by one-third, only a small decrease of B_{max} for β- [^{3}H] CCE occurred (Skolnick et al., 1982a,d). Irazepine increased the K_D more markedly for β-CCE than for Diaz, suggesting differences in the binding of agonists and antagonists.

Kenazepine (Fig. 3) was found to react noncompetitively and irreversibly with some BZ binding sites and competitively and reversibly with others (E. F. Williams et al., 1980). The cerebellum had the highest proportion of irreversibly bound sites, while cerebral cortex and hippocampus contained a preponderance of reversibly bound sites.

Injection of irazepine or kenazepine intracerebroventricularly to mice resulted in an antipentetrazol effect for about 4 hr, while Diaz and Ro 7-1986 (Fig. 3) (the nonalkylating parent compound) had lost their activity 15 min after the injection (E. F. Williams et al., 1981).

5.9.2 Flunitrazepam

When Möhler et al. (1980) attempted photoaffinity labeling with azide derivatives of BZs, they realized that, in the presence of Flu (used to determine nonspecific incorporation of the radioligand), the irreversible loss of BZ binding sites was in fact greater in the presence of Flu than in its absence. This chance observation led to the discovery of the excellent properties of Flu and other 7-nitro BZ derivatives as photoaffinity labels.

Incubation of membrane preparations or tissue slices with [^{3}H]Flu and subsequent exposure to UV light resulted in the time- and ligand concentration-dependent specific, irreversible incorporation of radioligand and a corresponding decrease of reversible binding. Other BZ ligands were able to inhibit the specific incorporation in relation to their affinity. Photoaffinity labeling reduced B_{max} but had little effect on K_D of subsequent reversible [^{3}H]Flu binding. Covalent incorporation of [^{3}H]Flu showed saturation with increasing concentrations of the ligand, half-maximal saturation occurring at about the K_D. The molecule covalently attached to Flu was a protein as shown by trypsin degradation. SDS–PAGE of the solubilized membranes showed a peak of radioactivity in a band corresponding to a protein of MW 49,600 ± 1400 (further studies on the proteins identified by photoaffinity labeling will be discussed later). Surprisingly, a maximum of one-fourth of the binding sites could be photolabeled. In addition, for one molecule of [³H]Flu specifically incorporated in membranes, four binding sites became inaccessible for subsequent reversible binding. Möhler et al. (1980) tentatively concluded that four BZ binding sites may be present on one receptor complex.

Photoaffinity labeling with [³H]Flu was shown to be useful for EM autoradiography. A fraction of labeled binding sites could be localized to known GABAergic synapses. In combination with the immunocytochemical reaction for glutamic acid decarboxylase it was possible to localize one-third of all photolabeled BZ binding sites to GABAergic synapses (Möhler et al., 1981b).

Flu was later shown not to photolabel nonneuronal type binding sites (Thomas and Tallman, 1983; Marangos et al., 1982; Richards and Möhler, 1984).

Of great interest has been the study of changes induced by photoaffinity labeling of membranes with Flu in the binding characteristics of various ligands, in particular of antagonists. Möhler (1982) observed that photolabeling of synaptic membranes with Flu reduced the number of [³H]Ro 15-1788 binding sites by the number of sites covalently bound to [³H]Flu. The affinity of the non-photolabeled binding sites for [³H]Ro 15-1788 was unaltered. Therefore, the use of [³H]Ro 15-1788 as reversible ligand in photolabeled membranes allowed for the rapid detection of changes on the affinity of various ligands after photoaffinity labeling (IC_{50} for inhibition of [³H]Ro 15-1788 binding to normal versus photolabeled membranes). The affinity of classical BZ agonist was found to be drastically reduced (20- to 50-fold) by photolabeling, that of the two non-BZ agonists zopiclone and CL 218,872 moderately (3- to 4-fold) reduced, that of suriclone (Blanchard and Cotrel, 1983) and of BZ antagonists (Ro 15-1788, CGS 8216) unaffected (Gee and Yamamura, 1983a), and the affinity of inverse agonists (β-CCM) even slightly enhanced. This suggested that binding to photolabeled membranes could be used to predict the (positive and negative) efficacy of ligands, a view supported by similar results of Gee and Yamamura (1982c), Brown and Martin (1982), Karobath and Supavilai (1982), and Sieghart et al. (1982) with β-[³H]CCE, β-[³H]CCM, β-[³H]CCPr, [³H]Ro 15-1788, and [³H]CGS 8216. However, Brown and Martin (1983b) surprisingly found that binding of pyrazoloquinolinones (CGS 8216, CGS 9895, and CGS 9896) was unaffected by photoaffinity labeling irrespective of the very different efficacies of the three compounds. They suggested that lack of occlusion of binding sites after photoaffinity labeling may be related to chemical structure rather than to efficacy; they speculated that an unknown fragment of Flu might be inserted in the vicinity of the BZ binding site in such a way that the proper site was not occupied, but that access to it was reduced for certain ligands, probably due to steric factors. Implicit in this idea is again the view that the actual binding sites for the different ligands may not be identical, but overlapping.

When Thomas and Tallman (1983) performed photoaffinity labeling such that about 25% of the BZ binding was covalently labeled and reversible [³H]Flu binding sites were reduced to 5%, the B_{max} for the BZ antagonists β-[³H]CCE, [³H]CGS 8216, or [³H]Ro 15-1788 was unaltered. And yet, each of these ligands was able to inhibit photoaffinity labeling with Flu when incubated with the photoaffinity label. Moreover, whereas BZ agonists were able to displace β-[³H]CCE in untreated membranes, the displacement curve for Diaz and other agonists in photolabeled membranes was shifted to the right and flattened. The displacement curves for antagonists was not altered to any significant degree. Accordingly, the Hill coefficient for β-[³H]CCE inhibition was close to 1 for agonists in untreated membranes, but around 0.5 in photolabeled preparations, however, remained at unity for antagonists. The Hill coefficient for CL 218,872 was less than unity in control as well as in photolabeled membranes. Essentially similar results were obtained with [³H]CGS 8216 as radioligand. The results suggested to Thomas and Tallman (1983) that the binding site photolabeled by [³H]Flu is not identical with the BZ antagonist binding site, however, that binding sites for β-carbolines and BZ agonists overlap in some but not all of their steric requirements for binding. The photolabeled site was even considered to be separate from both agonist and antagonist binding sites. The loss of BZ agonist binding sites in surplus of those actually photolabeled suggest that covalent binding converts high-affinity agonist binding sites to low-affinity sites which, due to technical difficulties to measure low-affinity binding, may simulate loss of binding sites ("cryptic" sites). The results of Thomas and Tallman (1983) are at variance with those of other authors, which rather suggest that the photolabeled site is a part of the BZ binding site. Möhler (1982) showed that the binding sites for [³H]Ro 15-1788 were occluded by photoaffinity labeling with Flu; their number was reduced by the extent to which binding sites were photolabeled. Similarly, Sieghart et al. (1982) found the number of binding sites for β- [³H] CCM reduced after photolabeling with the Flu. Thus, according to these results, the position of the photolabeled site would be within the BZ binding site.

Sherman-Gold (1983) suggested a mechanism that could be involved in photoaffinity labeling of BZ binding sites with Flu. She proposed that UV light induces resonance in the ligand molecule, resulting in a positively charged carbonyl carbon in position 2. With a hydrogen or halogen substituent in position 7 this resonance cannot occur. It was further suggested that the positively charged carboxyl carbon may interact with a nucleophilic group of the BZ binding site. This interaction would lead to the opening of the Diaz ring between positions 1 and 2 and the formation of a covalent bond between the nucleophil and the carbonyl carbon. The tyrosinyl residue, assumed to be involved in the reversible binding of BZ (Sherman-Gold and Dudai, 1981), could act as a nucleophile. Indeed, acetylation of the tyrosyl in the BZ binding protein abolished both reversible and covalent binding of [³H]Flu. Thus, reversible binding of BZ ligands may include an electrostatic interaction of the carbonyl carbon of the ligand with a nucleophilic component of the binding site and/or hydrogen binding of the carbonyl oxygen with a hydrogen donor of the receptor (Borea et al., 1982). Photoaffinity labeling would require a more positively charged carbon to form a covalent bond. If the role of the tyrosinyl residue turned out to be correct, this would support the view that BZ antagonists, such as Ro 15-1788 and β-carbolines, do not form the same bonds with the BZ binding site as agonists. However, considering the structural similarity of Flu with 4-nitrophenylethers—well-known high-yield photoreagents (Jelenc et al., 1978)—a different photoreaction appears likely. A nucleophlic group of the receptor protein, e.g., an amino group, might interact with Flu in position 9 or 5. No resonance in the ligand molecule, resulting in a positively changed caroxyl group in position 2 is needed for the photoreaction.

The intriguing question whether the BZR that is covalently linked to Flu is in an activated state or not has been answered only recently. Neurons from embryonic chick spinal cord in cell culture were exposed to Flu and UV light. The electrophysiological response of these photolabeled cells to GABA was rather depressed than increased, as one would have expected if photolabeling had produced an irreversible activation of BZRs (Chan et al., 1983).

5.9.3 Clonazepam

Sieghart and Möhler (1982) found clonazepam to have virtually identical properties to Flu as a photoaffinity label of BZ binding sites; the higher specificity of clonazepam for neuronal binding sites is of little relevance, as Flu does not photolabel nonneuronal binding sites.

5.9.4 Nitrazepam

Johnson and Yamamura (1979) obtained similar photoaffinity labeling results with nitrazepam, clonazepam, and Flu.

5.9.5 Other Irreversible Ligands

In order to better characterize the antagonist binding site, an azide analog of Ro 15-1788 (Ro 15-4513) was used as a photoaffinity label (Möhler et al., 1982). The compound is a partial inverse agonist (Bonetti et al., 1984). The labeling reaction was inhibited by agonists, antagonists, and inverse agonists. The autoradiographical distribution of [^{3}H]Ro 15-4513 sites corresponded well with the known pattern of neuronal BZ binding site distribution. Furthermore, the same protein bands (50K and 55K) were photolabeled with either [^{3}H]Ro 15-4513 or [^{3}H]Flu (Möhler et al., 1984). This suggests that the same binding protein contains both an agonist and an antagonist or inverse agonist binding site.

Phenoxybenzamine, which alkylates a number of transmitter receptors, was reported to inactivate GABA-Rs, but not BZ binding sites (Smokcum, 1983).

5.10 LOCALIZATION OF NEURONAL HIGH-AFFINITY BZ BINDING SITES

The uneven regional distribution of BZ binding sites in the CNS was already described in early biochemical studies on tissue homogenates (see Haefely et al., 1981b). The highest density of BZ binding sites is found in the cerebral cortex; the density is intermediate in the cerebellar cortex, hippocampus, amygdala, hypothalamus, and thalamus, and low in the lower brain stem and the spinal cord. The apparent affinity of classical BZ agonists for these sites is similar throughout the CNS. It was also reported rather early that in all brain areas the number of BZ binding sites is consistently lower than the number of GABA binding sites (Placheta and Karobath, 1979).

Great progress in the light-microscopic localization and regional quantifications of BZ binding sites has been made due to a new technique introduced by Young and Kuhar (1979b) and Palacios et al. (1981a) (see Section 4.2.1.1). This new autoradiographic approach has revealed, using [^{3}H]Flu as the radioligand, distinct intraregional differences in the density of BZ binding sites at the macroscopic and microscopic levels, e.g., in specific cell layers of the cerebral and cerebellar cortex, amygdala, substantia nigra, and spinal cord (Young and Kuhar, 1979a, 1980; Young et al., 1981; Palacios and Kuhar, 1980; Palacios et al., 1981a,b; Unnerstall et al., 1981, 1982; Niehoff and Kuhar, 1983; Richards et al., 1985).

Similarities as well as differences between species, e.g., human and rat brain, have been described for some of these regions, such as the cerebellum (Young and Kuhar, 1979b) or amygdala (Niehoff and Kuhar, 1983; Niehoff and Whitehouse, 1983). Using the autoradiographic technique it has also been possible to compare the regional distributions of BZ and various transmitter binding sites (Unnerstall et al., 1981). Moreover, it has helped to clearly distinguish central from peripheral type BZ binding sites by using displacing ligands or radioligands which are selective for the neuronal type ([^{3}H]clonazepam, [^{3}H]Ro 15-1788) or the nonneuronal type ([^{3}H]Ro 5-4864) (Richards et al., 1982; Gehlert et al., 1983; Richards and Möhler, 1984). In contrast to the former, the latter type of binding sites is concentrated in the olfactory nerve and the glomerular layer, in most ependyma and in the choroid plexus. The neuronal type of binding sites have been further differentiated in the putative BZ_1 and BZ_2 sites using CL

218,872 as a selective displacing agent for the former subtype. Autoradiographically they could be localized to specific brain regions (Young et al., 1981; Unnerstall et al., 1982; Niehoff and Kuhar, 1983; Richards and Möhler, 1984). Highest densities of BZ_1 binding sites occur in the cerebellum, substantia nigra, globus pallidus, inferior colliculus, central thalamus, ventral pallidum, and islands of Calleja, whereas the cerebral cortex and hippocampus appear to have a mixture of both BZ_1 and BZ_2 sites. The two subtypes have also been distinguished autoradiographically on the basis of their different sensitivity to detergent solubilization (Lo et al., 1983a). In lesion studies BZ_1 sites were reported to be located on intrinsic neurons of the substantia nigra and BZ_2 sites on terminals of striatonigral afferents (Lo et al., 1983b; see Section 5.15.6).

The pineal gland was found in biochemical studies to contain BZ binding sites of the central type, modulated by GABA (Lowenstein and Cardinali, 1983a,b); β-[^{3}H]CCE bound to about 60% of the [^{3}H]Flu binding sites, suggesting the presence of both BZR_1 and BZR_2 sites. In contrast, autoradiographical studies (Richards and Möhler, 1984) revealed exclusively peripheral type binding sites of a high density in the rat pineal.

The human anterior pituitary contains [^{3}H]Diaz binding sites which are only weakly stimulated by GABA (Grandison et al., 1982). In the rat intermediate lobe a small population of central type BZ binding sites, strongly stimulated by GABA, has been described (Anderson and Mitchell, 1983). However, autoradiographical studies (Richards and Möhler, 1984; De Souza et al., 1984) have demonstrated the exclusive presence of peripheral binding sites in the rat pituitary (higher density in the neurointermediate lobe).

The retina seems to contain BZ binding sites of both the central and peripheral type (Howells et al., 1979; Young and Kuhar, 1979b; Borbe et al., 1980; Willow and Morgan, 1980; Paul et al., 1980b; Skolnick et al., 1980d; Altstein et al., 1981; Guarneri et al., 1981, 1982). BZ binding sites are concentrated in the inner plexiform and ganglion cell layers. Kainic acid injection into the eye (destroying horizontal and amacrine cells) had little effect on high-affinity binding of [^{3}H]Diaz in the experiments of Willow and Morgan (1980) but reduced it in the experiments of Skolnick et al. (1980b). [^{3}H]Diaz binding sites in the rat retina were found to increase with age (along with GABA binding sites), whereas GABA stimulation of [^{3}H]Diaz binding decreased with age. Dark exposure was found to increase B_{max} for [^{3}H]Diaz.

The olfactory bulb is very rich in BZ binding sites. Autoradiographically (Richards et al., 1982), they are concentrated in the lamina plexiformis externa, rich in GABAergically innervated mitral cell dendrites (Ribak et al., 1977), and in the lamina glomerulosa, which contains primary mitral cell dendrites with dense GABAergic synapses. Nonneuronal type BZ binding sites, in contrast, are concentrated in the lamina nervosa, rich in glia (Jaffé and Cuello, 1981), and in the lamina glomerulosa containing peripheral inputs from the olfactory mucosa

(Richards et al., 1982). Recently, Anholt et al. (1984) have reported extremely high levels of [³H]Ro 5-4864 binding sites in the nasal epithelium, in presumed olfactory nerves.

BZ and GABA binding sites were also studied on isolated neurons, e.g., on isolated cell bodies of cerebellar Purkinje cells prepared with 90% purity from beef brain by filtering through a nylon mesh (Henn, 1980). GABA binding sites were of a low- and a high-affinity type. The total number of GABA binding sites was about three times higher than the number of [³H]Diaz binding sites.

In the spinal cord central type binding sites are present almost exclusively in the gray matter, being particularly concentrated in the dorsal horn (laminae II, III, and IV) and in lamina X around the central canal (Young and Kuhar, 1980). The fraction of [³H]Diaz binding sites belonging to the nonneuronal type (occurring in both white and gray matter) was considerably larger than in the brain (Del Zompo et al., 1983).

The study of the subcellular distribution of BZ binding sites (Yokoi et al., 1981) gave discrepant results (see Haefely et al., 1981a). The neuronal type of binding sites are undoubtedly highly concentrated in the neuronal cell membrane. Nonneuronal and, perhaps, low-affinity binding sites, are, in addition, located intracellularly. Some binding sites of the neuronal type are likely to be found intracellularly with sensitive methods, as they have to be transported to and from their functional site during receptor synthesis and degradation of recycling.

The GABA-induced increase in the apparent affinity of agonist ligands of the neuronal type BZ binding sites can be visualized autoradiographically (Unnerstall et al., 1981). The binding of [³H]Ro 15-1788, in contrast, is not stimulated by GABA (Möhler and Richards, 1981a). BZ binding stimulation by other agents, e.g., barbiturates (Valdes et al., 1981), can also be studied at high tissue resolution.

The controversy about BZ binding sites in glial cells is not resolved because of methodological problems with cells and ligands (Baraldi et al., 1979; Braestrup et al., 1978; Henn and Henke, 1978; Dudai et al., 1979; Syapin and Skolnick, 1979; McCarthy and Harden, 1981; Tardy et al., 1981).

The question of whether BZ binding sites are present both in the subsynaptic membrane of soma and dendrites and in the membrane of axon terminals has been studied, e.g., by lesion experiments (see below); the answer is inconclusive. Extraction of membranes with the detergent Triton X-100 under conditions thought to extract differentially proteins from pre- and postsynaptic membranes was interpreted as indication that a portion of BZ binding sites is located presynaptically (Sabato et al., 1981a–c). Fung and Fillenz (1983) studied the effect of chlordiazepoxide (an unsuitable BZ for in vitro experiments) on GABA-induced changes in the release of noradrenaline from hippocampal synaptosomes; a very complex picture emerged.

The photolabel [³H]Flu has been used after covalent binding to localize BZ binding sites by electron microscopic autoradiography (Möhler *et al.*, 1980). Photolabeled BZ binding sites were localized in areas of synaptic contact, some of which are GABAergic according to immunocytochemical identification (Möhler *et al.*, 1981b).

5.11 PHYLOGENY OF BZ BINDING SITES

A survey of the occurrence of specific binding sites in the animal kingdom is given in Braestrup and Nielsen (1983). BZRs appear to be phylogenetically young and restricted to vertebrates. Since GABA-Rs occur and are intensively investigated in invertebrates (e.g., crustaceae), it will be very interesting to compare the GABA-R/Cl$^-$ channel complex in vertebrates and invertebrates. The lack of a potentiating effect of BZs on GABA effects in invertebrates is fully in line with the results of binding experiments (see Haefely and Polc, 1983). Recently, typical central type BZ binding sites were identified in the brain of the rainbow trout (Wilkinson *et al.*, 1983a,b). GABA enhanced [^{3}H]Flu binding in the trout by a bicuculline-sensitive mechanism via a decrease of K_D. It would be very interesting to know whether BZs modulate the GABA-R in this poikilotherm animal at low temperature.

5.12 ONTOGENY OF BZ BINDING SITES

Biochemically, BZ binding sites have been found in fetal rodent brain from gestational day 16; at birth they are approximately 30% of the adult levels reached at 21 days post partum (Braestrup and Nielsen, 1978; Candy and Martin, 1979a,b; Mallorga *et al.*, 1983; Palacios *et al.*, 1979; Regan *et al.*, 1981; Richards *et al.*, 1985). The apparent affinity of the receptor for BZs is similar throughout development. The prenatal and postnatal development of BZ binding sites in rat brain has been recently studied autoradiographically (Palacios and Kuhar, 1982; Schlumpf *et al.*, 1983). *In vitro* binding is first detected on gestational day 14 in the spinal cord and lower brain stem, then spreads into the mesencephalon and parts of the diencephalon (particularly the ventral areas). By day 16 binding occurs in the developing caudate-putamen, the olfactory bulb, and the frontoventral parts of the neocortex and by day 21 throughout the neocortex and increasingly in diencephalic and telencephalic areas. At earlier stages of development, neocortical binding sites are confined to the superficial (days 16 and 18) and deep layers (day 18) above and below the cortical plate, the latter being unlabeled. This distinct ontogenetic pattern of BZ binding sites—the general caudo-rostral gradient and the development in individual brain regions such as the neocortex—appears to be linked with cell differentiation, though not necessarily with synaptogenesis.

Chisholm *et al.* (1983) have recently studied the development of BZ$_1$ and BZ$_2$ binding sites in three regions of rat brain. In contrast to the cortex and cerebellum, the hippocampus contains BZ_1 sites at birth, prior to periods of dendritic elaboration and synaptogenesis. High-affinity BZ_1 sites in the cerebellum show a delayed postnatal development. That some, at least, of the BZ binding sites present in the fetal brain are functional receptors is indicated by the finding that various BZ agonists reduce somatic movements of 4- and 5-day-old chicken embryos; this effect was blocked by Ro 15-1788 (Maderdrut et al., 1983). As a by-product of ontogenetic studies, knowledge about the period of most intense biosynthesis of BZRs is obtained that could be used in future experiments to obtain mRNA coding for BZRs. The other aspect is the use of BZ binding sites as biochemical markers for fetotoxic effects of chemical agents.

The postnatal development of [^{3}H]Diaz and [^{3}H]muscimol binding sites in rats was characterized by a decrease in density, whereas in the cerebellum there was an increase (Saito et al., 1983).

5.13 SEX DIFFERENCES

B_{max} for [^{3}H]Diaz was found to be 15% higher in female mice than in males, whereas K_D did not differ in the two sexes (Sonawane et al., 1980). A sex difference in [^{3}H]Flu binding was also reported for rats (Shephard et al., 1982). The number of [^{3}H]Flu binding sites in the cerebral and cerebellar cortex was higher in female rats, while the reverse was true in the striatum and hippocampus.

5.14 MONITORING THE IN VIVO OCCUPATION OF BZRS

A highly controversial issue in clinical pharmacology is whether a correlation exists over time between the intensity of effects of BZs and the blood levels of the original compound and possible active metabolites. Surprisingly little is known about the "pharmacokinetics at the receptor site," not only for BZs but for centrally acting agents in general. Even though the intensity of central effects is unlikely to reflect accurately the proportion of drug receptors in the CNS that is activated (because of rapid and slow physiological adaptation processes both in neuronal circuits that are directly affected by the drug and circuits that are not direct targets of the drugs), receptor occupancy (fraction of available receptors that are liganded at a given time) is certainly the main determinant of the intensity of drug effect. Fractional receptor occupancy is determined by, and reflects, the drug concentration in the biophase, i.e., the concentration of free drug able to interact with the receptor according to the law of mass action.

Pioneer studies (see Haefely et al., 1981a) have shown that it is possible in the animal to estimate fractional receptor occupancy "in vivo" (measurement of specifically bound radioligand in tissue samples removed as rapidly as possible after sacrifice) at any time after drug administration. The principle is, of course, based on the competition between radiolabeled and unlabeled drug molecules for specific binding sites. A tracer dose of the radioligand is injected iv after (in some experiments before, e.g., Fehske and Müller, 1982) a pharmacologically active dose of the unlabeled drug. The amount of specifically bound radiolabel in a tissue sample is measured at a fixed time after its injection and at various times after administration of the unlabeled drug and compared to the value of specific binding in the absence of the cold ligand.

The details of the technique used by the various investigators varied considerably. The following variables are relevant: (1) The radioligand used; whereas [³H]Diaz was used in early investigations (Williamson et al., 1978a,b; Chang and Snyder, 1978; Lippa et al., 1978b; Tallman et al., 1979) and is still used by Mennini and Garattini (1982) and Mennini et al. (1982a,b), [³H]Flu was soon realized to be superior to [³H]Diaz because of higher affinity, lower nonspecific binding, and a slower off-rate (at low temperature), reducing the dissociation during wash-out of unbound radioligand on the filters; (2) the time of sacrifice after injection of the radioligand; (3) the way specifically bound ligand is estimated. This was done in some studies by measuring totally bound radioactivity in one aliquot of tissue and nonspecifically bound activity in another aliquot in which the specifically bound ligand was displaced by a cold ligand. The problem is to prevent new binding "ex vivo" as well as dissociation to occur during the homogenization (Minchin and Nutt, 1983). A variation of the procedure was to measure nonspecifically bound radioligand after inhibiting specific binding by prior administration of a very high "saturating" dose of a cold ligand (Braestrup and Nielsen, 1983). Duka et al. (1979) measured total, free, as well as specifically and nonspecifically bound radioactivity in rapidly removed tissue samples after combustion. This activity minus that found when the radiolabel was injected after high "saturating" doses of cold ligand (representing unbound plus nonspecifically bound ligand) gave the amount of specifically bound radioligand. The total radioactivity was highest in hippocampus, medium in the cerebral cortex, hypothalamus, and striatum, and only 54–58% of the cortical concentrations in midbrain, pons–medulla, and cerebellum. "Displaceable binding" was highest in the cerebral cortex (53%) and lowest in the brainstem (30%) and cerebellum (11%). The dose of cold Flu inhibiting "displaceable binding" as defined above by 50% was 0.44 mg/kg (about 1.4 μmol/kg), which resulted in a level of Flu in the hippocampus of 8×10^{-7} mol/kg.

Results of in vivo fractional receptor occupancy studies are expressed by the ID_{50}, the calculated doses for 50% inhibition of specific binding. Comparative studies on in vivo potency were made by Müller and Stillbauer (1983) in mice. Sethy et al. (1983a,b) compared the time course of brain-specific binding of Diaz, triazolam, alprazolam, and some ring-open prodrugs of triazolobenzodiazepines. Braestrup and Nielsen (1983) have collected other data from the literature and their own experiments. Mennini and Garattini (1982) present data obtained with their method. The relative potencies agree overall with pharmacological experience; the absolute figures, however, differ considerably from one paper to the other. Mennini *et al.* (1982b) administered equieffective anticonvulsant doses of various BZs po to rats. Animals were sacrificed 1 min after the iv injection of [^{3}H]Diaz. Total and specifically bound [^{3}H]Diaz were determined in crude homogenates of various brain parts *ex vivo*. The percent of specifically bound [^{3}H]Diaz was highest in the cerebral cortex (37%) and lowest in the cerebellum (16.2%), the hippocampus, brainstem and striatum showing intermediate values. All BZs tested and given in equieffective doses inhibited specifically bound [^{3}H]Diaz by roughly 50% in all areas except in the cerebellum, where displacement was very weak and, in addition, highly variable. The concentration of Diaz plus desmethyldiazepam in the brain was 8×10^{-7} mol/kg. Pieri *et al.* (1981) compared time course of pharmacological activity and of *in vivo* BZR occupancy for Diaz and midazolam and found a correlation. Jones and Oakley (1982) studied *in vivo* binding of [^{3}H]Flu in mice. When Diaz was administered po 1 hr before [^{3}H]Flu (iv, sacrifice 20 min later), the doses inhibiting total binding by 25 and 50% were 1 and 4 mg/kg, respectively, for both cortex and cerebellum. CL 218,872 was about 1.5 to 2 times more potent in the cerebellum (10 and 39 mg/kg for 25 and 50% inhibition) than in the cortex (15 and 80 mg/kg). β-CCPr gave ID_{25} and ID_{50} values of 0.75 and 0.3 mg/kg iv in cerebellum and 1.2 and 5.0 mg/kg in the cortex. Minchin and Nutt (1983) studied the *in vivo* displacing potencies of Diaz, β-CCE, and Ro 15-1788 in various regions of the rat brain. Whereas Ro 15-1788 had the same affinity in cortex, hippocampus, striatum, and cerebellum, β-CCE was four times more potent in the cerebellum than in the cortex and for Diaz the situation was the reverse. Most investigators made one important error, at least in formulating their results: the reported ID_{50} values are not the doses that produce 50% occupancy of available BZ binding sites, as suggested by the authors, but simply 50% inhibition of an unknown fraction of binding sites that is occupied by the radioligand, which was always given in a dose much too small to saturate binding sites. In fact, the really saturating doses of BZs are still unknown. The statements, repeated uncritically in the literature, that a certain effect is obtained by a measured degree of receptor occupancy (e.g., Paul *et al.*, 1979; Skolnick *et al.*, 1983a), are necessarily wrong. This is unfortunate, as the true amount of receptor occupancy for a given intensity of effect would be an urgently needed index of intrinsic activity (or efficacy). An approach to obtain at least an approximation value of receptor occupancy has recently been used by Jensen and Petersen (1983) and has proven of value in detecting partial agonists at BZRs.

In vivo binding played a crucial role in the discovery of the first specific BZ antagonist (Hunkeler *et al.*, 1981). It will be even more important in characterizing partial agonists and for the identification of possible inter- and intraregional differences of affinity *in vivo*.

Valuable information is obtained, when not only the amount of specifically bound ligand is determined, but when this value is followed over time in relation to totally present and totally bound ligand, as first done by Chang and Snyder (1978). These studies give clear evidence for nonparallel changes in the amount of specifically bound and totally present ligand over time, indicating that a redistribution occurs within the brain with greater tendency toward nonspecific binding (most probably in brain lipids) with time.

Determination of *in vivo* binding is useful to explain apparent discrepancies between *in vitro* affinity to BZ binding sites and *in vivo* pharmacological activity. For instance, the ring-open prodrug of a 1,4-benzodiazepine, the peptidoaminobenzophenone 450088-S, inactive *in vitro,* was more potent *in vivo* than Diaz after iv and po administration as an [3H]Flu displacer (Wong and Bymaster, 1983). *In vivo* studies also demonstrate convincingly that some drugs, having a weak but possibly relevant affinity *in vitro,* do not occupy BZ binding sites to any significant degree after the highest tolerated doses, e.g., harmane (Fehske and Müller, 1982). Findings that wait for an explanation are, e.g., the dose-dependent enhancement of *in vivo* binding of [3H]Flu in mice (Oakley and Jones, 1983) and of [3H]Diaz (but not of [3H]Flu) in rats (Garattini *et al.,* 1982) by buspirone. The distribution of BZRs *in vivo* can be visualized autoradiographically. Two to 5 min after intravenous injection of the radioligand, e.g., [3H]Ro 15-1788, the regional density of radiolabeling in tissue sections was virtually identical with that found by *in vitro* labeling (Richards and Möhler, 1984a).

Vizualization of BZ distribution and displacement in the brain of intact baboons has been obtained using [11C]-labeled BZR ligands (Flu, Ro 15-1788) and positron emission tomography (PET) (Comar *et al.,* 1979, 1981; Mazière *et al.,* 1983a,b). After iv injection of [11C]Ro 15-1788 specific accumulation of radioactivity occurred in brain areas; this was rapidly displaced by cold lorazepam as seen in sequential tomographic pictures. Although the level of resolution of PET is yet too small for quantitative brain receptor pharmacokinetics of drugs, the method would seem to have interesting prospects. Recently, preliminary results with a positron emitting radioligand containing [75Br] in position 7 have been published (Scholl *et al.,* 1983).

5.15 *IN VIVO* MODULATION, ADAPTATION, AND PATHOLOGY OF BZRS

Receptors for neurotransmitters and hormones are known to display plasticity of varying intensity, i.e., adaptive changes to physiological, pathological, and drug-induced perturbations of CNS activity. It was of obvious interest, therefore, to search for changes in BZRs in various conditions. Theoretically, such changes, if they occur at all, may be simply associated with other, more important alterations, and be of no functional relevance, or they may themselves have functional consequences and be the cause of altered behavior or altered drug response.

5.15.1 Diurnal Rhythms and Influences of Light

B_{max} for [³H]Diaz binding to rat forebrain membranes was found to display a diurnal rhythm (monophasic decrease during the daylight period, biphasic increase toward the end of the dark phase), which was completely abolished by a 2-week treatment with lithium in the food (Kafka *et al.*, 1982).

In the retina of dark-adapted rats the affinities of BZ and GABA binding sites for their ligands were reported to be higher than in light-adapted rats (Biggio *et al.*, 1981a). Neither REM sleep deprivation nor REM sleep rebound affected [³H]Diaz binding in cerebral cortex and brainstem (Mueser *et al.*, 1983).

5.15.2 Ageing

While no differences in [³H]BZ binding characteristics between young adult and old rats were found by Haefely *et al.* (1980), Heusner and Bosman (1981), Cook and James (1982), Tsang *et al.* (1981), Reeves and Schweizer (1983), Pedigo *et al.* (1981), B_{max} for [³H]Diaz binding was found to increase in the cerebellum, hippocampus, and striatum, but not in the cerebral cortex of aged Sprague–Dawley rats and GABA stimulation of [³H]Diaz binding to decrease (Calderini *et al.*, 1981). An increase of B_{max} for [³H]Diaz binding in the cortex of senescent mice was found by Lal *et al.* (1982). A quantitative difference between adult and old rats was found in their increase of BZ_1Rs 1 hr after a single acute administration of 5 mg/kg Diaz (Reeves and Schweizer, 1983). Both GABA and BZ binding sites were found to increase in the rat retina with age (Biggio *et al.*, 1983), while the stimulation of BZ binding by GABA decreased. In old rats, dark exposure no longer activated BZ binding in the retina. Binding of [³H]Ro 5-4864 was found to be decreased in kidney membranes of senescent rats (Pedigo *et al.*, 1981).

5.15.3 Stress and Various Emotional States

Various forms of stress (repeated electric footshock, postnatal isolation of newborn pups, immobilization, swim stress, amphetamine intoxication, isolation-induced aggression) were considered not to lead to relevant changes in [³H]Diaz binding by Braestrup *et al.* (1979b). In male mice, which developed intramale aggression after 4 weeks of socioenvironmental isolation, the number of BZ_1Rs was reported to be reduced in the cerebral cortex, while in the diencephalon and cerebellar cortex it was the number of BZ_2Rs that was reduced (Essman and Valzelli, 1981). Mice exposed to forced swimming for 3 min in warm water showed no change in [^{3}H]Diaz binding in the forebrain but an increase of both low- and high-affinity sites for [^{3}H]GABA (Skerritt *et al.*, 1981). In rats killed immediately after a 15-min swimming stress, B_{max} for [^{3}H]Flu and β-[^{3}H]CCE binding was reduced by 30% in the cerebral cortex and hippocampus, but not in other CNS regions. B_{max} had recovered 1 hr after stress (Medina *et al.*, 1983a–c). An increase in the number of [^{3}H]Flu binding sites was found by Soubrié *et al.* (1980) in the cerebral cortex of rats after forced swimming in cold water. Rats of the Maudsley nonreactive strain ("nonemotional") bound more [^{3}H]Diaz in all areas of the brain than animals of the Maudsley reactive strain ("emotional") (Robertson *et al.*, 1978); the difference was most marked in the hippocampus and hypothalamus. Similar results were obtained by Robertson (1979) when comparing [^{3}H]Diaz in "emotional" or "anxious" mice. In Roman Low and Roman High Avoidance rats, differing clearly in their emotionality, no difference in specific [^{3}H]Flu was found (Shephard *et al.*, 1982). A slightly (nonsignificant) higher binding of [^{3}H]Diaz was found in Roman High Avoidance (low emotionality) rats (Gentsch *et al.*, 1981). B_{max} for [^{3}H]Flu binding was reduced by 25% in cortex membranes of rats sacrificed during a conditioned emotional response (Lane *et al.*, 1982), but not in animals conditioned but exposed to footshock alone or in animals nonconditioned but presented with the conditioned stimulus. While diazepam, given ip prior to the session, eliminated the conditioned emotional response, it did not affect the change in B_{max}. A similar 25% decrease of [^{3}H]Diaz binding sites in the frontal cortex was reported by Lippa *et al.* (1978b) in rats exposed to a conflict situation (punished drinking) for 5 min. Exposure to repeated, unavoidable footshocks for 5 min had a less pronounced effect. The reduced binding of [^{3}H]Diaz was ascribed to the release of an endogenous compound in anxiety producing situations. In rats housed in isolation for 3 months muricide behavior develops, which is not reduced by BZs (Petkov and Yanev, 1982); affinity and number of [^{3}H]Flu binding sites were significantly reduced in the cerebral cortex.

5.15.4 Epileptic Activity

Generalized clonic–tonic seizures induced in rats by electroshock or pentetrazol were followed by a 20% increase of specific [^{3}H]Diaz binding in a crude synaptosomal membrane preparation of the cerebral cortex (Paul and Skolnick, 1978; Skolnick *et al.*, 1983a); the effect was significant as early as 15 min after seizures and was completely reversed after 60 min. No alteration of [^{3}H]Diaz and β-[^{3}H]CCE binding was found in rat brain at various times after a single electroconvulsive shock (Nutt and Minchin, 1983). Kindling seizures induced by repeated stimulation of the basolateral nucleus of the right amygdala led to an increase of [^{3}H]Flu binding on somata and the dendritic tree of granule cells in the fascia dentata (Valdes *et al.*, 1982; Fanelli and McNamara, 1983); daily induction of full electroshock seizures had the same effect. Amygdala kindling increased [³H]Flu binding in the amygdala itself and somewhat less in the hippocampus, but lowered it in the caudate (Tuff et al., 1983). Two months after amygdala kindling a decrease in B_{max} for [³H]Flu in cortex and hypothalamus was found (Burnham et al., 1983; Niznik et al., 1983); [³H]Ro 5-4864 binding was unchanged. Kindling induced by repeated iv injections of initially subconvulsive doses of pentetrazol in mice resulted in an ~ 30% increase of B_{max} for [³H]Diaz in the forebrain without change of K_D (Syapin and Rickman, 1981); there was no correlation between changes in BZ binding and the kindling response. Lal et al. (1981) failed to find any changes in [³H]Diaz and [³H]Flu binding in the cortex of rats treated acutely or chronically with pentetrazol except for a slight increase in B_{max} within the 30 min after overt seizure activity. No change in [³H]Diaz binding in several brain regions of rats was observed by Bowdler and Green (1982) and Bowdler et al. (1983) after a series of electroconvulsive seizures induced daily for 10 days. In DBA/2 mice with genetically determined susceptibility to generalized seizures upon exposure to auditory stimulation, [³H]Flu binding was not convincingly different from control animals (Horton et al., 1982); however, the number of high-affinity binding sites for [³H]GABA was lower at all ages in susceptible mice. Also in an inbred strain of mice with susceptibility to audiogenic seizures at about 22 days of age, the density of [³H]Flu binding sites in brain synaptosomal membranes was significantly higher than in a nonsusceptible control strain (Robertson, 1980); this increase was seen only during the short period of seizure susceptibility and was present whether the animals had had seizures before sacrifice or not. The affinity of [³H]Flu was increased in all main areas of Mongolian gerbils 10 min after seizures had been induced by strong manipulation (Asano and Mizutani, 1980); changes in B_{max} were not significant. Twenty minutes after seizures binding was again at control levels. Pups of rats exposed to three maximal electroconvulsive shocks at gestational days 14, 18, and 20 showed a 20% decrease in specific neuronal [³H]Diaz binding sites in cerebral cortex membranes at the age of 3 weeks (Gallager and Wakeman, 1982). Electrolytic lesions of the entorhinal cortex of rats consistently produces limbic seizures; a bilateral and symmetrical decline in the number of [³H]Flu binding site in the dentate gyrus was found (Kraus et al., 1983). Treatment with phenobarbitone suppressed seizures and prevented the changes in BZ binding.

5.15.5 Drugs

The modulation of BZRs by drugs can be separated into homospecific receptor modulation, i.e., changes induced by ligands of these receptors, and into heterospecific receptor modulation, i.e., changes induced in BZRs by agents that do not bind themselves to the BZ binding sites.

5.15.5.1 Benzodiazepines. BZ, when given over long periods in sufficiently high doses, can induce tolerance and physical dependence. The simplest (and certainly too simple) explanation would be a change in BZRs.

No changes in [³H]Diaz binding were found in the brain of rats given 3 mg/kg Diaz ip daily for 3 weeks and sacrificed 24–28 hr after the last injection (Möhler *et al.*, 1978b). The huge dose of 90 mg/kg po daily for 8 weeks apparently did not result in any change in [³H]Diaz binding (Braestrup *et al.*, 1979d). Daily exposure of rats to Diaz from 10 days before birth until 7 days after birth also failed to produce significant changes in BZ binding. Rats treated for 7 to 10 days twice daily with flurazepam ip up to 150 mg/kg and sacrificed 14 hr after the last dose had a 15% decrease in B_{max} for [³H]Diaz binding in cortex (Rosenberg and Chiu, 1979b, 1981a,b; Chiu and Rosenberg, 1978). The same authors found a decrease of B_{max} for [³H]Flu binding in synaptosomes of rats treated for 4 weeks with 100–150 mg/kg flurazepam once daily. DiStefano *et al.* (1979) treated rats with 170 mg/kg Diaz po daily for 35 days. Binding of [³H]Diaz and [³H]Flu to forebrain membranes was tested at 5 n*M* over the first 7 days of withdrawal. Binding was markedly increased on the third to seventh day, but normal again at day 10. These early studies of possible alterations in BZRs that could account for tolerance and/or physical dependence were summarized by Overstreet and Yamamura (1979); they considered that the highly contradictory results provided no firm evidence for a modulation of the BZ binding characteristics after chronic administration. In more recent studies Abbracchio *et al.* (1983) and Coen *et al.* (1983) reported a marked decrease of B_{max} for [³H]Flu in the cerebral cortex and hippocampus, but not in the cerebellum of rats treated with moderate doses of chlordiazepoxide either during the first 3 postnatal weeks or for 3 weeks at adult age. The authors speculated that a specific down regulation of the number of BZ_2R had occurred. Conversely, the number of [³H]muscimol binding sites was increased by pretreatment. Enhancement of [³H]GABA binding by Diaz was reduced. Medina *et al.* (1983c) found a small, nonsignificant decrease of [³H]Flu and β-[³H]CCE binding in the cortex of rats treated with a daily dose of 4 mg/kg Diaz in the drinking water over 14 days. In contrast, a similar treatment with Ro 15-1788 markedly increased the density of binding sites for both ligands in synaptosomes of the cerebral cortex and hippocampus.

A single acute dose of 50 mg/kg Diaz to rats increased the apparent density of [³H]Flu binding sites measured 1 h later and decreased apparent affinity (Speth *et al.*, 1979a). An acute single administration of 5 mg/kg Diaz led to a 73% increase of density in aged and to a 42% increase in adult rats 1 hr after administration (Reeves and Schweizer, 1983); the increase in adult rats was due to a massive increase of BZ_1Rs and a slight decrease of BZ_2Rs, whereas in aged rats BZ_2Rs were doubled and BZ_1R only slightly increased. A chronic administration of 0.4 mg/kg Diaz ip twice daily produced an approximately 30% increase of BZ binding site density (exclusively BZ_1R) in adult and aged rats. One hour after a single high ip dose of alprazolam and Diaz (50 mg/kg) B_{max} of [^{3}H]Flu binding was roughly doubled in water-washed rat brain membrane preparations; this effect was no longer seen 20 hr after dosing (Sethy and Harris, 1982). The authors speculated that this change may be artifactual, e.g., that the presence of a BZ might protect membrane-bound sites from solubilization by distilled water. Treatment of rats on 7 consecutive days with the "short-acting" lorazepam, the "intermediate acting" clonazepam, or the "long-acting" BZs flurazepam and Diaz led to an 80% increase of B_{max} with no change in K_D for [^{3}H]Diaz binding 18 to 25 hr after the last injection of the two former drugs; Diaz and flurazepam did not produce any change (Scharf and Feil, 1983). It was speculated that repeated intake of a BZ may inhibit the production of an endogenous BZR ligand by a feedback mechanism and that the lack of the endogenous ligand would increase the available sites; rebound phenomena that are thought to occur after short-acting BZs were tentatively explained by these highly speculative processes. In mice injected twice daily with increasing doses (up to 7.5 mg/kg ip of clonazepam or chlordiazepoxide for 3 weeks, [^{3}H]Diaz binding in the forebrain showed a marked reduction of B_{max} 2 hr and 2 days after the last dose of clonazepam, but not of chlordiazepoxide; binding was found to be normalized 10 days later (Crawley et al., 1982). The same treatments resulted in an increase of the apparent number of high-affinity [^{3}H]muscimol binding sites (Marangos and Crawley, 1982).

Neurons were also exposed to BZs in cell culture conditions to study changes in BZ binding sites. Shibla et al. (1981) exposed dissociated cell cultures of fetal mouse brain to 1 μM Diaz for 3 weeks. No change in [^{3}H]Diaz binding could be found in membranes prepared from the cell culture. Exposure to 1 μM GABA or muscimol was also without effect on [^{3}H]Diaz binding. Sher (1983) and Sher et al. (1983) exposed dissociated mouse spinal cord cell cultures, containing both neurons and nonneuronal cells, to 10 μM Diaz for 7 days. [^{3}H]Diaz binding was very markedly reduced immediately after withdrawal of Diaz and recovered on the tenth day after withdrawal. Binding to the (clonazepam displaceable) neuronal type of site was considerably more affected than that to the nonneuronal type. A parallel electrophysiological study showed that the ability of Diaz to enhance the membrane conductance increase produced by iontophoretic GABA was depressed with a similar time course as the decrease of [^{3}H]Diaz binding. The results were explained either by a down regulation of BZRs by Diaz or by a "tight" binding of Diaz to its binding sites. A contrasting conclusion was drawn by Prezioso and Neale (1983) from similar experiments.

Twice daily intracerebroventricular injection (10 μg) of β-CCE for 8 days increased the number of [^{3}H]Diaz binding sites in the cortex, cerebellum, and hippocampus by 63, 51, and 38%. Binding of β-[^{3}H]CCE was unaffected (Concas et al., 1983). The results were taken as evidence that β-CCE is an antagonist at BZRs.

5.15.5.2 Ethanol.   Continuous inhalation of ethanol by rats for 19 days, resulting in a mean blood ethanol concentration of 28.5 mg/100 ml, did not affect [^{3}H]Flu binding (Karobath *et al.*, 1980a). Mice ingesting alcohol for 3 to 4 weeks showed no change in [^{3}H]Flu or [^{3}H]Diaz binding in whole brain and several brain areas (Freund, 1980; Bosio *et al.*, 1982); after 7 months of ethanol ingestion a slight decrease in B_{max} and an increase in K_D was observed, which was considered to be possibly due to neuronal lesions (Freund, 1980). It may be of interest that ethanol treatment of rat brain membranes produced a concentration-dependent increase of [^{3}H]Diaz binding (Burch and Ticku, 1980). [^{3}H]Flu binding was decreased in cerebral and cerebellar cortex of rats 1 hr after the last of three daily doses of ethanol for 6 days; this effect was only seen in membranes preincubated with Triton X-100 and was due to a decrease in B_{max} (Volicer and Biagioni, 1982b). Binding was normal 16 hr later. The complex and partially contradictory results reported on the effect of ethanol on the GABA-R-BZR complex are discussed by Hunt (1983).

5.15.5.3 Barbiturates.   Möhler *et al.* (1978b) found no change in [^{3}H]Diaz binding in the brains of rats treated for 30 days with 30 mg/kg phenobarbitone ip daily. Treatment of mice for 4 days with 60 mg/kg phenobarbitone ip daily markedly reduced B_{max} (by 36% in males, by 53% in females) and slightly reduced K_D (Sonawane *et al.*, 1980). After 10 days of barbitone twice daily up to 125 mg/kg ip binding of [^{3}H]Diaz to cortical synaptosomal membranes was unaffected (Rosenberg and Chiu, 1979b). In membranes obtained from primary cultures of isolated neurons of chick embryo cerebral hemisphere exposed to 10^{-4} *M* pentobarbitone for 5 days, the GABA-induced enhancement of [^{3}H]Diaz binding was markedly attenuated (Roth-Schechter *et al.*, 1983).

5.15.5.4 Other agents.   Methylmercury (10 mg/kg po), which produced no visible effects on rats, increased the number of [^{3}H]Diaz binding sites in the retina and in various areas of the brain (Corda *et al.*, 1981).

Mice were made physically dependent on morphine by sc pellet implantation. Twenty-four hours after removal of the pellet the animals were sacrificed and synaptic membranes prepared from a whole brain homogenate for equilibrium binding of [^{3}H]Flu (Sivam and Ho, 1982). No change in B_{max} and K_D for [^{3}H]Flu binding occurred; however, the apparent affinity of GABA and muscimol to stimulate BZ binding was significantly reduced.

A 4-week lithium diet reduced [^{3}H]Flu binding sites selectively in the cerebral cortex of rats (Hetmar *et al.*, 1983).

Rats ingesting during 4 weeks the GABA-transaminase inhibitor ethanolamine *O*-sulfate, which increased GABA levels in the brain approximately fourfold, increased the number of $GABA_A$ and $GABA_B$, but not that of BZ binding sites (Horton *et al.*, 1983).

5.15.6 Lesions

Since autoradiographic methods do not allow the precise localization of BZ binding sites on identified neurons, the seemingly simple procedure of determining BZ binding after neuronal lesions has been used. The pitfalls of this technique are among other things the problematic selectivity of neuronal cell loss, the possibility that BZ binding sites may remain intact for quite some time in cell membrane debris, and the present ignorance whether cell loss may have induced modulatory effects on BZ binding sites. The use of radioligands highly specific for the neuronal high-affinity binding site is imperative, as lesions induce variable degrees of gliosis with the corresponding increase of nonneuronal type binding sites. Changes in BZ binding sites have been sought after spontaneous (genetic) degenerations, after neurotoxins, and after mechanical lesions.

Changes in BZ binding sites in mice with genetic neurological defects will not be described in detail here, since this topic has been reviewed very recently (Biscoe and Fry, 1984). A generally accepted conclusion is that cerebellar Purkinje cells contain a considerable part of the BZ binding sites in the cerebellum (perhaps one-half) (Lippa *et al.,* 1978a; Speth and Yamamura, 1979; Vaccarino *et al.,* 1983).

Neurotoxins with more or less selectivity for certain types of neurons have been used. Kainic acid which, upon local application, lesions cell bodies in the injected area, but not through-axons, was injected into the cerebellum; a marked decrease of [^{3}H]Diaz and [^{3}H]Flu binding in the molecular layer was found with little change in the (modest) density of high-affinity [^{3}H]muscimol binding sites (Braestrup *et al.,* 1979a; Biggio *et al.,* 1980a,b; Palacios *et al.,* 1981a,b). A decrease of [^{3}H]Flu binding was found in the striatum after local injection of kainic acid (Sperk and Schlögl 1979; Chang *et al.,* 1980; Biggio *et al.,* 1981b); intracaudate injection of kainic acid increased K_D for [^{3}H]Diaz binding without change in B_{max} in the substantia nigra (Biggio *et al.,* 1979). Intranigral injections of kainic acid reduced [^{3}H]Diaz binding sites by 30% (Biggio *et al.,* 1981b). Ibotenic acid lesions of the striatonigral fibers resulted in a 30–60% increase of total specific binding of [^{3}H]Flu and [^{3}H]Ro 15-1788 in the substantia nigra (Lo *et al.,* 1983b); [^{3}H]muscimol binding also increased by 70%. Differentiating putative BZ$_1$Rs and BZ$_2$Rs by differential extraction and displacement with CL 218,872, the authors concluded that BZ$_1$Rs increased (and therefore represented postsynaptic sites with respect to the striatonigral pathways), whereas BZ$_2$Rs decreased (and therefore were assumed to be located to endings of striatonigral afferents). Owen *et al.* (1983) reported an increase of [^{3}H]Ro 5-4864 binding in the rat striatum after kainic acid injection. After subcutaneous injection of kainic acid to rats, there was no change in GABA and BZ binding sites at the peak of convulsive state (2 hr); however, in the following long-term hyperexcitable syndrome neuronal type BZ binding sites were decreased and nonneuronal type

BZ binding sites markedly increased (Kish *et al.*, 1983a). Neurotoxic (6-hydroxydopamine) degeneration of noradrenergic neurons ending in the cerebral cortex of rats resulted in a moderate decrease of B_{max} and a fivefold increase of the apparent affinity of [^{3}H]Diaz; it was suggested that catecholamines could modulate BZRs. Lesions by 6-hydroxydopamine of the noradrenergic innervation of the rat cerebellar produced a 20% decrease of BZ binding with no change in GABA binding (Doble *et al.*, 1981).

Neonatal chemical lesions of central noradrenergic neurons by 6-hydroxydopa and DSP 4 [*N*-(2-chloroethyl)-*N*-ethyl-2-bromobenzylamine] results in a permanent noradrenergic hyperinnervation of the brainstem and cerebellum. In the adult animals, the number of BZ binding sites was decreased in the cerebral cortex and increased in the brainstem and cerebellum (Medina and Novas, 1983). When adult rats treated at birth with 6-hydroxydopa were given DSP 4 (to destroy the regenerated noradrenergic neurons) there was a marked decrease of [^{3}H]Flu binding sites in all three regions 7 days later. Unfortunately no attempt was made to identify the type of BZ binding sites.

Surgical lesions of the fimbria–fornix led to a decrease of [^{3}H]Flu binding sites in the rat hippocampus (Sabato *et al.*, 1981b), suggesting the presence of part of the binding sites on afferents to the hippocampus. Olfactory bulbectomized mice, surprisingly, were found to have no relevant changes in [^{3}H]Diaz binding in limbic regions (Hirsch, 1981); however, [^{3}H]Diaz binding was increased 30% in the frontal cortex and 24% in the thalamus, but decreased 26% in the striatum and 28% in the brainstem.

In the brain of patients who had suffered from Huntington's chorea, [^{3}H]Diaz binding was markedly reduced in putamen and caudate nucleus but not in frontal cortex, cerebellar cortex, thalamus, and dendate gyrus (Möhler and Okada, 1978). Both B_{max} and affinity of [^{3}H]Flu binding was decreased in the putamen, while there was an increase of B_{max} in the cerebellum and frontal cortex (Reisine *et al.*, 1979, 1980). An increase of BZ binding was also found in the substantia nigra. In the cerebellum of patients who had suffered from adult-onset Huntington's disease [^{3}H]Flu binding was found to be unaffected; a normal GABA-induced shift of the binding occurred (Kish *et al.*, 1983b). Binding of [^{3}H]Ro 5-4864 was increased in the temperal cortex obtained postmortem from patients with Alzheimer's disease, whereas [^{3}H]Flu binding was lowered (Owen *et al.*, 1983).

5.16 *IN VITRO* MODULATION OF NEURONAL HIGH-AFFINITY BZ BINDING

5.16.1 *Modulation of BZ Binding by GABA-Rs*

Around 1978 several groups of investigators reported almost simultaneously that GABA (and muscimol) are able to enhance BZ binding *in vitro* (Briley and

Langer, 1978; Gallager et al., 1978; Müller et al., 1978; Martin and Candy, 1978; Tallman et al., 1978; Wastek et al., 1978; Chiu and Rosenberg, 1979; Dudai, 1979; Karobath and Sperk, 1979; Karobath et al., 1979; Speth et al., 1979a–c; Squires et al., 1979; Williams and Risley, 1979). The phenomenon became, for several years, one of the most intensively studied single aspects in the molecular pharmacology of BZs. These early studies indicated that the stimulant effect of GABA (and muscimol) was concentration dependent, blocked by bicuculline, present at 0°C as well as at 37°C, and affected the apparent affinity of BZs. The blocking effect of picrotoxin was controversial. The effect of GABA was found to depend critically on the level of endogenous GABA in the tissue studied. The less endogenous GABA was present, the more marked was the stimulant effect of exogenous GABA on BZ binding. Indeed, it seems that the maximum stimulation of BZ binding in thoroughly washed membranes results in a binding similar to that observed in tissue preparations in which no attempt had been made to remove endogenous GABA. Bicuculline reduced [^{3}H]BZ binding in membrane preparations with high levels of endogenous GABA. The increased affinity of the BZ binding site for BZs is due to an increased rate of association (k_{+1}); the effect on the rate of dissociation (k_{-1}) is controversial, some investigators (e.g., Wong et al., 1980) having found a decrease, others no change at all.

A few particular aspects of the GABA-stimulated BZ binding are discussed here. Gabamodulin, a brain peptide of about 126 amino acids, inhibited (IC_{50} = 0.5 μM) stimulation of [^{3}H]diazepam binding by GABA due to its noncompetitive interaction with high affinity GABA binding sites in synaptic membranes (Guidotti et al., 1982). A bicuculline-sensitive GABA stimulation of BZ binding was also observed in intact living neurons from the rat cerebral cortex in dissociated cell culture (White et al., 1981), in primary cultures of fetal mouse brain and spinal cord (Huang et al., 1980), and in primary cultures of chick brain (Mallorga et al., 1983). In contrast to membrane preparations, GABA was inactive in the absence of Cl^- ions. In the same neurons, White et al. (1981) found Diaz to enhance the conductance increase induced by GABA and THIP or occurring during IPSPs. Whereas similar stimulatory effects of GABA on BZ binding were observed in various brain regions (Wastek et al., 1978), other studies suggested regional differences in the affinity of GABA (Supavilai and Karobath, 1980a; Mitchell and Wilson, 1983). The stimulant effect of GABA on [^{3}H]BZ binding ("positive GABA shift") was also seen in autoradiographic studies (Unnerstall et al., 1981); the conclusion of the latter authors was that there exists a tonic GABAergic influence, because bicuculline attenuated [^{3}H]Flu binding, and that all BZ binding sites seemed to be modulated by GABA. Muscimol (5 mg/kg ip) and AOAA (40 mg/kg po) given 1 hr before the iv injection of [^{3}H]Diaz increased its binding by 45 and 265%, respectively (Tallman and Gallager, 1979). In other experiments, pretreatment with AOAA in a dose that doubled the brain GABA level did not alter [^{3}H]Diaz binding in cortical membranes (Rosenberg and Chiu, 1979a). When [^{3}H]Diaz was injected iv after AOAA, the total radioactivity of the ligand in the brain was higher than in untreated animals; however, this increase affected specific and nonspecific binding alike. These authors concluded that the normal levels of GABA in the brain are supramaximal for BZ binding and that fluctuations of endogenous GABA are unlikely to modify BZ binding. In primary cell cultures of neurons from the cerebral hemispheres of chick embryos [^{3}H]Diaz binding was found to be stimulated by GABA (Roth-Schechter et al., 1983); this effect was markedly reduced in cultures exposed for 5 days to pentobarbitone (0.5 mM). The convulsant BZ Ro 5-3663 was reported to block the stimulant effect of GABA or muscimol (O'Brien and Spirt, 1980; Ticku, 1981). While Klepner et al. (1979) proposed that BZ$_1$Rs were not coupled to GABA-Rs, others observed a positive GABA shift with [^{3}H]CL 218,872 as a ligand (Stapleton et al., 1982) and with CL 218,872 as displacer of [^{3}H]Ro 15-1788 binding (Möhler and Richards, 1981a) and of β-[^{3}H]CCE binding (Skolnick et al., 1982c). The displacing activity of zopiclone on [^{3}H]Ro 15-1788 binding was not enhanced by GABA, while that of CL 218,872 was increased (Skerritt et al., 1982c). Möhler and Richards (1981a) found a positive GABA shift for zopiclone in [^{3}H]Ro 15-1788 binding, when tested at 37°C, but not at 4°C. Binding of the congener of zopiclone, [^{3}H]suriclone, was reported by Blanchard and Julou (1983) to be unaffected by GABA at 0°C, although the latter protected [^{3}H]suriclone binding sites from thermal inactivation. Maggi et al. (1980) investigated the phylogenesis of the "GABA shift" (using in this case muscimol) of [^{3}H]Diaz. Muscimol stimulated [^{3}H]Diaz binding in brain membranes of all vertebrates studied, except in those of hagfish. The potency of muscimol was greater in human brain than in other species. The conclusion was that BZ and GABA binding sites develop separately, but that most, if not all, BZ binding sites are coupled to GABA-Rs. In the frog spinal cord, Oka et al. (1981) found no significant modulation of [^{3}H]Diaz binding by GABA and, electrophysiologically, Diaz failed to enhance GABA effects. It was suggested that this coupling may vary in different conditions and, perhaps, brain regions; Gee et al. (1983a–c) proposed, on the basis of GABA shift experiments, that in the cerebral cortex and hippocampus GABA regulation of BZ binding may be predominantly associated with BZ$_2$ sites, while BZ$_1$ sites may show regional differences in the way they are associated with GABA-Rs. As for the ontogeny of the "GABA shift," Gallager et al. (1980a) found it to be highest at the end of fetal life, gradually declining to adult values 3–4 weeks after birth. The GABA shift at 37°C was at least as marked as at low temperature (e.g., Burch and Ticku, 1981; Burch et al., 1983). The GABA shift at 37°C was increased by Cl$^-$ (Ehlert et al., 1981, 1982). AgNO$_3$ not only increased irreversibly the binding of [^{3}H]muscimol, but also irreversibly enhanced the muscimol-induced stimulation of [^{3}H]Flu binding (Supavilai et al., 1982a). Propranolol in nanomolar concentrations inhibited

GABA stimulation of [³H]Diaz binding and enhanced it at micromolar concentrations (Morgan and Stone, 1982b); no stereospecificity was observed for the propranolol enantiomers. The stimulant effect of GABA on [³H]BZ binding was also studied on solubilized "receptors." A similar effect as in the membrane-bound state was observed by Gavish and Snyder (1980b, 1981) with an [³H]Flu binding protein extracted with 1% Triton X-100 from calf brain membranes. Similar findings were obtained by Asano and Ogasawara (1981b) with a "BZR" solubilized after extraction with Triton X-100 and deoxycholate; these authors believed that the GABA-R mediating this shift was the high-affinity type. A GABA shift was also observed in a highly purified preparation of BZ binding sites where half-maximal stimulation occurred at 0.1 μM GABA (Schoch and Möhler, 1983).

All these results strongly suggest that the effect of GABA on the binding of BZR ligands is a receptor-mediated mechanism; it was, therefore, of great interest to identify the type of GABA-R that was responsible for the "GABA shift." A large series of GABA mimetics were accordingly tested for a stimulant action on [³H]BZ binding (Karobath *et al.,* 1979; Maurer, 1979; Krogsgaard-Larsen and Arndt, 1980). The structures studied and their potencies as GABA agonists and stimulants of [³H]BZ binding are reviewed by Braestrup and Nielsen (1983). While it was believed in an early phase that the stimulation of BZ binding did poorly correlate with the affinity for GABA binding sites (in particular for structurally rigid molecules), it was later found that some GABA mimetics, that were inactive as stimulants at low temperature, were quite active at 24°C (Supavilai and Karobath, 1980b). Moreover, some of the ligands for GABA binding sites were found to act as specific antagonists of GABA-induced increase of BZ binding or to behave as partial agonists (Braestrup *et al.,* 1979b; Karobath and Lippitsch, 1979; Krogsgaard-Larsen *et al.,* 1984). Ethylenediamine, a compound that mimicks to some degree the electrophysiological effect of GABA on neurons and displaces [³H]GABA, [³H]muscimol, and [³H]baclofen in the low micromolar concentration range, was surprisingly weak as a stimulant of [³H]Diaz binding (Davies *et al.,* 1982; Morgan and Stone, 1982a,b, 1983); moreover, the small stimulation seemed to involve an increase of B_{max} rather than K_D, in contrast to GABA. The cyclic analog of ethylenediamine, piperazine, increased [³H]Diaz binding only minimally at room temperature and even reduced it at 0°C. Histamine H_2-antagonists structurally derived from imidazole (cimetidine > metiamide > tiolidin) were found to be as potent as GABA as inhibitors of specific [³H]muscimol binding and as stimulants of [³H]Flu binding (Lakoski *et al.,* 1983); ranitidine, which does not contain an imidazole moiety, was inactive. Progabide, and one of its metabolites, enhance [³H]Diaz binding to cortical membranes by increasing affinity; membranes of rats given 1 mmol/kg progabide ip had an elevated B_{max} for [³H]Diaz (Koe, 1983).

Another interesting finding was that the intensity of the GABA shift varied with different agonists at BZRs, that the GABA shift was absent with competitive BZ antagonists, and even negative with the stronger inverse agonists (Möhler, 1984b; Möhler and Richards, 1981a; Skolnick *et al.*, 1982b; Skerritt *et al.*, 1982c; Ehlert *et al.*, 1981, 1982, 1983a). Interesting results were obtained by Burch and Ticku (1981), Burch *et al.* (1983), Ticku (1983), and Ticku *et al.* (1983). They used the group reactive agents diethylpyrocarbonate (thought to modify histidine selectively) and diazotized sulfanilate (modifies histidine or tyrosine groups) to inactivate binding sites for [^{3}H]BZ and β-[^{3}H]CCPr. Under the conditions used these reagents produced only a partial occlusion of binding sites; those sites not occluded showed normal K_D values for the three types of ligands. While diethylpyrocarbonate left the GABA (and barbiturate) stimulation of the radioligands to the unoccluded sites intact, diazotized sulfanilate abolished GABA (and barbiturate) stimulation of unoccluded sites. These results were interpreted as indication that the latter reagent also altered GABA (and barbiturate) binding sites or the coupling with BZRs. Fong *et al.* (1982b) found a greater percent GABA shift for [^{3}H]Flu binding in membranes, where approximately 50% of the binding sites were occupied by a BZ antagonist, than when 50% displacement was achieved with a (cold) BZ agonist. While the authors supposed that antagonists displaced the radioligand preferentially from a GABA-insensitive conformational state or binding site subtype, their finding could simply reflect the fact that GABA increased equally the binding of the cold and radioactive agonist ligand, but did not affect the antagonist binding.

The "negative GABA" shift, i.e., the decrease of BZ inverse agonist binding by GABA, is discussed in the paragraphs on the individual inverse agonists.

5.16.2 Modulation of BZ Binding by Ions

In the early days of [^{3}H]BZ binding studies, the investigation of a possible modulatory effect of ions was more or less a routine exercise. Later on, the association of BZRs with the GABA-gated Cl^- ionophore came into the focus of interest, and, hence, the study of ion effects took on a different meaning.

5.16.2.1 Anions. While Mackerer and Kochman (1978) observed a slight decrease of [^{3}H]Diaz binding in the presence of anions, T. Costa *et al.* (1979) and Rodbard *et al.* (1979) found 5 out of 18 anions tested to be able to enhance [^{3}H]Diaz binding to crude rat brain membranes by enhancing the affinity, namely I^-, BR^-, Cl^-, SCN^-, and NO_3^-. These anions are those that were found in electrophysiological experiments to selectively penetrate cat motoneurons *in situ* during the (GABA-mediated) IPSP. In analogy to opiate binding, T. Costa *et al.* (1979) assumed that the ion effect was suggestive of an agonist action of BZs on BZRs. Candy and Martin (1979a) questioned the general validity of this conclusion. [^{3}H]Diaz binding was decreased in the presence of $SO_4{}^{2-}$ and acetate (T. Costa et al., 1979). Further studies of anions were reported by Squires (1981, 1982).

The stimulant effect of Cl^- anions was absent at 37°C (T. Costa et al., 1979) and even decreased [^{3}H]Flu binding in the experiments of Gee and Yamamura (1982b, 1983a). Also at 37°C, Cl^- slightly enhanced the stimulant effect of GABA on [^{3}H]Flu binding (Ehlert et al., 1982); Cl^- did not effect the (smaller) GABA shift of [^{3}H]CL 218,872 binding. In neurons in dissociated cell culture omission of Cl^- increased [^{3}H]BZ binding (White et al., 1981). Binding of [^{3}H]Ro 15-1788 was unaffected by Cl^- ions at 4°C (Möhler and Richards, 1981a). Cl^- anions also stimulate the specific binding of the inverse agonist [^{3}H]DMCM (Honoré et al., 1983).

5.16.2.2 Cations.   Chloride sales of the divalent cations Ca^{2+}, Ni^{2+}, Cu^{2+}, and Zn^{2+} markedly enhanced [^{3}H]Diaz binding to rat brain membranes, whereas chloride salts of monovalent cations had no effect (Mackerer and Kochman, 1978; Hirsch et al., 1982; Kochman and Hirsch, 1982; Mizuno et al., 1982). In the presence of these divalent cations a second binding site for [^{3}H] Diaz with higher affinity appeared (''super high-affinity binding site''). The effect of these divalent cations, which are known to form complexes with protein and to activate various enzymes, seems to be independent of the GABA binding site. $NiCl_2$ had no effect on [^{3}H]Ro 15-1788 binding (Möhler and Richards, 1981a). Hirsch and Kochman (1983) observed that Ni^{2+} and Ca^{2+}, while enhancing binding of [^{3}H]Diaz, decreased that of β-[^{3}H]CCPr. Ca^{2+} inhibited the effect of Ni^{2+} and Ca^{2+}. They suggested that a Ca^{2+} binding site is associated with the BZR/GABA-R channel complex.

5.16.3 Modulation of BZ Binding by Barbiturates

Damm et al. (1979) first described that barbiturates potentiate the stimulant effect of GABA on [^{3}H]Diaz binding, and MacDonald et al. (1979) found a direct stimulant effect of barbiturates on Cl^- channels. This effect of barbiturates was confirmed and studied in more details and variations by many investigators (Leeb-Lundberg et al., 1980, 1981b; Skolnick et al., 1980b, 1982b; Asano and Ogasawara, 1981a; Davis and Ticku, 1981; Olsen and Leeb-Lundberg, 1981; Ticku, 1981; Leeb-Lundberg and Olsen, 1982; Olsen, 1982). The earliest systematic study of Leeb-Lundberg et al. (1980) concluded that all anesthetic barbiturates investigated stimulated [^{3}H]BZ binding by decreasing K_D, that this effect of barbiturates was strictly dependent on the presence of Cl^- ions or of other anions able to permeate the open Cl^- channel, that there was a marked stereoselectivity of action, that even excitatory barbiturates stimulated [^{3}H]BZ binding, and that the effect of barbiturates was seen even after maximal stimulation by GABA. Leeb-Lundberg *et al.* (1981b) found anticonvulsant barbiturates to lack a stimulant effect, but to block the stimulant effect of anesthetic barbiturates. Skolnick *et al.* (1980b, 1981) found two components in the action of pentobarbitone: at low (subanesthetic) concentrations the compound further increased GABA-enhanced [³H]BZ binding, at about 10 times higher (anesthetic) concentrations it stimulated basal [³H]Diaz binding in the absence of GABA. The effect of pentobarbitone was reduced by bicuculline as well as by picrotoxin and by the omission of Cl⁻. According to Skolnick *et al.* (1982b) the potency and maximum effect of pentobarbitone varied in different brain regions and was blocked by the convulsant BZ Ro 5-3363. The barbiturate stimulation of [³H]BZ binding was also seen on solubilized BZ binding molecules (Davis and Ticku, 1981; Ticku and Davis, 1981; Skolnick *et al.* 1982b). In the latter study, phenobarbitone was inactive by itself but blocked the stimulant effect of pentobarbitone. Barbiturate stimulation was also seen in slide-mounted sections of hippocampus (Valdes *et al.,* 1981); surprisingly, the few binding sites in the corpus callosum also bound more [³H]Flu in the presence of pentobarbitone or GABA. Pentobarbitone diminished [³H]DMCM binding in a partially Cl⁻-dependent and picrotoxinine-sensitive manner (Honoré *et al.,* 1983). Niehoff *et al.* (1983) reported that pentobarbitone stimulated [³H]Flu binding to BZ₁, but not to BZ₂ binding sites in rat cerebellum and cerebral cortex. Skerritt *et al.* (1983a,b) found a significant correlation in a series of barbiturates between the degree of enhancement of [³H]Diaz and of high-affinity binding of [³H]GABA.

The very complex effects of barbiturates on [³H]BZ binding have been reviewed by Olsen (1982), Richter and Holtman (1982), and Leeb-Lundberg and Olsen (1983); the reader is referred to these reviews for detailed information. Three classes of barbiturates were distinguished which all inhibited [³H]DHP binding: full agonists [e.g., (±)-pentobarbitone], partial agonists (e.g., derivatives substituted with methyl at N-1), and antagonists (e.g., phenobarbitone). These three classes do not correlate perfectly with the three groups of "anesthetic," "antiepileptic," and "excitatory" barbiturates. The type of interaction with [³H]BZ binding, therefore, does not predict global CNS activity. In a very detailed study Leeb-Lundberg and Olsen (1983) have studied BZ binding stimulation by pentobarbitone, etazolate, and GABA in various brain regions and its modification by bicuculline, β-CCE, Ro 15-1788, and CL 218,872. The conclusion from these very complex interactions was that multiple coupling states of a single type of GABA-R, BZR, and pentobarbitone/picrotoxinin/pyrazolopyridine binding site could explain the heterogeneity observed and for which there is, at present, no pharmacological correlate.

The multiple effects of barbiturates on [³H]BZ binding strongly suggest the existence of close physical and functional contacts between BZ and barbiturate binding sites; they do not, however, suggest that barbiturates would produce their *in vivo* pharmacological effects by altering the BZ binding sites, unless one accepts the speculative existence of an endogenous ligand for the BZ binding site, with which barbiturates would compete or whose action they would modulate. So far, it seems reasonable to assume that barbiturates produce at least part of their effects in the intact CNS by altering the function of the Cl^- channel, e.g., by increasing the mean channel open time (MacDonald and Barker, 1978, 1979a,b; Study and Barker, 1981; Barker *et al.*, 1984); the interaction with [^{3}H]BZ binding would then simply indicate that altered conformations of the Cl^- channel do indeed change the affinity of BZ agonists (but not of BZ antagonists) for their binding site. Of more relevance for the mechanisms of action of barbiturate would be the effect of these drugs on the interaction of GABA with its receptor. Willow and Johnston (1980, 1981) have found that pentobarbitone enhances GABA binding in a lower micromolar range, this effect disappears with increasing concentrations, suggesting the direct interaction with GABA binding sites (direct GABA mimetic action).

5.16.4 Regulation of BZ Binding by Miscellaneous Compounds and Procedures

5.16.4.1 Diphenylhydantoin. Diphenylhydantoin has no relevant affinity for BZ binding sites (Speth *et al.*, 1979a), although Tunnicliff *et al.* (1979) found an IC_{50} of about 1 μM in a centrifugation assay and in spite of a presumed structural similarity with BZ_2Rs (Camerman and Camerman, 1983). BZ and diphenylhydantoin have very different anticonvulsant profiles; however, their combination results in an enhanced anticonvulsant effectiveness (Czuczwar *et al.*, 1981; Ticku *et al.*, 1983). Similarly, the decrease in locomotor activity by Diaz was enhanced by diphenylhydantoin (Turski *et al.*, 1982). Gallager *et al.* (1980a,b) and Gallager and Mallorga (1980) reported that the ip injection of 100 mg/kg diphenylhydantoin increased the binding of [^{3}H]Diaz *in vivo;* diphenylhydantoin enhanced the depressant effect of Diaz on the firing rate of dorsal raphé cells (Gallager *et al.*, 1980b). Such an acute effect was not seen by Mimaki *et al.* (1980), who observed, however, after subchronic daily administration of diphenylhydantoin a dose-dependent decrease of [^{3}H]Flu density in the cerebellum, which correlated with a degeneration of Purkinje cells. Tallman and Gallager (1979) then found that diphenylhydantoin enhances [^{3}H]Diaz binding at low concentration by increasing the affinity; they argued that this effect could be due to an alteration of cell membranes, as extensive washing did not reverse the enhancement. [^{3}H]Diphenylhydantoin itself has been found to bind specifically to a saturable high-affinity, low-capacity site and a low-affinity, high-capacity site (Shah *et al.*, 1981; Okazaki *et al.*, 1983). The high-affinity site is unevenly distributed in the CNS and also occurs in liver, kidney, and lung. Prior incubation of membranes in micromolar concentrations of various BZs enhanced [^{3}H]diphenylhydantoin binding (Shah *et al.*, 1981; Okazaki *et al.*, 1983). (+)-

Bicuculline also stimulated [³H]diphenylhydantoin binding, suggesting that this stimulation may not reflect a pharmacological effect.

5.16.4.2 Avermectin B_{1a} and etomidate. These two compounds are discussed under one heading, although their pharmacological activities could hardly differ more. Avermectin B_{1a} is a macrocyclic lactone disaccharide anthelmintic agent which increases Cl^- conductance in lobster muscle, whereas etomidate is a short-acting intravenous anesthetic. Both compounds either act directly on GABA-Rs or on Cl^- channels.

Paul *et al.* (1980a, 1982) described an irreversible enhancement of [³H]Diaz binding by avermectin B_{1a} by an increase of affinity and, less markedly, of B_{max}. The compound was also reported to enhance the muscle relaxant and locomotor depressant effect of Diaz in mice (Williams and Yarbrough, 1979). Binding of β-[³H]CCPr and β-[³H]CCE was also enhanced, but less than that of [³H]Diaz (Williams and Risley, 1982a); there was an exclusive, bicuculline-insensitive increase of B_{max}. Avermectin B_{1a}, in addition to increasing the number of [³H]Diaz binding sites, also enhanced [³H]GABA binding in a picrotoxin-sensitive manner (Pong *et al.*, 1982); the drug also protected BZ binding sites from heat inactivation. The stimulant effect of avermectin B_{1a} is Cl^- ion dependent (Supavilai and Karobath, 1981a). Pretreatment of membranes with Triton X-100 annihilated the effect of avermectin B_{1a}. Since these authors found etazolate and cartazolate, as well as GABA and other GABA mimetics, to inhibit the stimulant effect of avermectin B_{1a}, the anthelmintic was speculated to act somehow on the Cl^- channel, but at a site different from that mediating the effect of pyrazolopyridines. Pong *et al.* (1981) found a stimulation by avermectin of [³H]Flu binding also to digitonin-solubilized BZ binding sites.

Etomidate increases binding of [³H]Diaz (Ashton *et al.*, 1981; Thyagarajau *et al.*, 1983) and [³H]Flu (Ehlert *et al.*, 1982), but not of β-[³H]CCPr binding. [³H]DMCM is reduced (Honoré *et al.*, 1983). The active isomer is (+)-etomidate. The potency for stimulation of [³H]BZ binding was in the order of that of GABA, but the maximum stimulation was higher with the former; neither picrotoxin nor bicuculline blocked the stimulant effect of etomidate. (+)-Etomidate failed to stimulate [³H]Diaz binding in synaptosomes from rat cerebellum.

5.16.4.3 Ethanol. Ethanol was found to enhance [³H]Diaz binding to a crude preparation of BZR/GABA-R/Cl^- ionophore complex solubilized with Lubrol (Ticku and Davis, 1981). Ethanol was inactive on the 61 kDa BZ binding protein obtained by gel filtration. While ethanol did not inhibit [³H] muscimol binding, it displaced [³H]DHP.

5.16.4.4 Tofisopam. Tofisopam, a 3,4-benzodiazepine with an ill-documented claim of tranquillizing activity, enhanced [³H]Flu binding (Saano *et al.*, 1981; Saano and Urtti, 1982; Saano, 1982b). After 300 mg/kg tofisopam po the *in vivo* binding of [^{3}H]Flu was increased by 26%, while at 25 mg/kg the binding of [^{3}H]Diaz was inhibited. No specific binding was found with [^{3}H]tofisopam. At 1 mM tofisopam increased [^{3}H]Flu binding through a 30% rise in B_{max} (Mennini *et al.*, 1982c). Tofisopam at 1 μM was reported to increase [^{3}H] muscimol binding by 17% (Saano, 1982a).

5.16.4.5 Clomethiazole.   Clomethiazole, used in the treatment of acute alcohol withdrawal, did not stimulate BZ binding, but blocked the stimulant effect of pentobarbitone and etazolate (Leeb-Lundberg *et al.*, 1981b). This may be related to inhibition of [^{3}H]DHP binding at 0.5 mM.

5.16.4.6 Pyrazolopyridines.   Several pyrazolopyridines have been reported to produce anticonflict effects in animals suggestive of a possible anxiolytic activity in man. They were initially expected to be ligands of BZRs, but surprisingly were found to enhance, rather than inhibit, [^{3}H]BZ binding. The hypothesis has been advanced that these compounds may act by enhancing the effect of an endogenous ligand at BZRs. The pyrazolopyridines were found to interact with the [^{3}H]DHP binding site (Olsen *et al.*, 1981; Leeb-Lundberg *et al.*, 1981a).

Etazolate (SQ 20009). Etazolate induces a dose-dependent increase of [^{3}H]Diaz binding (Williams and Risley, 1979). No effect on [^{3}H]muscimol binding was observed. The stimulant effect was found to be blocked by bicuculline, but not by picrotoxin. Supavilai and Karobath (1979) found etazolate to be a more potent stimulant of [^{3}H]Flu binding in the cerebellum than in the cerebral cortex, hippocampus, and striatum. According to these authors the stimulant effect of etazolate depends on Cl$^-$ anions and is blocked by picrotoxin. No significant effect of etazolate on β-[^{3}H]CCPr binding (Ehlert *et al.*, 1982) or [^{3}H]Ro 15-1788 binding (Möhler and Richards, 1981a) was found. [^{3}H]Flu binding is enhanced by etazolate via an increase in apparent affinity (Karobath *et al.*, 1980a; Supavilai and Karobath, 1981b). The stimulant effect depended on Cl$^-$, Br$^-$, I$^-$, NO$_3^-$, and NO$_2^-$, but not on F$^-$, acetate, formate, or sulfate. Bicuculline as well as IBTBO and picrotoxin and were found to block the etazolate effect. An enhancement by etazolate of [^{3}H]Diaz binding was also found in a Lubrol-solubilized fraction containing specific binding sites for [^{3}H]BZs, [^{3}H]muscimol, and [^{3}H]DHP (Ticku and Davis, 1982). Etazolate is believed by Leeb-Lundberg *et al.* (1981a) to stimulate BZ binding in a similar way as barbiturates: they all affect K_D, barbiturates and etazolate are nonadditive, but additive to GABA. Recently, Barnes *et al.* (1983) found that etazolate in a range of 0.3 to 100 μM produces a large increase in the duration, but not in the amplitude of spontaneous, GABAergic IPSPs in cerebral cortex neurons of fetal rats in primary dissociated cell culture (in contrast, Diaz increased the amplitude, but not the duration). Above 10 μM etazolate produced a hyperpolarization and a conductance increase even in the absence of GABA; the effect was due to a Cl$^-$-conductance. The effects of Diaz and etazolate on IPSPs were additive, i.e., in combination they increased both duration and amplitude. The direct membrane effect of etazolate was blocked by both bicuculline and picrotoxin. In these living cells in culture, etazolate had a biphasic, bell-shaped dose–effect curve for modulation of [^{3}H]Flu binding at 23°C, increasing it at lower and decreasing it at higher concentrations.

Cartazolate (SQ 65396). Beer *et al.* (1978), Karobath *et al.* (1980a), and Supavilai and Karobath (1981b) found cartazolate to stimulate [^{3}H]Diaz and [^{3}H]Flu binding in rat cerebellar membranes in the presence of Cl$^-$, and to potentiate the stimulant effect of GABA. At high concentrations, cartazolate inhibited [^{3}H]Diaz binding (Williams and Risley, 1979). The latter effect was shown to be due to an enhancement of the apparent affinity of GABA. Cartazolate, like etazolate, was more potent at [^{3}H]BZ binding enhancer in the cerebellum than in the forebrain (Supavilai and Karobath, 1979). No significant effect of β-[^{3}H]CCPr binding was found (Ehlert *et al.*, 1982). Cartazolate also inhibits [^{3}H]DHP binding (Leeb-Lundberg *et al.*, 1981a).

Tracazolate (ICI 136753). Tracazolate also enhances [^{3}H]BZ binding in a Cl$^-$-dependent manner (Ehlert *et al.*, 1982; Meiners and Salama, 1982). GABA binding is also enhanced (Pong *et al.*, 1982). Tracazolate was reported to be one-fourth to one-half as potent as chlordiazepoxide as an anticonflict agent (Patel and Malick, 1982). This effect was not blocked by Ro 15-1788 or CGS 8216 (Patel *et al.*, 1983).

5.16.4.7 LY 81067. This anticonvulsant diaryltriazine increased [^{3}H]Flu and [^{3}H]GABA binding in the high nanomolar range (Bymaster *et al.*, 1982; Wong *et al.*, 1983a,b).

5.16.4.8 EMD 28422. This synthetic purine derivative with sedative, anticonvulsant, and anticonflict activity (Skolnick *et al.*, 1980e) was studied in a SAR study of nucleosides related to the putative endogenous ligand inosine. It increased [^{3}H]Diaz binding in mouse brain synaptosomes after ip injection (Skolnick *et al.*, 1980a,e). The effect seemed to be independent of Cl$^-$ and GABA, but was antagonized by bicuculline. *In vitro*, EMD 28422 increased [^{3}H]Diaz binding by increasing B_{max}. In an anticonflict test and in a drug discrimination test EMD 28422 showed no anxiolytic-like activity (Lal *et al.*, 1983).

5.16.4.9 Changes of membrane phospholipids. Treatment of synaptic membranes from rat cortex with phospholipase C or phospholipase A$_2$ increased binding of [^{3}H]Diaz and [^{3}H]Flu by increasing B_{max} of the former and affinity of the latter (Ueno and Kuriyama, 1981; Kuriyama and Ueno, 1983). The effect of the two enzymes was abolished by adding the phospholipids phosphatidylserine and phosphatidic acid. Treatment with phospholipase A_2 attenuated the GABA-induced increase of [^{3}H]Diaz binding. Agents interacting with membrane cholesterol, such as digitonin and polyene antibiotics, did not affect BZ binding. These results suggest that BZ binding can be modulated, in part, by phospholipids of membranes. In rat cerebellar membranes, the two phospholipases likewise increased [^{3}H]Diaz binding; the stimulant effect of GABA remained unaltered while stimulation by Cl^- was decreased (Fujimoto and Okabayashi, 1983).

When phospholipid methylation in membranes was increased by incubating crude synaptic membranes from rat cerebellum with S-adenosylmethionine, a dose-dependent increase of [^{3}H]Diaz occurred, due to an increase in B_{max} (Toffano, 1983).

5.16.4.10 Convulsants binding to the Cl^- channel. While picrotoxin and IPTBO enhanced [^{3}H]Flu binding to cerebellar membranes in a Cl^--dependent manner at 0°C (by an increase in B_{max}) (Fujimoto and Okabayashi, 1981; Karobath *et al.*, 1981), the two convulsants were inactive by themselves at 37°C and inhibited GABA-stimulated binding. Picrotoxinin was found to enhance specific binding of [^{3}H]DMCM only in the absence of Cl^- ions (Honoré *et al.*, 1983). Anisatin, a toxic substance isolated from the seeds of a Japanese anise plant with picrotoxin-like GABA antagonistic activity, inhibited GABA stimulation of [^{3}H]Diaz binding, but not its basal binding (Matsumoto and Fukada, 1982b). For a review of the interaction of "Cl^- channel agents" with [^{3}H] muscimol and [^{3}H]Flu binding see Supavilai *et al.* (1982a,b).

5.16.4.11 Guanosine triphosphate (GTP). GTP decreased [^{3}H]Flu binding by increasing k_{-1}, but also the binding of the BZ antagonist [^{3}H]CGS 8216 (Fong *et al.*, 1982a,b). However, the effect was probably due to an impurity of GTP (M. Golstein, personal communication).

5.16.4.12 Estrogen. Three-month treatment of rats with estrogen slightly increased B_{max} for [^{3}H]Flu binding in hypothalamus, but not in amygdala and cortex (Wilkinson *et al.*, 1983b). Induction of experimental hyperthyroidism in rats by chronic administration of D-thyroxine or L-triiodothyronine did not alter pentetrazole seizure threshold or the anticonvulsant effect of flurazepam or the preconvulsant effect of FG 7142 (Atterwill and Nutt, 1983).

5.17 HETEROGENEITY OF BZ BINDING

The early studies of BZ binding in the mammalian brain gave no hint to suspect the presence of qualitative differences among the high-affinity BZ binding sites. The radiolabeled BZs used as ligands gave saturation isotherms that on Scatchard analysis resulted in straight lines. Displacement with nonradioactive BZs yielded inhibition curves also consistent with conventional mass action law terms for simple bimolecular interactions. All BZ ligands had roughly the same apparent affinity for binding sites in all CNS areas.

However, in 1979 Squires *et al.* (1979, 1980) published data obtained with a new class of non-BZ ligands of BZRs which suggested that BZ binding sites may not all belong to a single class. These triazolopyridazines inhibited [³H]BZ binding with Hill slopes significantly smaller than unity in most (but not all) brain areas, indicating the inconsistency of this binding with the law of mass action for a single class of equal and independent binding sites. In addition, multiphasic dissociation curves with classical BZs and multiphasic heat inactivation curves were found. Klepner *et al.* (1979) proposed the hypothesis of two classes of BZRs, one class called BZ_1R and characterized by high affinity for CL 218,872, the other class called BZ_2R and characterized by a lower affinity for CL 218,872. BZ_1Rs were to prevail in the cerebellum, whereas a considerable fraction of BZ binding sites in cerebral cortex and hippocampus would be of the BZ_2R type. Classic BZs do not discriminate between the two types. Even more hypothetically, BZ_1Rs were believed not to be coupled with GABA-Rs and Cl^- channels and to mediate the anxiolytic effect of BZs and triazolopyridazines, while BZ_2Rs would be responsible for muscle relaxant and sedative effects. Further support for the two-class hypothesis of BZRs was seen in the binding behavior of certain β-carbolines. Studies of solubilized peptides covalently bound to [³H]Flu after photoaffinity labeling of membranes seemed to provide strong evidence for the existence of multiple molecular species of [³H]Flu binding polypeptides (Sieghart and Karobath, 1980). For some scientists, the existence of multiple BZRs seems to be a well-proven fact (Dubnick *et al.*, 1983). We, therefore, review in this paragraph the evidence for and against the existence of subclasses of BZRs.

Also for this particular aspect of BZ receptorology semantic shortcomings are a source of confusion. Heterogeneity of BZ binding could reflect at least five different situations: (1) Presence of distinct independent protein species differing in their primary structure (true multiplicity of receptors or binding proteins); the different protein species could be the products of separate receptor genes or may result from posttranslational modifications; (2) existence of different, interconvertible conformational states of a single species of binding molecules; (3) existence of different coupling states of binding molecules with other components of a supramolecular complex; (4) differences in the microenvironment of a single class of binding molecules; (5) cooperativity of ligand binding to coupled BZ binding sites.

5.17.1 Curvilinear Scatchard Plots of Radioligand Equilibrium Binding

[³H]Diaz binding to chicken retina provided evidence for two binding sites with differing affinity (Willow and Morgan, 1980). In synaptosomal membranes of the rabbit forebrain two sites for [³H]Diaz binding with K_D values of 5 and 84 nM were calculated, however, in microsomal preparations only a high-affinity site was found (Yokoi *et al.*, 1981). A linear Scatchard plot for [³H]Diaz binding was obtained in the cerebellar and cerebral cortex, but a curvilinear plot was obtained in the hippocampus, where a high- (K_D 4.6 nM) and a low-affinity (K_D 1077 nM) site were calculated (Volicer and Biagioni, 1982a). The high-affinity binding site in the hippocampus was similar to the apparent single site in the two areas. The number of low-affinity binding sites was 20 times higher than the number of high-affinity sites. There was also a clear difference between the affinity of [³H]Flu in the cerebral cortex and in the hippocampus. However, it should be realized that it is not clear to what extent interregional differences in affinity merely reflext different GABA concentrations in the membrane preparation.

Scatchard analysis of equilibrium binding data reveal deviations from simple bimolecular interactions obeying the mass action law, but do not provide an explanation for this deviation.

5.17.2 Association and Dissociation Kinetics

Two exponential components, a fast and a slow one, were found in the association of [³H]Flu, [³H]Diaz, and [³H]Ro 15-1788 (Chiu and Rosenberg, 1982, 1983a,b; Chiu *et al.*, 1982). This does not support a simple bimolecular reaction mechanism in the binding of these ligands to their binding sites. The interpretation proposed by the authors was that a fast initial complex isomerizes to a more stable one.

Wong *et al.* (1980) observed two different dissociation rates of [³H]Flu in the absence and presence of GABA. Chiu and Rosenberg (1982, 1983a,b) and Chiu *et al.* (1982) found two exponential components of dissociation of [³H]Flu, [³H]Diaz, and [³H]Ro 15-1788. The ratio of the slow to the fast dissociation complex was higher at lower concentrations of [³H]Flu, which was taken as evidence for the existence of low- and high-affinity conformations of BZ binding sites. The rate of dissociation was decreased if the membranes had been preincubated at 37°C, moreover, the ratio of slow to fast dissociation complexes increased. The authors interpreted these findings as indicating a shift of binding sites to a high-affinity (or slow dissociation) conformation after preincubation at physiological temperature. This would be consonant with the findings of Gee and Yamamura (1982a) that physiological temperature causes intraregional heterogeneity of binding for CL 218,872 to disappear. The dissociation rate of [³H]Flu complexes was found to be faster when induced at preequilibrium than at equilibrium, further suggesting an isomerization step for the BZR complex (Chiu and Rosenberg, 1983a,b).

5.17.3 CL 218,872

Following the original proposal (Squires *et al.*, 1979; Klepner *et al.*, 1979; Lippa *et al.*, 1979a,b) a number of studies have been made using CL 218,872 as the assumed selective ligand for putative BZ_1Rs. The above authors found that the Hill coefficient for [³H]BZ displacement by CL 218,872 was close to 1 in the cerebellum, but significantly below 1 in other areas; the inhibition by CL 218,872 of [³H]BZs was reported to be competitive at the putative BZ_1 sites, but noncompetitive at BZ_2 sites. The triazolopyridazine was confirmed to be five times more potent in displacing [³H]Flu in the cerebellum than in the hippocampus but was found to be equipotent in displacing β-[³H]CCPr in the two regions (Stapleton *et al.*, 1982). The Hill coefficient was <1 for displacement of [³H]Flu by β-CCE and CL 218,872, but around 1 for the displacement of β-[³H]CCPr in both areas. GABA enhanced the displacing potency of Diaz to the same extent in the cerebellum and the hippocampus, but increased that of CL 218,872 more in the cerebellum than in the hippocampus. Unnerstall *et al.* (1982), using quantitative autoradiography, observed regional differences in the amount of inhibition of [³H]Flu binding by Cl 218,872 and β-CCM. Also in the ovine brain, the degree of displacement of [³H]Diaz by CL 218,872 differed in the various brain regions (Villiger *et al.*, 1982); in the ovine cerebral cortex CL 218,872 did not differentiate low- from high-affinity binding sites for [³H]Diaz.

The value of CL 218,872 as an argument in favor of BZR multiplicity has been greatly weakened by Gee *et al.* (1982b, 1983a–c). They observed that the intraregional heterogeneity for putative BZ_1 and BZ_2 binding sites disappeared at 37°C. What .emained at physiological temperature is a moderately higher affinity of CL 218,872 for binding sites in the cerebellum than in, e.g., the hippocampus. The authors interpreted their results as an indication that temperature was altering different conformations rather than different binding proteins. Multiple conformations might only be detected at low temperature. They also proposed that the profile of action of CL 218,872, which differs somewhat quantitatively from that of classic BZs, may be explained by a partial agonistic activity of the triazolopyridazine rather than by selectivity for multiple BZRs.

5.17.4 K_D and B_{max} Values for [³H]Flu

Supavilai and Karobath (1980a) found the affinity of [³H]Flu to be consistently higher in the hippocampus than in the cerebellum. GABA was more potent in stimulating [³H]Flu binding in the hippocampus than in the cerebellum, although the maximum stimulation was the same in the two areas.

Stapleton *et al.* (1982) obtained a B_{max} value for [³H]Flu binding that was equal to that for β-[³H]CCPr in the cerebellum. It was twice as high as in the hippocampus.

5.17.5 Differences in Thermostability

Biphasic curves of heat inactivation of [³H]BZ binding was one of the earliest arguments of Squires *et al.* (1979) in favor of receptor multiplicity. In a more recent study (Squires and Saederup, 1982), complex actions of GABA and divalent cations on thermoinactivation were believed to reflect the existence of more than just two different binding sites. Schacht and Baecker (1982) confirmed the biphasic inactivation of BZ binding sites at 60°C, however, they found a greater fraction of binding sites that resisted incubation at 60°C for 60 min. They coined these sites BZ_3 binding sites. While clobazam was much less potent than Diaz in displacing BZ_1 and BZ_2 binding, it was almost as potent as Diaz in inhibiting binding to the presumed BZ_3 sites.

5.17.6 β-Carbolines, Pentetrazol

Binding of β-carbolines and β-carboline inhibition of [^{3}H]BZ binding show certain similarities with CL 218,872 (Braestrup and Nielsen, 1981a; Stapleton *et al.*, 1982; Ehlert *et al.*, 1983). A Hill coefficient <1 for β-[^{3}H]CCPr binding, considered originally as evidence for an intraregional heterogeneity of binding sites, disappears at 37°C (Gee and Yamamura, 1982a,b; Gee *et al.*, 1982a, 1983a). Interregional differences remain at physiological temperature but are smaller than at low temperature. β-CCE was reported to be more potent in displacing β-[^{3}H]CCPr than [^{3}H]Flu in both cerebellum and hippocampus (Stapleton *et al.*, 1982). Martin and Doble (1983) concluded from binding studies with β-[^{3}H]CCE at 0°C in membranes from whole rat brain that the BZR is a single entity that can exist in two conformations.

Pentetrazol has been reported to discriminate between the putative BZ_1 and BZ_2 binding sites (Chweh *et al.*, 1983a,b).

5.17.7 Kenazepine and Etazolate

Kenazepine reacts noncompetitively and irreversibly with some sites and competitively and reversibly with other sites. The cerebellum has the largest proportion of the noncompetitive type, while in the hippocampus and cortex the competitive type prevails (E. F. Williams *et al.*, 1980).

Etazolate was found by Supavilai and Karobath (1980a) to stimulate [^{3}H]Flu more in the cerebellum than in the hippocampus.

5.17.8 Multiplicity of Monomers Photoaffinity Labeled with [^{3}H]Flu

Battersby *et al.* (1979) and Möhler *et al.* (1980) found only one protein species of about MW 49,000 photolabeled with [^{3}H]Flu when separating on SDS–PAGE the denatured proteins extracted from membranes. Similar findings were reported by Thomas and Tallman (1983). However, Sieghart and Karobath (1980), using fluorography as detection system, found that [^{3}H]Flu bound irreversibly to a polypeptide of MW 51,000 (P_{51}) in the cerebellum, but to three additional polypeptides (P_{53}, P_{55}, P_{59}) in other brain regions, notably in the hippocampus. Diaz, but not Ro 5-4864, inhibited covalent binding to all four peptides. Conversely, GABA enhanced covalent binding in a bicuculline-sensitive way to all four peptides. CL 218,872 inhibited irreversible binding of [³H]Flu more to P_{51} than to P_{55}. In the early days of life, [³H]Flu was reported to label preferentially P_{55} and P_{59}, and labeling of P_{51} to start to increase in the second postnatal week (Sieghart and Mayer, 1982a,b). The presence of multiple photolabeled proteins is thought not to be due to artifactual proteolysis *in vitro* (Sieghart and Drexler, 1983); the authors speculated that interregional differences in the posttranslational processing of a receptor precursor may contribute to the hetrogeneity. CL 218,872 and β-CCE differed in their potency to inhibit irreversible [³H]Flu binding to the four individual peptides (Sieghart *et al.*, 1983). Quazepam and two of its metabolites were found by Sieghart (1983) to interact preferentially with BZ binding sites in the cerebellum.

5.17.9 Different Localization of BZ₁R and BZ₂R in the Substantia Nigra

Lo *et al.* (1983b) made localized chemical lesions in the caudate-putamen of rats using the neurotoxic amino acid ibotenic acid, with the aim of inducing the degeneration of striato-nigral afferents. About 10 days after the lesion the total specific [³H]BZ binding in the substantia nigra was increased by 70%, whether [³H]Flu or [³H]Ro 15-1788 was used as radioligand. To distinguish between BZ₁Rs and BZ₂Rs, tissue sections were treated with 2% sodium cholate, which completely solubilizes BZ₂Rs; in addition β-[³H]CCE, which has about 10 times higher affinity for BZ₁Rs, was used. The striato-nigral degeneration increased BZ₁Rs by 100–170% and decreased BZ₂Rs. Ibotenic acid lesions within the substantia nigra reduced BZ₁Rs by 50% without changing binding to BZ₂Rs. The conclusions were that BZ₂Rs were located on striato-nigral nerve endings, whereas BZ₁Rs were localized to neurons within the substantia nigra.

5.17.10 Different Ontogenetic Development

Lippa *et al.* (1981) found that binding sites for [³H]Flu in the rat cerebral cortex on postnatal day 1 were BZ₂Rs according to their definition. These binding sites increased rapidly during the first week and reached adult levels after 3–4 weeks. BZ₁Rs were present in only a few percent on the first day. They increased mainly during the second week.

5.17.11 Differential Solubility in Detergents

Lo *et al.* (1982, 1983a,b) and Lo and Snyder (1983) described a differential extraction of BZ₁ and BZ₂ binding sites from membranes due to different sensitivity to detergents. While GABA was found to enhance binding of [^{3}H]Flu to both types, anions and divalent cations selectively stimulated solubilized BZ_2 binding sites (Lo and Snyder, 1983).

5.17.12 Conclusions

Although heterogeneous binding of various ligands to BZ binding sites is a well-documented fact, the actual reasons for this heterogeneity are totally unknown (see Martin and Brown, 1983; Martin *et al.*, 1983, 1984). It is certainly premature to assume the existence of multiple receptor species (mediating different effects) from heterogeneity of binding. Part of this heterogeneity is due to the highly unphysiological conditions of radioligand binding assays, because part of the heterogeneity disappears, e.g., at physiological temperature. The distinction of two types of BZRs, one mediating the most desired effects, such as anxiolytic and anticonvulsant effects, the other those effects considered (correctly?) to be unwanted side effects in current therapy of anxiety and epilepsy, such as sedation and muscle relaxation, certainly reflects wishful thinking rather than realistic views on how the CNS works. On the other hand, BZs and some novel non-BZ agonists at BZRs differ sufficiently in their prevalent actions to call for an explanation other than pharmacokinetic differences. As an alternative (or addition) to receptor multiplicity for explaining differences in the pharmacological profile, partial agonistic properties of the ligands have to be considered. Partial agonists are ligands which require a higher fractional receptor occupancy to produce a given intensity of effect than full agonists (for a brief review of this concept see Ruffolo, 1982). Assuming the presence of spare receptors for BZs at some GABAergic synapses but not at others, partial agonists may produce a maximum effect (like full agonists) at the former and only a weak effect at the latter synapses. This possibility has been recently reviewed by Haefely and Polc (1985).

5.18 PUTATIVE ENDOGENOUS LIGANDS OF BZRS

The BZR appears now to be a component of the GABA-R/Cl$^-$ channel complex, and the protein bearing the BZ binding site may well be identical with the protein carrying the GABA binding site. All available evidence indicates that the BZ binding site mediates a modulation of the GABA-R/Cl$^-$ channel function. While it seems clear that BZs can produce their effects on the GABA-R/Cl$^-$ channel complex in the absence of an endogenous ligand (Smart *et al.*, 1983), the question arises whether this modulatory site, called BZR, has any physiological function by responding to one or more endogenous modulators. Although there is no a priori reason to postulate that such an endogenous ligand has to exist, there is also no compelling argument against a possible physiological role of the BZR. It was logical, therefore, to search for endogenous compounds present in the CNS that would bind to the BZ binding site, as soon as a simple radioligand assay became available. The topic of endogenous ligands for the BZR has been reviewed several times and we refer to these reviews for more detailed information (Möhler, 1981; Skolnick and Paul, 1982; Hamon and Soubrié, 1983; Braestrup and Nielsen, 1983). We present here a very brief overview of the compounds that have been considered at some time as candidates for the role of endogenous ligands of the BZR.

5.18.1 Purines

Hypoxanthine and inosine were isolated from the brain by virtue of their affinity to BZ binding sites by Marangos et al. (1978), Skolnick et al. (1978, 1979, 1980c), Möhler et al. (1979), and Asano and Spector (1979). The affinity of these two purines for BZ binding sites is in the high micromolar to low millimolar range. A number of other nucleosides, e.g., adenosine, have similar low affinities for BZ binding sites and, in addition, are weak inhibitors of [^{3}H]DHP binding (Olsen and Leeb-Lundberg, 1980). It has been calculated that inosine and hypoxanthine may reach concentrations in the brain under pathological conditions (e.g., ischemia) that might allow some interaction with BZ binding sites. Whether the two purines act as agonists or antagonists when they reach sufficiently high concentrations, is not clear. Inosine administered intracerebroventricularly has been reported to have "BZ-like" effects (increase of the latency of pentetrazol-induced seizures) by Skolnick et al. (1979, 1983a) and by Lapin (1980) as well as to block BZ effects (Slater and Longman, 1979; Skolnick et al., 1982a,b). An electrophysiological comparison of inosine and flurazepam on cultured mouse spinal cord neurons yielded somewhat confusing and inconsistent results (MacDonald et al., 1979). Matsumoto and Fukuda (1982a) reported that inosine failed to enhance low-affinity [^{3}H]muscimol binding or to protect GABA binding sites from heat inactivation as they found BZ agonists to do. According to Ticku and Burch (1980) inosine and hypoxanthine inhibit both [^{3}H]muscimol and [^{3}H]Diaz binding. Levine and Morley (1982) proposed that inosine may be an endogenous modulator of satiety acting through BZRs; inosine suppressed spontaneous and diazepam-induced food intake. Inhibition of guanase, which metabolizes guanine and hypoxanthine to xanthine, decreased BZ binding in brain areas where this enzyme is present in abundance (Norstrand et al., 1983); inhibition of adenosine deaminase, which converts adenosine to inosine, increased BZ binding in the frontal lobe, but to a very small extent in other areas.

5.18.2 Nicotinamide

Nicotinamide was identified in bovine and rat brain as a compound with low affinity for BZ binding sites (Möhler et al., 1979). While these and other authors (Iwata and Mikumi, 1980; Kennedy and Leonard, 1980; Bourgeois et al., 1983) reported some BZ-like effects of nicotinamide in extremely high systemic and locally applied doses, other investigators failed to confirm this (Slater and Longman, 1979; Lapin, 1980; Petersen and Buus-Lassen, 1981).

5.18.3 β-Carbolines

The story of β-CCE has already been narrated (see Section 5.8.3.2). β-Carboline-3-carboxylate esters are very unlikely to be formed in the body and, therefore, are no candidates for endogenous ligands (see Braestrup and Nielsen, 1983). Dihydro- and tetrahydro-β-carbolines (which have a very low affinity for BZ binding sites) may occur in the CNS, and it has been speculated that harmane or a congener may function as an endogenous ligand of BZRs (Rommelspacher *et al.*, 1980; Morin *et al.*, 1981).

5.18.4 Tryptophan Derivatives

Of several tryptophan derivatives tested, melatonin (K_i 450 μM) and its metabolite N-acetyl-5-methoxy-kynurenamine (K_i 49 μM) were the most potent inhibitors of [^{3}H]Diaz binding (Marangos *et al.*, 1981b).

5.18.5 Unidentified Factors

A number of medium- to high-molecular-weight compounds with some affinity for BZ binding sites have been isolated, mostly from the brain.

Inhibition of benzodiazepine binding by a high-molecular-weight fraction (MW = 40,000–70,000) from porcine brain was reported by Colello *et al.* (1978). The inhibitory factor was heat stable and susceptible to trypsin treatment.

Karobath *et al.* (1978) found a low-molecular-weight inhibitor (MW <500) in rat brain which was not inactivated by proteolytic enzymes.

Marangos *et al.* (1979a) found two fractions in bovine brain, heat stable and resistant to protolytic degradation, in addition to inosine and hypoxanthine.

A highly hydrophilic low-molecular-weight factor was isolated by Chen *et al.* (1983b) from bovine cerebral cortex; a theoretical K_D of 1–2 nM was determined in an usual receptor binding assay.

Nepenthin is a protein of about MW 16,000 isolated by Woolf and Nixon (1981) from the small intestine and the bile duct of rats. It was reported to be heat stable, resistant to proteolytic digestion, and to have weak protease activity. An immunoreactive similar peptide was found in deep cortical regions of the forebrain. The displacing potency of nepenthin is said to be very high (K_D 46 nM).

Poddar *et al.* (1980) found that the supernatant of a brain homogenate of awake, but not of sleeping hamsters, contains a factor that inhibits [^{3}H]Diaz binding to membrane preparations of cerebral cortex and less so of other brain areas. They suggested that this inhibitor may be an endogenous ligand with BZ-like activity.

Davis et al. (1981) separated a peptide-containing fraction from aqueous brain extracts that competitively inhibited [³H]Diaz binding and that produced Diaz-like effects upon intracerebroventricular injection.

Nagy et al. (1981) described an endogenous compound from porcine brain with a MW of about 3000 that partially inhibited [³H]Diaz binding in the P_2-fraction but not in the synaptic membrane fraction. The compound also inhibited GABA binding. Injection into the amygdala of Diaz inhibited convulsions evoked by systemic pentetrazol; this Diaz effect was prevented by prior local injection of the brain factor.

Kuhn et al. (1981) reported on three peaks with [³H]Diaz binding inhibitory activity separated by Sephadex chromatography of human cerebrospinal fluid.

Chiu and Rosenberg (1981) obtained a heat stable protein by digitonin extraction that inhibited in a purely noncompetitive manner [³H]Flu binding to solubilized BZ binding sites.

Clow et al. (1983) isolated unidentified material from human urine that displayed both MAO inhibitory and [³H]Flu displaying activity. The output of this material (also termed tribulin; Sandler, 1982) seems to be increased in stress and drug withdrawal periods.

Korneyev and Factor (1983) reported that washing rat brain homogenates in 10 to 20 volumes of distilled water at 20°C resulted in a decrease of the K_D for [³H]Flu binding. Adding the supernatant of this first washing to the washed residue or to the solubilized [³H]Flu binding material obtained by further washing with distilled water decreased specific binding of [³H]Diaz dose dependently. The authors considered these results as evidence that the first washing in distilled water (but not in several tested buffers) extracted an endogenous inhibitor of BZ binding. This inhibitor seemed to be thermostable and to have an MW between 2000 and 10,000. Subsequent washings did not yield further inhibitory activity; however, it decreased B_{max} for [³H]Flu binding in the insoluble membranes until complete disappearance. This also occurred at 5°C. The presence of Flu or, even better, of Ro 15-1788 at 1 μM, prevented the solubilization of membrane-bound binding material.

Diaz binding inhibitor (DBI) is a name coined by Costa et al. (1983a–c) for a peptide isolated from rat brain. It has an MW of approximately 11,000, contains 104 amino acids with an abundance of lysine, is basic in nature, has a tyrosine at the carboxy terminus and a blocked N-terminal amino acid (Corda et al., 1983a,b; Costa and Guidotti, 1982; Costa et al., 1980, 1983a,b; Costa, 1983a,b; Guidotti, 1983). This peptide is present in high concentrations in the rat brain (10–25 μmol/kg), but only in traces in peripheral organs. DBI inhibits competitively the specific binding of [³H]BZs and, more effectively, of β-[³H]carbolines. Its displacing activity of [^{3}H]Ro 15-1788 is unaffected by GABA, in contrast to BZ agonists. DBI does not affect GABA binding directly, but inhibits the enhancement of [^{3}H]GABA binding by BZs. When injected intracerebroventricularly to rats in a punished drinking test, DBI seemed to enhance the punishment effect, i.e., acted like an anxiogenic. Moreover, injected by this route, DBI antagonized the anticonflict action of Diaz. Overall, the biological properties of DBI resemble those of inverse agonistic β-carboline derivatives (Guidotti et al., 1983a–c, 1984). DBI is speculated to be synthesized in GABAergic neurons and released as a cotransmitter together with GABA, perhaps only at very high activity of these neurons and, by down modulating the BZR, would avoid overstimulation of GABA-Rs. A lot remains to be done before this very attractive speculation can be tested.

5.19 SOLUBILIZATION AND PURIFICATION OF BZR

The early studies on BZ binding had already suggested, based on enzymatic inactivation, that the BZ binding molecules are proteins (Bosmann et al., 1977; Braestrup and Squires, 1977; Möhler and Okada, 1977a,b). The membrane-bound site seems to be rather stable, as there is no loss of activity when stored at low temperature, and autoradiographic investigations show normal binding properties of mildly prefixed tissue slices. Very few attempts have been made to identify chemical groups that may be responsible in reversible bond formation with ligands. For instance, the involvement of a tyrosyl residue has been postulated on the basis of the loss of binding capacity after treatment with group reactive reagents (Fehske et al., 1979; Sherman-Gold and Dudai, 1981). Treatment of membranes with the alkylating agent N-ethylmaleimide decreased irreversibly the number of [^{3}H]Diaz binding sites, an effect that could be prevented by the presence of BZs (Martini and Lucacchini, 1982).

Molecular mass estimation of the BZ binding molecule in extensively washed and dried membrane preparations of cattle and rat cortex, using radiation inactivation, yielded a value of about MW 220,000. Binding of [^{3}H]Diaz, [^{3}H]muscimol, and β-[^{3}H]CCE disappeared at the same rate on electron bombardment, suggesting that all three ligands bind to the same oligomer (Chang and Barnard, 1982). With the same technique Doble and Iversen (1982) obtained a molecular weight of only 90,000 to 100,000. According to Nielsen and Braestrup (1983) the molecular target size of binding sites for the convulsant TBPS, thought to represent the anion translocation site, is 134,000 Da and, thus, different from both the BZ and GABA binding sites.

BZ binding material can be extracted from membranes and solubilized under nondenaturating conditions by various ionic detergents, such as deoxycholate, lysolecithin, and CHAPS {3-[(3-cholamidopropyl)dimethylammonio]propane sulfonate}, and nonionic detergents, such as digitonin, Lubrol PX (polyethyleneglycolmonododecyl ether), Triton X-100 (polyethyleneglycol-*p*-isooc-tylphenyl ether) as well as, perhaps, by distilled water.

5.19.1 Extraction and Solubilization with Ionic Detergents

Gavish *et al.* (1979) solubilized [³H]GABA binding material with *lysolecithin*, while 50% of the membrane-bound [³H]Flu binding sites were solubilized with 1% digitonin. Cross binding to the binding material obtained by the two detergents was not investigated.

Sodium deoxycholate was used in 0.5% concentration to extract BZ binding material from calf cerebral cortex by Sherman-Gold and Dudai (1980); 30–40% of the membrane-bound binding capacity was solubilized. The solubilized material lost [³H]Flu binding capacity at 4°C with a half-life of 30 hr. Addition of 0.5 *M* KCl slowed down this loss of activity. Affinity and ligand specificity of the solubilized material did not differ markedly from the membrane-bound binding sites. Detergent treatment diminished but did not completely eliminate the GABA shift. After photolabeling with [³H]Flu and separation on SDS–PAGE in the presence of β-mercaptoethanol a major polypeptide with MW 51,000 ± 200 was revealed. Components with higher molecular weight were sometimes also present (Sherman-Gold and Dudai, 1983a–c); in the absence of β-mercap-toethanol a 57K protein was detected. Assuming a globular protein, the sedimentation coefficient suggested a molecular weight of the solubilized polymer of 200,000 to 250,000. Part of the binding sites for [³H]Flu solubilized in 2% deoxycholate could be protected from heat inactivation by 100 μ*M* GABA (Gavish, 1983). Asano and Ogasawara (1981b) solubilized GABA and BZ binding material from a rat cerebral cortex synaptosomal fraction with 0.2% deoxycholate and 1 *M* KCl. Ammonium sulfate fractionation and gel filtration on Sepharose 6-B showed the peaks of both [³H]GABA and [³H]Flu binding to be in the same fraction with a molecular weight of approximately 670,000. This value, which is not corrected for the presence of detergent, was much higher than that estimated by sucrose gradient. Further attempts at separating the two binding sites by DEAE-cellulose chromatography failed. In later studies, Asano *et al.* (1983a,b) found that solubilized binding material from rat cerebellar membranes, photoaffinity labeled with [³H]muscimol and [³H]Flu, yielded peptide bands of approximately 50,000 Da on SDS–PAGE. Photolabeling with [³H]muscimol may be prone to artifacts since, in contrast to the photolabeling with [³H]Flu, UV light of short wavelength was used, which affects protein structure. In a study of BZ binding sites in various regions of the bovine brain, deoxycholate was found to extract 20–25% of [³H]Flu binding sites from the cerebellum and 50–60% from the hippocampus. Gel filtration through Sephadex of the solubilized [³H]muscimol and [³H]Flu binding material revealed peaks in the same fractions. The molecular weight estimated by gel filtration was 600,000 to 650,000.

Sucrose density gradient centrifugation also showed the binding peaks to be in the same fraction. SDS–PAGE of photoaffinity labeled sites revealed a 48,000 subunit in the cerebellum and two (48,000 and 52,000) in the cortex and hippocampus. GABA stimulated [^{3}H]Flu binding to the solubilized fraction from the cerebellum by 40% and from the hippocampus by 70%. Diaz and Ro 15-1788 inhibited [^{3}H]Flu binding to solubilized material from the three regions. CL 218,872 was most potent in the cerebellar material, half as potent in the cerebral cortex, and one-fifth as potent in the hippocampus. The Hill coefficient for CL 218,872 binding was 0.98 in the cerebellar material, 0.64 for material from cortex and 0.58 from hippocampus. Stephenson et al. (1982) used 0.5% deoxycholate to solubilize GABA- and BZ-binding material from bovine cortex. About 58% of the membrane-bound [^{3}H]muscimol binding activity was extracted. On gel filtration as well as on sedimentation in a sucrose density gradient the soluble [^{3}H]GABA and [^{3}H]Flu binding material comigrated. A molecular weight of 355,000 was calculated for the presumed receptor–detergent complex. GABA and, less regularly, pentobarbitone, enhanced BZ binding to the soluble protein. Sigel et al. (1982) extracted BZ binding material from bovine cortex membranes with deoxycholate in the presence of protease inhibitors.

CHAPS, a zwitterionic derivative of the detergent cholic acid, was used by Stephenson and Olsen (1982, 1983) to extract bovine cerebral cortex and by Mernoff et al. (1983) to solubilize BZ binding material from rat brain. At 20 mM CHAPS extracted 67% of the total membrane BZ binding sites. The number of [^{3}H]GABA binding sites was two to four times higher than that of BZ binding sites. Pentobarbitone enhanced in a concentration-dependent way [^{3}H]Flu binding to the soluble BZ binding material by increasing affinity. Other barbiturates enhanced [^{3}H]Flu binding in relation to their relative potencies as anesthetics. Pentobarbitone produced only a slight enhancement. The barbiturate effect was stimulated by Cl$^-$ ions and blocked by picrotoxin. Pentobarbitone also enhanced [^{3}H]muscimol binding to the material solubilized by CHAPS by increasing B_{max} and without altering K_D, apparently by unmasking "cryptic" binding sites. The studies of Stephenson and Olsen (1982) were the first to show a barbiturate stimulation of BZ binding to solubilized material. Whereas the solubilized material retained its [^{3}H]Flu binding capacity for days, the ability of barbiturates to stimulate BZ binding was gradually lost, suggesting that CHAPS has a slow destabilizing effect selective for the barbiturate binding site.

5.19.2 Extraction and Solubilization with Nonionic Detergents

Digitonin (1%) extracted 50% of membrane-bound [^{3}H]Flu binding sites (Gavish et al., 1979); K_D values for [^{3}H]Flu binding were similar for membranes and for the solubilized material. Pong et al. (1981) used digitonin for extraction with a yield of 42%. Avermectin B$_{1a}$ and GABA increased [^{3}H]Flu binding in a bicuculline-sensitive manner. In digitonin/Na cholate extracts Chen *et al.* (1983a,b) found an influence of temperature on the steepness of competition curves in [³H]Flu binding for CL-218,872 and β-CCPr (Hill coefficient 0.7 and 1.0 at 0 and 37°C, respectively).

Lubrol-PX (0.5%) was used by Yousufi *et al.* (1979), Tallman and Gallager (1979), and Tallman (1980) for extraction of rat cortex membranes; the yield was 50–60%. Molecular weight estimation by gel filtration gave a value of 210,000 to 230,000. The affinity of various BZs to the solubilized material was about half that to membranes. Increasing temperature decreased binding. Treatment with urea and guanidine inactivated binding. GABA did not enhance BZ binding to this material. Solubilized and membrane-bound material showed different heat denaturation. Ticku and Davis (1981) and Davis and Ticku (1981) also used Lubrol for extraction of rat brain membranes. The solubilized material apparently contained a functional complex consisting of [³H]Diaz, [³H]muscimol, and [³H]DHP binding sites. Pentobarbitone, ethanol, and muscimol increased [³H]Diaz binding. Subsequent gel filtration on a Sephadex G-200 column yielded a 61 and a 185 kDa peak. The former was associated with BZ binding, the latter to [³H]muscimol and [³H]DHP binding.

Triton X-100 (0.7%) extracted about 60–70% of BZ binding sites from rat whole brain crude synaptosomal membranes (Lang *et al.*, 1979). The K_D of binding to the soluble form was about one-third of that to membranes. Massotti *et al.* (1981) claimed to have separately solubilized GABA and BZ binding proteins from rat brain membranes by using, at a crucial point, different concentrations of Triton X-100. A high proportion of GABA binding material virtually free of BZ binding capacity was solubilized by incubation at 0°C with 1% Triton X-100, whereas the reverse was obtained by using 0.05% Triton at 37°C. While GABA and BZ binding to the respective material was similar to that found to membrane-bound sites, the mutual modulation was absent. These findings were interpreted as proof that GABA and BZ binding sites reside in two different molecules. The authors also solubilized an inhibitory factor that selectively inhibited GABA binding ("gabamodulin") (Toffano, 1983; Toffano *et al.*, 1980) and another thermostable protein which selectively inhibited BZ binding (later to be named DBI; Guidotti *et al.*, 1983b). Chang and Barnard (1982) extracted photoaffinity-labeled material with Triton X-100. On gel filtration on two different columns they obtained a protein with an approximate molecular weight of 220,000. It gave a single peak for both [³H]Flu and [³H]muscimol binding. When the extracted material was subjected to SDS–PAGE, all the extracted radioactivity migrated in a single band at MW 51,000. Chang and Barnard (1982) concluded that the BZ binding site and GABA$_A$-R in membranes are a single (oligomeric) protein structure of about MW 220,000. Korneyev (1982) extracted 60–70% of BZ and 50% of [³H]muscimol binding sites from rat brain with 2% Triton X-100. GABA stimulated [³H]Flu binding to proteins that did not permeate the ultrafilter XM-300, but not to the 10% of soluble sites permeating through the filter. On CM Sepharose [³H]Flu and [³H]muscimol binding material was eluted together; however, with this eluted material muscimol failed to stimulate [³H]Flu binding. Lo et al. (1982) and Lo and Snyder (1983) extracted pellets of cow brain homogenate with 2% Triton X-100. The solubilized BZ and GABA binding glycoproteins were immobilized on concanavalin A–agarose beads and then assayed for [³H]ligand binding. Using whole cow brain and 2% Triton X-100 no more than 30% of BZ binding sites and no more than 42% of GABA binding sites could be solubilized. The portion of BZ binding sites that could be extracted varied with the brain regions. The most extensive solubilization was achieved in tissues from brainstem and hippocampus, the least in the cerebellum and corpus striatum. β-CCM and CL 218,872 were more potent ligands of the residual sites in the membrane than of the solubilized sites (six- to eightfold potency difference). β- [³H] CCPr had only a low-affinity component of binding in the solubilized sites, only a high-affinity component on residual membrane-bound sites, and multiphasic binding in native membranes (not treated with detergent). The ratio of B_{max} values for β-[³H]CCPr binding to soluble and insoluble sites varied at least fivefold in different brain regions. About one-half of the Triton X-100-insoluble BZ binding sites could be solubilized by the combination of a high salt solution (1 M) and Triton X-100. The affinity of β-CCM and CL 218,872 for the material solubilized by salt plus Triton X-100 was the same as for the residual membrane-bound sites after Triton X-100 alone. In marked contrast, Diaz, clonazepam, and flurazepam had the same affinity for native membranes, membranes after Triton X-100 treatment, sites solubilized by Triton X-100 and for material solubilized by salt plus Triton X-100. The results were interpreted as support for the notion of two different BZ binding sites: BZ_1Rs corresponding to the Triton X-100-resistant and BZ_2Rs to the Triton X-100-soluble sites. The effects of anions and divalent cations on physically separated, solubilized BZ_1 and BZ_2 binding material differed markedly (Lo and Snyder, 1983). Nonidet P-40 was found by Kuriyama and Ito (1983) to be the most suitable detergent for extracting GABA-Rs and BZ binding sites. A further copurification was achieved by an affinity chromotography on nitrazepam–autoamide–AH–Sepharose 4B. While bidirectional interaction between GABA- and BZ-binding sites was preserved, the barbiturate effect on GABA and BZ binding was lost. Most of the [³H]Flu binding sites solubilized in 2% Triton X-100 could be protected by GABA from heat inactivation (Gavish, 1983).

5.19.3 Extraction with Distilled Water

As discussed in Section 5.20, Korneyev and Factor (1983) extracted an inhibitor of BZ binding by a first washing of membranes with distilled water and a BZ binding material with subsequent washings. The solubilized BZ binding material in the supernatant of the second and subsequent washings was easily detectable by its specific [^{3}H]Flu binding capacity. The K_D was 1.7 nM. About 25 to 30% of the binding sites lost from the membranes was recovered in the distilled water supernatant. It would be surprising if this method were successful in further purification of BZRs, because one would expect membrane proteins to aggregate and precipitate after removal of endogenous membrane lipids that may form micelles initially.

5.19.4 Purification of BZ Binding Sites by Affinity Chromatography

The first attempts at purifying solubilized BZ binding material by affinity chromatography appear to have been those of Tallman and Gallager (1979). They prepared an affinity column by coupling Ro 7-1986 to activated Sepharose beads. Material extracted and solubilized with Lubrol was absorbed on the column. Problems with the recovery and stability of the eluted fraction prevented further progress. Sigel et al. (1982) used essentially the same affinity column. Over 87% of the [^{3}H]Flu binding material extracted with deoxycholate was retained on the column. It was eluted with the water-soluble BZ chlorazepate in a Triton X-100 containing buffer. The eluted fraction could not be assayed for BZ binding capacity because of the presence of high concentrations of chlorazepate; however, the fraction was highly enriched in [^{3}H]muscimol binding capacity. Separation of the protein from chlorazepate on DEAE-Sephacel resulted in a 1800-fold enriched receptor fraction containing a high-affinity binding site for GABA and BZs. A low-affinity GABA binding site (GABA shift) was not detected. The receptor fraction consisted of two major protein bands of MW 57,000 and 53,000, which were both photolabeled with [^{3}H]Flu (Sigel et al., 1983a,b).

With a similar purification procedure, but a different method of separating chlorazepate from the protein, Schoch and Möhler (1983) obtained a receptor fraction which contained, in addition to the high-affinity sites for GABA and BZs, a low-affinity GABA site; positive and negative GABA shifts were observed. Monoclonal antibodies raised against the binding material immunoprecipitated a complex containing both the high-affinity sites for GABA and BZs and the low-affinity site for GABA, suggesting that these sites are localized on the same molecular entity (Schoch et al., 1984).

Martini et al. (1981) used an affinity column made of chlorazepate or delorazepam immobilized via an adipic hydrazide spacer on Sepharose. Chlorazepate was attached through C-3 and delorazepam through N-1. Clonazepam–agarose (clonazepam attached through the nitrogen in position 7) did not work. The affinity columns retained [^{3}H]Diaz binding material from human serum and rat kidney, lung, skeletal muscle, and brain. Purification of rat brain material (Martini et al., 1981; Martini and Lucacchini, 1982) started with extraction and solubilization with 0.7% Triton X-100. Specific elution from the columns was performed with 6 mM chlorazepate. The latter was removed from the eluate by exhaustive dialysis. [^{3}H]Diaz bound with a K_D of 8 nM. Molecular weight determination by gel filtration gave a value of about 240,000. SDS–PAGE showed a single peptide band of about MW 60,000. Modulation of BZ binding by GABA and other agents was not investigated, however, [^{3}H]muscimol binding to the purified BZ binding site was demonstrated (Martini et al., 1983b).

5.20 BIOSYNTHESIS AND MEMBRANE INCORPORATION OF THE BZR/GABA-R/Cl$^-$ CHANNEL COMPLEX IN FROG OOCYTES

In the course of their studies on the nicotinic acetylcholine receptor Barnard et al. (1982) and Miledi and Sumikawa (1982) had microinjected into oocytes of Xenopus laevis a crude mRNA fraction extracted from the Torpedo electric organ or from the denervated cat skeletal muscle. The message for the receptor in the exogenous mRNA was translated in the oocyte, which normally does not possess nicotinic acetylcholine receptors; the receptor was not only synthesized, but also incorporated into the cell membrane in a functional form, because intracellular electrophysiological techniques now showed the oocyte membrane to respond to nicotinic agonists with a conductance increase that could be blocked by nicotinic antagonists. In an attempt to induce de novo synthesis in oocytes of a central neuronal type of nicotinic acetylcholine receptor, a mRNA fraction from the chicken brain was injected into frog oocytes. Instead of the acetylcholine receptor, functional GABA-Rs were synthesized and incorporated in the oocyte membrane (mediating a typical chloride conductance in response to GABA), which normally lacks GABA-Rs. Smart et al. (1983) therefore decided to see whether the mRNA fraction coding for the chick GABA-R also directed the synthesis and membrane insertion of these components of the complex that mediated the modulatory effects of BZs and barbiturates. First, they showed that GABA enhances [^{3}H]Flu binding in membranes of embryonic chick brains. Poly(A)-mRNA extracted from embryonic chick whole brain was then injected into Xenopus oocytes. After 1 to 2 days the oocytes were inserted with two intracellular microelectrodes. GABA applied to the bath increased membrane input conductance and depolarized the cell (the Cl$^-$ equilibrium potential being close to -15 mV). Muscimol and 3-aminopropanosulfonate were more potent than GABA. Baclofen (a GABA$_B$ agonist) was inactive, suggesting the GABA$_A$ nature of the receptor in question. Chlorazepate (1–10 μM) as well as pentobarbitone (25–100 μM) enhanced the conductance change and depolarization evoked by GABA. The effect of chlorazepate was not reversible within 1 hr. Control and enhanced responses to GABA were blocked by bicuculline and picrotoxin. Neither chlorazepate nor pentobarbitone had a direct effect on the conductance of the oocyte membrane.

5.21 EFFECTS OF BZS ON GABA BINDING

The foregoing sections have shown the tremendous work that has been done in the past few years in analyzing the effect of GABA, GABA mimetics, and GABA-R blockers on binding of BZs. Compared with this, the obviously more relevant aspect of the molecular mechanism of action of BZs, namely the possible modification by BZs of the interaction of GABA with its receptor, has been grossly neglected.

In 1978 Costa et al. reported that BZs reduced the K_D of [^{3}H]GABA binding to freshly prepared synaptic membranes (to which GABA apparently binds in a manner consistent with the presence of a single population of binding sites) but not to membranes further treated by freeze-thawing and extraction with 0.01% Triton X-100 (in which GABA binding suggested the presence of two binding sites with different affinities). Moreover, the supernatant of fresh membranes treated with Triton contained a factor that decreased the high-affinity component of GABA binding to treated membranes. BZ competitively inhibited the effect of this supernatant. The authors concluded that an endogenous peptide (later called gabamodulin; Guidotti et al., 1978, 1979; Costa, 1979, 1983a,b; Costa et al., 1980, 1983a,b; Massotti and Guidotti, 1980) was present in fresh membranes and acted as an endogenous down regulator (inhibitor) of GABA-Rs (reducing the affinity of GABA-Rs for GABA), therefore shifting the proportion of GABA-Rs from a high-affinity state to a low-affinity state. BZs were proposed to interact with gabamodulin on the regulatory site for GABA-R affinity. Hence, the effect of BZs on the level of the GABA-R would be to increase their affinity for GABA or, in other words, to make them more sensitive to their transmitter. Phosphorylation of gabamodulin was recently found to reduce its ability to decrease the number of high-affinity binding sites for GABA in synaptic membranes (Wise et al., 1983).

A number of investigators have tried, according to personal communications, to confirm the early findings on gabamodulin, but were unable to reproduce these results. For instance, Gavish and Snyder (1980a) failed to find an enhancement of [^{3}H]muscimol binding to rat brain membranes by Diaz and clonazepam, while several BZs were able to protect [^{3}H]muscimol binding proteins from heat inactivation. More recently, the original observations of Costa et al. (1978) were reproduced in a few laboratories, albeit with modifications.

Matsumoto and Fukuda (1982a) found an enhanced binding of [^{3}H]muscimol to low-affinity sites, but not to high-affinity sites in rat brain membranes frozen and treated with 0.05% Triton X-100. The effect was due to a decrease of K_D for muscimol. The maximum stimulation of [^{3}H]muscimol binding was about 20% (with 10^{-7} M Diaz). Clonazepam, more potent as a BZR ligand, seemed to be rather less effective than Diaz on [^{3}H]muscimol binding. The slowly denaturating phase of heat inactivation of GABA-Rs was markedly reduced in the presence of Diaz.

Also in Triton X-100-treated membranes Diaz, Flu, and chlordiazepoxide in the nanomolar range increased [³H]GABA binding in a concentration-dependent manner (Meiners and Salama, 1982). Maximum stimulation was 15 to 18%. Tracazolate further increased GABA binding. The stimulant action of BZs was not enhanced by Cl⁻ ions. Using a centrifugation assay and fresh, well-washed synaptosomes from rat central cortex, Abbracchio et al. (1983) found evidence for the presence of two [³H]GABA binding sites differing in K_D and B_{max}. Diaz (300 nM) increased B_{max} for both component of binding, but reduced the affinity of both. Kuriyama and Ito (1983) describe an increase of the high-affinity binding of [³H]muscimol by 10^{-5} of diazepam in frozen synaptic membranes treated with 0.05% Triton X-100; a similar effect was seen with a solubilized GABA binding material (Ito and Kurijama, 1982). Flu increased [³H]muscimol binding by 20% according to Borea et al. (1983). Korneyev (1983) also found a 20% increase in high-affinity [³H]muscimol binding by Diaz (10 μM), Flu (1 μM), and Clon (1 μM), which was not apparent in the presence of Ro 15-1788 (1–10 μM). Treatment of the membranes with Triton X-100 reduced the stimulant effect of BZs.

The most systematic investigation of the stimulant action of BZs on GABA binding was made by the Sydney group (Skerritt and Johnston, 1983a,b; Skerritt et al., 1982a–c, 1983a,b; Johnston and Skerritt, 1984). Using fresh, well-washed synaptic membranes of rat brain, a number of BZs were seen to produce a dose-dependent increase of [³H]GABA binding to its low-affinity (K_D 800 nM) sites. The EC_{50} for Diaz was determined as 20 nM and the maximum stimulation, achieved at 300 nM, amounted to 44% over unstimulated binding. The effect is due to an increase of affinity (decrease of K_D to 600 nM) for GABA without change in B_{max}. High-affinity (K_D 30 nM) binding of GABA was unaffected. The magnitude of the effect was higher at higher temperature, although the potency of BZs decreased. While Diaz enhanced binding of [³H]GABA and [³H]muscimol, it failed to affect that of [³H]THIP. Non-BZ ligands, such as zopiclone, CL 218,872, and β-CCPr also enhanced GABA binding, whereas the nonneuronal type ligand Ro 5-4864 was ineffective. Ro 15-1788 by itself did not affect GABA binding, but blocked the stimulation by agonists; this compound was more potent in this respect than β-CCM and β-CCE. Stimulation of GABA binding by Diaz was not inhibited by picrotoxin and not affected by Cl⁻ ions. Johnston and Skerritt (1984) propose several explanations for the failure of other investigators to observe BZ-induced stimulation of GABA binding and for the phenomenon being less robust than GABA stimulation of BZ binding. Among factors determining the occurrence of BZ stimulation of GABA binding they mention the GABA concentration used (only low-affinity binding is affected), the method of membrane preparation (a putative endogenous inhibitor of GABA binding has to be present for the phenomenon to occur), and the method used to separate bound and free GABA (centrifugation being required because of the rapid dissociation of low-affinity binding of GABA). The peak enhancement of [³H]GABA binding was not the same for all BZ agonists; however, the large scattering of data make this parameter unsuitable as a possible criterion of "intrinsic efficacy." No satisfactory correlation between stimulation of GABA binding, *in vitro* affinity for BZ binding sites, and *in vivo* pharmacological activity is apparent from the above studies.

Unfortunately, the stimulant effect of BZs on GABA binding has not been examined in intact cells, e.g., in cell membranes in which the GABA potentiating effect of BZs can be monitored by electrophysiological methods.

Attempts to see a stimulant effect of BZs on GABA binding *ex vivo* have failed (Pérez and Rubio, 1981; Marangos and Crawley, 1982).

5.22 EFFECTS OF BZS ON "Cl⁻ CHANNEL AGENTS"

BZ agonists (Diaz, Flu, clonazepam, zopiclone, CL 218,872) enhance and inverse BZR agonists (β-CCM, β-CCE, FG 7142, DMCM) reduce the binding of the "cage convulsant" [³⁵S]TBPS to membranes of rat cerebral cortex (Supavilai and Karobath, 1983). BZ antagonists (Ro 15-1788, β-CCPr) have little, if any, intrinsic activity on the binding of the convulsant ligand, but block the effects of both BZ agonists and antagonists. Etazolate-stimulated [³H]muscimol binding was found by Borea *et al.* (1983) to be further enhanced by BZ agonists, little or not affected by BZ antagonists, and reduced by inverse agonists (Borea *et al.*, 1983).

Out of a series of BZs tested for inhibition of *[³H]DHP binding* to rat brain membranes the convulsant BZ Ro 5-3663 was the most potent, with an IC_{50} of $10^{-7}\ M$ (Leeb-Lundberg *et al.*, 1981c); electrophysiological studies also suggest that Ro 5-3663 may share a common site with picrotoxin (Harrison and Simmonds, 1983). Nitrazepam, flurazepam, and Diaz had IC_{50} values equal to or above $10^{-6}\ M$. Other BZ derivatives, such as, e.g., midazolam (which is a more potent anxiolytic–sedative than Diaz) and the nonneuronal type ligand Ro 5-4864, were ineffective on [³H]DHP binding at $10^{-4}\ M$. Thus, there is no correlation between anxiolytic–sedative potency of BZs and their affinity for the picrotoxinin binding site (Leeb-Lundberg *et al.*, 1981c). Depression of GABA effects has been observed by several investigators with very high concentrations of BZs. Whether this might be due to a convulsant-like action on Cl⁻ channels remains to be shown.

6 The Nonneuronal ("Peripheral") Type of BZ Binding Site

Braestrup and Squires (1978a,b) already found specific high-affinity binding of [³H]Diaz to peripheral tissues, most markedly in kidneys, liver, and lung; they also realized that the ligand specificity of these peripheral binding sites is quite different from that of the BZ binding sites that had been characterized in the brain. The still classic distinction between central and peripheral BZ binding sites was proposed, based on Ro 5-4864 as specific ligand for the latter and clonazepam for the former. Specific, saturable binding sites with the same ligand specificity were found, in addition, in testes, heart (Davies and Huston, 1981; Le Fur et al., 1983a,b), skeletal muscle, erythrocytes (Marangos et al., 1982), rat blood platelets (Wang et al., 1980), in mouse thymocytes, spleen T cells and peripheral lymphocytes (Wang et al., 1981; Moingeon et al., 1983), rat peritoneal mast cells (Taniguchi et al., 1980), astrocytes in primary culture (Hertz and Mukerji, 1979), crude membranes of rat diaphragm (Wilkinson et al., 1982), in cultured cell lines of neural origin, the rat C_6 glioma and the mouse NB41A2 neuroblastoma (Syapin and Skolnick, 1979), B16/C3 mouse melanoma (Matthew et al., 1981), longitudinal muscle–myenteric plexus of the guinea pig ileum (Hullihan et al., 1983), rat intestinal mucosa (Zimmerman, 1983), and cultured transformed murine fibroblast cells (Feller et al., 1983). The early distinction between central (or ''brain'') BZ binding sites and peripheral (extracerebral) BZ binding sites soon turned out to be incorrect. Indeed, binding sites with all characteristic properties of ''peripheral'' BZ binding sites were discovered in the brain (Gallager et al., 1981a,b; Quast and Mählmann, 1982; Gehlert et al., 1983); increase of these binding sites by gliosis induced by kainic acid lesions indicated their glial localization. A very high density of these binding sites were found (by displacement studies and [^{3}H]Ro 5-4864 autoradiography) in the bulbus olfactorius, pineal, neurohypophysis, the choroid plexus, and the ependyma (Richards et al., 1982; Weissman et al., 1983a,b; Möhler and Richards, 1983c; Richards and Möhler, 1984; Richards et al., 1984). A relatively dense, uniform distribution in the gray matter of the spinal cord was also seen. The typical distribution of [^{3}H]Ro 5-4864 binding sites was also observed after iv injection of the radioligand (Richards and Möhler, 1984a). It seems very likely, therefore, that typical high-affinity binding sites for Ro 5-4864 occur almost exclusively in nonneuronal cells (Gallager et al., 1981b; McCarthy and Harden, 1981); it cannot be excluded that nuclear membranes of neurons also contain this type of BZ binding site (Bosmann et al., 1980). The proportion of nonneuronal BZ binding sites with respect to neuronal type sites was found to be higher in guinea pigs than in other species (Weissman et al., 1983a). Photoaffinity labeling of brain BZ binding sites does not affect [^{3}H]Ro 5-4864 binding (Marangos et al., 1982; Richards and Möhler, 1984). The term nonneuronal high-affinity site seems, therefore, to be more appropriate. B_{max} for [^{3}H]Ro 5-4864 in the brain was about one-fourth of that of [^{3}H]Diaz or [^{3}H]methylclonazepam (Skerritt et al., 1982d; Marangos et al., 1982).

The nonneuronal BZ binding sites do not seem to be coupled with GABA-Rs; at least, GABA was unable to stimulate binding to these sites (Regan et al.,

1981; Taniguchi *et al.*, 1982; Patel and Marangos, 1982; Rohde and Harris, 1982; Schoemaker *et al.*, 1982a, 1983b; Marangos *et al.*, 1982). There was also no stimulant effect of Cl$^-$ ions, barbiturates, and convulsants (Schoemaker *et al.*, 1982a, 1983b). β-Carbolines, Ro 15-1788, and CGS 8216 have no significant affinity for these binding sites. Only restricted SAfR data are available (Richards *et al.*, 1982; Schoemaker *et al.*, 1983b). Chirality in position 3 does not affect binding affinity; substitution in position 4' of the phenyl ring assures specificity for the nonneuronal type and a methyl substituent at the N-1 is essential for optimal affinity. At 37°C the affinity of [^{3}H]Ro 5-4864 was only 1/20 of that found at 0°C. Whereas the neuronal type binding sites are highly concentrated in the microsomal fraction (P_3), [^{3}H]Ro 5-4868 is preferentially bound to the nuclear fraction (P_1). Slow channel blockers of the dihydropyridine class have been found to inhibit [^{3}H]Ro 5-4864 binding in the low micromolar concentration range (Kenessey *et al.*, 1983).

A convincing connection of nonneuronal BZ binding sites with any pharmacological activity has not been found so far. For instance, the ability to inhibit electrically induced contractions of guinea pig ileum strips by various BZs was not correlated with affinity to binding sites in the same tissue (Hullihan *et al.*, 1983). Although Ro 5-4864 is convulsive (Pieri *et al.*, 1983; Weissman *et al.*, 1983b), there is no evidence that convulsions are mediated by the nonneuronal BZ binding site. Although the prototype inhibitor of adenosine uptake, dipyridamol, has a high affinity for [^{3}H]Ro 5-4864 binding sites in rat and guinea pig hearts (Davies and Huston, 1981), the adenosine uptake site is clearly not identical with the nonneuronal BZ binding site. Taniguchi *et al.* (1981) reported that B_{max} for binding of [^{3}H]Diaz on platelets from spontaneous hypertensive rats was significantly higher than on platelets from normotensive control rats, while the reverse was true for B_{max} in the kidney. Treatment of unilaterally nephrectomized rats with DOCA and NaCl for 6 weeks resulted in a 70% increase of arterial blood pressure; specific [^{3}H]Flu binding in the kidney was increased by 35%, due to an increase of B_{max} (Regan *et al.*, 1981). B_{max} for [^{3}H]Diaz binding in the kidney was found to be increased in Brattleboro rats homozygous for diabetes insipidus (Del Zompo *et al.*, 1983). Treatment of those animals with arginin–vasopressin for 7 days increased the affinity for [^{3}H]Diaz. A possible coupling between BZ binding sites and some ion channels was proposed.

In neuroblastoma cells ethanol failed to affect the (nonneuronal type) binding of [^{3}H]Flu; pentobarbitone decreased it by 20% (Rohde and Harris, 1982). Chronic exposure of mice to ethanol significantly increased [^{3}H]Ro 5-4864 binding site density (43%) without affecting affinity (Schoemaker *et al.*, 1983a). Following kainic acid injection into the striatum of rats, binding of [^{3}H]Ro 5-4864 increased to about 100% of control after the first week and remained so for up to 6 weeks; the effect was selective on B_{max} (Schoemaker *et al.*, 1982b).

These investigators also found a selective increase of binding sites in the putamen of patients with Huntington's disease. When primary neuronal cell cultures were grown in the presence of diphenylhydantoin for 7 days, the total number of [³H]Diaz binding was not affected; however, a ligand displacement analysis indicated that diphenylhydantoin, in fact, decreased the number of neuronal binding sites, possibly because survival of nonneuronal cells was increased over that of neuronal cells in the presence of diphenylhydantoin (Gallager et al., 1981b). In amelanotic cells of a melanoma cell line, specific ligands of the nonneuronal type BZ binding sites accelerated melanogenesis after entry of the cells into the stationary phase, without affecting cell growth (Matthew et al., 1981).

Le Fur et al. (1983a–c) and Benavides et al. (1983a,b) described an isoquinoline carboxamide derivative, PK 11195, which is a potent ligand for the nonneuronal type BZ binding site labeled by [³H]Ro 5-4864. The compound very potently inhibited radioligand binding after ip or po administration. Tritiated PK 11195 showed the characteristic topographical distribution of nonneuronal binding sites. While [³H]Ro 5-4864 binding to the heart was enthalpy driven, that of [³H]PK 11195 was entropy driven (Le Fur et al., 1983c); the authors concluded that this difference in thermodynamics could indicate an agonist property of Ro 5-4864 and an antagonist property of PK 11195 at nonneuronal binding sites. There is no pharmacological evidence to support this claim.

Martini et al. (1983a) reported on the solubilization of [³H]Ro 5-4864 binding protein from rat kidney using Triton X-100. Ultrafiltrates of human plasma and urine were found to contain a factor with an affinity 120 times higher for nonneuronal than for neuronal BZ binding sites (Beaumont et al., 1983).

At the present state of knowledge it is certainly not correct to use the term receptor for the nonneural type BZ binding site.

7 The Low-Affinity BZ Binding Site

Bowling and De Lorenzo (1982) described specific, saturable [³H]Diaz binding in membranes of rat brain, which started at concentrations (around 1 μM) where the high-affinity binding is already fully saturated. Saturation of this low-affinity binding occurred at about 0.3 mM Diaz. Whereas they found the K_D for [³H] Diaz binding to the high-affinity sites to be about 3 nM, K_D for low-affinity binding was 85 μM (thus 27,000 times higher). Also the binding capacities of the two types of binding sites were very different, 0.893 pmol/mg protein and 360.4 pmol/kg protein (a 400-fold difference). Scatchard analysis of equilibrium binding data gave a straight line. The ratio of specific/nonspecific binding was not indicated by the investigators. GABA and muscimol did not alter [³H]Diaz binding to these sites. While various BZs competitively inhibited specific [³H]Diaz binding to low-affinity sites, the rank order of inhibitory potency did not correlate at all with the rank order of high-affinity binding. For instance, clonazepam and bromazepam were less potent on the low-affinity site than the prodrug medazepam. Ro 5-4864 was 10 times weaker than Flu, hence, the ligand specificity was also very different from the nonneuronal type. The low-affinity site differentiated strongly between the two optical isomers of 3-methyl-flunitrazepam Ro 11-6893 and Ro 11-6896. Bowling and De Lorenzo (1982) claim that binding affinity to the low-affinity site is correlated best with potency against electroshock seizures, although this is not apparent from their paper. Diphenylhydantoin was found to be nearly as potent a displacer of [³H]Diaz binding as Diaz itself. Carbamazepin was not tested. Association and dissociation rate constants at 4°C were similar to those for the high-affinity binding. Dissociation was drastically enhanced at 37°C ($t_{1/2} = 26$ sec at 4°C and <3 sec at 37°C).

De Lorenzo et al. (1981) had found various BZs to inhibit membrane-bound Ca–calmodulin-stimulated protein kinase in the micromolar range. The relative potencies seem to correspond roughly to the inhibitory affinities for the low-affinity binding site. Therefore, Bowling and De Lorenzo (1982) proposed that potency in the low-affinity binding correlates with potency in protecting from electroshock (this correlation is, however, not perfect, as Ro 5-4864 does not protect, whereas clonazepam does).

One certainly has to wait for confirmation of low-affinity binding by other investigators, and for more extensive SAR before accepting the hypothetical connection of these sites with electroshock protection. Nevertheless, the assumption is very interesting, because industrial pharmacologists working in this field have been troubled by the lack of activity in the electroshock seizure model of certain BZ derivatives with very high affinity for the nanomolar binding site and very high potency in antipentetrazole tests. A weak correlation between affinity for high-affinity binding sites and activity in the maximal electroshock seizure model has been reported (Möhler et al., 1978; Chweh et al., 1983b). The existence of a second type of BZR with greatly differing ligand specificity and affinity would also explain effects of BZs at high concentrations on neuronal and muscle cell membranes that were so far laid aside as "nonspecific" membrane effects.

8 Possible GABA-Independent Actions of BZs

The overwhelming evidence favoring an interaction of BZs with GABA-mediated postsynaptic processes as the main mechanism by which BZs produce their therapeutic effects should not make us blind to the possibility that additional, minor or major, sites and mechanisms of action exist. Some speculative alternative or additional actions will be discussed very briefly. Effects of BZs in invertebrates, which lack BZ binding sites, have to be explained by a mechanism other than GABA potentiation (Corradetti *et al.*, 1980).

8.1 INHIBITION OF ADENOSINE UPTAKE

Phillis and collaborators (see Haefely *et al.*, 1983; and Phillis and Wu, 1982) have proposed that some, at least, of the effects of BZs are due to an interaction with adenosine. The facts are that a number of BZs inhibit the cellular uptake of adenosine, albeit at rather high concentrations (York and Davies, 1982), with an extremely shallow dose–effect curve, and with no apparent correlation with *in vivo* pharmacological activity. An interaction of BZs with adenosine receptors is very unlikely (Williams *et al.*, 1981; Patel *et al.*, 1982).

Adenosine uptake sites and BZRs were at some time proposed to be identical. This is not supported by comparing BZR ligands and adenosine uptake inhibitors for their affinity for BZ binding sites and for inhibition of adenosine uptake (Hammond *et al.*, 1981, 1983; Barker and Clanachan, 1982; Skerritt *et al.*, 1982d; Davies and Hambley, 1983). Moreover, the BZ antagonists Ro 15-1788 and CGS 8216 do not affect the inhibitory effect on adenosine uptake (Morgan *et al.*, 1983a,b). Adenosine might be released from cell neurons and even non-neuronal elements as a consequence of intracellular metabolism or may act as neurotransmitter in specific neurons. Adenosine has a strong depressant effect on neuronal activity, in part due to an inhibitory action of adenosine with the calcium-mediated transmitter release mechanism in nerve endings. While it seems unlikely that adenosine potentiation is a major factor in BZ actions, it may be involved, in addition to GABAergic mechanisms, in some particular effects (e.g., sedation) of some BZ derivatives (Bruns *et al.*, 1983; Haefely *et al.*, 1983). An adenosine component may explain why certain BZs have a more sedative–hypnotic profile than others in spite of similar interaction with BZRs coupled with GABA-R. Potentiation of adenosine (Slater and Bennett, 1981) may play a minor role in some cardiovascular effects of high BZ doses, e.g., in coronary vasodilation (Clanachan and Marshall, 1980; Clanachan *et al.*, 1981). Potentiation by BZ of adenosine effects were observed in various peripheral organs, e.g., the anococcygous muscle (Oriowo, 1983). The adenosine uptake inhibitor dipyridamole weakly inhibited [^{3}H]Diaz binding to rat brain membranes (Davies *et al.*, 1980).

8.2 PHOSPHOLIPID METHYLATION

Strittmatter *et al.* (1979) reported a stimulant effect of some BZs on phospholipid methylation in C_6 astrocytoma cells [increased incorporation of [^{3}H]methyl incorporation into phospholipids from S-methionine]. The order of potency was Ro 5-4864 > clonazepam > chlordiazepoxide. While this order of potency was taken as evidence that phospholipid methylation is mediated by the nonneuronal type of BZ binding sites, it seems that more BZ derivatives ought to be tested in order to identify the type of receptor, if any, that is involved in this effect. It should also be mentioned that in murine fibroblast cells in cultures, which contain peripheral type BZ binding sites, no stimulation of phospholipid methylation was observed with Ro 5-4864 or clonazepam.

8.3 Ca^{2+} TRANSPORT IN NERVE TERMINALS

Paul *et al.* (1982) reported that in intact synaptosomal membranes of rat brain Diaz (1 μM) enhanced the depolarization-induced, but not the basal uptake of Ca^{2+}. Clonazepam was active already at 10 nM whereas Ro 5-4864 was inactive. CGS 8216 completely blocked the effect of Diaz, without affecting Ca^{2+} uptake by itself. Diaz also stimulated the intrasynaptosomal ATP-dependent, nonmitochondrial sequestration of Ca^{2+}. At higher concentrations chlordiazepoxide and Diaz had been found to have the opposite effect on Ca^{2+} uptake into synaptosomes, namely to depress it (Leslie *et al.*, 1980; Ferendelli and Daniels-McQueen, 1982). No electrophysiological results supporting an enhanced neurotransmitter release by nerve terminals are available.

8.4 ENHANCEMENT OF Ca^{2+}-MEDIATED K^+-CONDUCTANCE INCREASE

In guinea pig hippocampal slices midazolam was found to hyperpolarize CA_1 pyramidal cells, to increase membrane input conductance in some cells and to enhance calcium spikes (Carlen *et al.*, 1983b). Midazolam also enhanced after hyperpolarization that follows a burst of (normal) sodium or calcium spikes (in the presence of tetrodotoxin) induced by intracellular depolarizing current injection. Removal of Ca^{2+} or addition of Mn^{2+} prevented the above effects of midazolam. Very strikingly, these effects of midazolam were observed at 1 and 5 nM, but no longer occurred at higher concentrations. Equally surprising is the finding that Ro 14-7437, a close congener of Ro 15-1788 with BZ antagonistic activity, produced effects opposite to those of midazolam, namely a depolarization, a conductance decrease, and an increase of spontaneous firing; Ca^{2+} spikes and afterhyperpolarization were decreased (Carlen *et al.*, 1983a). The Ca^{2+}-regulated K^+ conductance provides an important intrinsic inhibitory mechanism of neurons. Whether BZs affect this mechanism and, if so, why they do it at concentrations that are rather unlikely to produce pharmacological effects and not at concentrations that are pharmacologically relevant, are questions that require strongly controlled investigations.

8.5 MITOCHONDRIAL UPTAKE OF Ca^{2+}

Matlib and Schwartz (1983; Matlib *et al.*, 1983) obtained a depression of Na^{+}-induced release of Ca^{2+} from isolated heart and brain mitochondria with Diaz and clonazepam; the effect was very similar to that observed with the so-called Ca^{2+} entry blocker diltiazem. The IC_{50} for the active (+)-cis isomer of the latter was 7 μM, those for Diaz and for clonazepam 5 μM and 40 μM, respectively. None of these compounds affected the mitochondrial uptake of Ca^{2+}. Ro 15-1788 was inactive by itself and did not block the effect of Diaz or diltiazem. The relevance of these effects of BZs for their pharmacological activity is questionable.

8.6 SLOW Ca^{2+} CHANNEL BLOCKADE AND CALMODULIN ANTAGONISM

Evidence that flurazepam in micromolar concentration blocks voltage-dependent slow Ca^{2+} channels in the myocardium has been obtained by Ishii *et al.* (1982) and Akutagawa *et al.* (1983). Chlordiazepoxide was found to be very weak as an inhibitor of calmodulin-induced activation of phosphodiesterase with an IC_{50} of 0.3 mM (Prozialeck and Weiss, 1982).

8.7 EFFECTS MEDIATED BY THE PUTATIVE LOW-AFFINITY BZ BINDING SITES

This type of BZ binding site has been discussed in Section 8.6. Whatever the changes that might be induced in neuronal activity through these sites, they would be independent of endogenous GABA.

9 Conclusions

BZ tranquillizers, in the low doses that correspond to those used in therapy of anxiety and related states, epilepsy, and sleep disorders, appear to act with a high specificity on central GABAergic synapses by enhancing the effect of endogenous GABA released in these synapses. No other convincing effects on neuronal activities have been found. The potent and highly selective interaction with the main synaptic inhibitory system of the mammalian CNS explains the broad range of doses over which desired therapeutic effects are achieved with minimal side effects, as well as the extraordinarily low toxicity. At high doses, other effects may be relevant, e.g., the inhibition of adenosine uptake or the modification of nonsynaptic membrane properties of neurons. In contrast to the GABA potentiation, these latter mechanisms are not common to all BZs.

With the radioligand technique BZs have been found to bind with different affinity to sites of varying binding selectivity. The sites mediating the characteristic central effects of BZs are called the central or neuronal type of binding sites or, simply, BZRs. The relative affinities of a great number of BZs for these sites in general correlate well with the relative potencies for anxiolytic, anticonvulsant, muscle relaxant, and sedative activity. Hence, and because these effects can be blocked by specific antagonists that bind selectively to high-affinity neuronal binding sites, the latter are the recognition sites of receptors mediating the main effects of BZs. In addition to these central BZRs, binding of BZs also occurs, although not with the same rank order of affinity, to plasma albumin, to binding sites in nonneuronal cells in the periphery (e.g., kidney, adrenals, lung, blood cells), but also in the CNS (ependyma, choroid plexus, glia, olfactory afferents), for which a pharmacological receptor function has not been found. In addition to these sites, some BZs also bind with a different selectivity to the dermis of schistosomes; a further binding site for BZs has been described in the brain; it is characterized by low affinity and a ligand specificity differing from that of both the central high-affinity site and the nonneuronal site. The biological relevance of these sites is not yet established.

Electrophysiological studies have shown that BZs enhance the gating function of GABA-Rs on Cl^- channels in the membrane. While probably not affecting the properties of the single Cl^- channel, these drugs seem to increase the probability of channel opening events in response to GABA-R activation.

A vast literature on the interaction of BZs with their high-affinity binding sites clearly indicates that BZRs are intimately connected with a fraction of GABA-Rs and their associated Cl^- channels. Indeed, there is a strong mutual interaction between agents acting on the GABA-R and Cl^- channel on the one hand, and BZR ligands on the other hand. The major finding is the higher affinity of BZ agonists for their receptors in the presence of GABA. These interaction studies and recent advances in the extraction of BZRs from membrane, their solubilization and chemical analysis, strongly suggest that BZRs are in close physical connection with the GABA-R/Cl^- channel complex and may even be an allosteric regulatory site of this complex. Agonists of BZRs allosterically increase the affinity of GABA-Rs for GABA and, perhaps, facilitate (sensitize) the gating of Cl^- channels by the activated GABA-R, thus increasing the gain of the GABA-R function. This view is in excellent agreement with electrophysiological studies showing that BZs are ineffective on neuronal membranes in the absence of GABA and that they shift the concentration–response curve for the Cl^- conductance activating effect of GABA to the left, without affecting the maximum conductance induced by GABA.

While ligand–BZR interaction studies have so far been restricted to determinations of characteristics of the affinity of binding, there is not yet a consistent and direct way to determine intrinsic activity or efficacy. This property, however, is as relevant as the affinity for the effect of BZR ligands. The recently identified specific competitive antagonists at BZRs, such as, e.g., Ro 15-1788, some β-carboline derivatives, and CGS 8216, are characterized by high binding affinity, but low or virtually lacking efficacy, as indicated by their interaction with GABA and BZ agonists *in vivo*. Even more surprising than these competitive antagonists are compounds which produce effects that are the exact opposite of agonist effects, and which can be readily blocked by competitive antagonists. These compounds have been called inverse agonists to indicate that they have an efficacy, albeit a negative one, on BZRs. This unique finding in pharmacology is probably related to the fact that the BZR is an allosteric regulatory site on a neurotransmitter receptor. The existence of three prototypes of BZR ligands is a great stimulus for receptor research. Hypothetically, this complex situation could be explained by assuming that the BZR can exist in two spontaneously interconvertible states, one decreasing the gain of the GABA-R/Cl$^-$ channel function, the other increasing it. While inverse agonists might stabilize the former state, agonists might bind preferentially to the second one and stabilize it. Competitive antagonists would show no preference for either state. This attractive hypothesis rests on the unproven assumption that (1) the receptor has only two energetically similar conformational states between which it oscillates spontaneously, and not more than two, and (2) that the respective ligands are bound selectively to one conformer. This hypothesis rejects the possibility that the two conformations resulting in two opposite receptor–effector functions may require complex formation with a ligand. The three-state hypothesis assumes that the two states with opposite functions are induced by the respective ligands, while pure antagonists would bind to a neutral "inactive" form.

The obvious possibility, but not necessity, that the BZR is activated in physiological or pathological conditions by an endogenous ligand, has stimulated an intensive search for brain constituents with affinity for these receptors. None of the candidates found to date can be considered seriously as the putative ligand, but ongoing investigations in several laboratories may well change our views on the physiological role of BZRs.

Although BZ as well as non-BZ agonists at BZRs all have an essentially similar profile of activity, relevant differences in the relative importance of individual effects exist. They are not easily explained by the presence of one single type of BZR. Multiplicity (existence of subtypes) of BZRs has, therefore, been sought and claimed to be found. Since almost all these studies were done under very artificial conditions and since other likely explanations for heterogeneity of binding exist, true multiplicity of BZRs cannot yet be accepted as a fact. At least as attractive as the heterogeneity of receptors for explaining differences in activity profiles are differences in the efficacy of ligands coupled with differing receptor reserves in the various GABAergic synapses. Most recent experience with partial agonists of BZRs are in accord with such a view.

Structure–activity relations in the various classes of BZR ligands have been elaborated. In the BZ series agonists and antagonists have the same steric requirements for high binding affinity. Attempts were made to include all three types of ligands (agonists, antagonists, and inverse agonists) in a common molecular model; this may explain one property of these ligands, namely their affinity for the receptor. The procedure does not seem to be adequate to explain why a given ligand belongs to one of the prototypes of ligands. A proper receptor mapping has not yet been possible. No model is available that would allow one to draw any conclusions about the peptide and sugar residues of the receptor binding domain involved in recognition and binding of ligands. It seems obvious that the three prototypes of ligands (agonists, antagonists, and inverse agonists) cannot interact in exactly the same way with the probably adjacent and overlapping parts of the binding domain.

Isolation of BZRs is making rapid progress. The translation of a chicken brain mRNA coding for the GABA-R/BZR/Cl$^-$ channel complex has been obtained in frog oocytes; the newly formed complex, which normally does not exist in these cells, was incorporated into the oocyte membrane and found to function as expected in the presence of GABA and a BZ. This system offers the opportunity to study, in the future, the synthesis and assembly of the receptor.

The question remains why not all GABA-Rs are regulated by BZRs. Is the BZR lacking, e.g., in GABA-Rs of invertebrates or nonaccessible to ligands because of differences in the receptor microenvironment? Modern technology will probably provide answers to many of these questions within the not too far future.

The great progress made in the elucidation of the molecular aspects of BZR function should not divert from the formidable task of inserting molecular events into a coherent understanding of how subtle changes in one neurotransmitter system are translated into complex alterations of the neuronal activity subserving the somatic and psychic effects of BZs.

Acknowledgments

We thank Mrs. Ruth Tschudin, Miss Caroline Meyer, and Mrs. Sophia Lardelli for secretarial help, Dr. J. G. Richards for assistance with the topic of autoradiography, Drs. K. Bernauer, E. P. Bonetti, M. Da Prada, and R. Schaffner for critical comments on the manuscript.

References

Abbracchio, M. P., Balduini, W., Coen, E., Lombardelli, G., Peruzzi, G., and Cattabeni, F. (1983). In ''Benzodiazepine Recognition Site Ligands: Biochemistry and Pharmacology'' (G. Biggio and E. Costa, eds.), pp. 227–237. Raven, New York.

Akutagawa, K., Makino, M., and Ishii, K. (1983). Jpn. J. Pharmacol. **33**, 845–850.

Altstein, M., Dudai, Y., and Vogel, Z. (1981). Brain Res. **206**, 198–202.

Anderson, R. A., and Mitchell, R. (1983). Br. J. Pharmacol. **79**, 290P.

Anholt, R. R., Murphy, K. M. M., Mack, G., and Snyder, S. H. (1984). J. Neurosci. **4**, 593–603.

Antoniadis, A., Müller, W. E., and Wollert, U. (1979). Ann. Neurol. **8**, 71–73.

Antoniadis, A., Müller, W. E., and Wollert, U. (1980). *Neuropharmacology* **19**, 121–124.

Asano, T., and Mizutani, A. (1980). *Jpn. J. Pharmacol.* **30**, 783–788.

Asano, A., and Ogasawara, N. (1981a). *Brain Res.* **225**, 212–216.

Asano, A., and Ogasawara, N. (1981b). *Life Sci.* **29**, 193–200.

Asano, A., and Ogasawara, N. (1982). *Eur. J. Pharmacol.* **80**, 271–274.

Asano, T., and Spector, S. (1979). *Proc. Natl. Acad. Sci. U.S.A.* **76**, 977–981.

Asano, T., Sakakibara, J., and Ogasawara, N. (1983a). *FEBS Lett.* **151**, 277–280.

Asano, T., Yamada, Y., and Ogasawara, N. (1983b). *J. Neurochem.* **40**, 209–214.

Ashton, D., Geerts, R., Waterkeyn, C., and Feysen, J. E. (1981). *Life Sci.* **29**, 2631–2636.

Atterwill, C. K., and Nutt, D. J. (1983). *J. Pharm. Pharmacol.* **35**, 767–768.

Ball, H. A., Davies, J. A., and Nicholson, A. N. (1979). *Br. J. Pharmacol.* **66**, 92P–93P.

Baraldi, M., Guidotti, A., Schwartz, J. P., and Costa, E. (1979). *Science* **205**, 821–823.

Barker, P. H., and Clanachan, A. S. (1982). *Eur. J. Pharmacol.* **78**, 241–244.

Barker, J. L., Gratz, E., Owen, D. G., and Study, R. E. (1984). *In* "Actions and Interactions of GABA and Benzodiazepines" (N. G. Bowery, ed.), pp. 203–216. Raven, New York.

Barnard, E. A., Miledi, R., and Sumikawa, K. (1982). *Proc. R. Soc. London Ser. B* **215**, 241–246.

Barnes, D. M., White, W. F., and Dichter, M. A. (1983). *J. Neurosci.* **3**, 762–772.

Battersby, M. K., Richards, J. G., and Möhler, H. (1979). *Eur. J. Pharmacol.* **57**, 277–278.

Beaumont, K., Cheung, A. K., Geller, M. C., and Fanestil, D. D. (1983). *Life Sci.* **33**, 1375–1384.

Beer, B., Klepner, C. A., Lippa, A. S., and Squires, R. F. (1978). *Pharmacol., Biochem. Behav.* **9**, 849–851.

Benavides, J., Malgouris, C., Imbault, F., Begassat, F., Uzan, A., Renault, C., Dubroeucq, M. C., Gueremy, C., and Le Fur, G. (1983a). *Arch. Int. Pharmacodyn.* **266**, 38–49.

Benavides, J., Quarteronet, D., Imbault, F., Malgouris, C., Uzan, A., Renault, C., Dubroeucq, M. C., Gueremy, C., and Le Fur, G. (1983b). *J. Neurochem.* **41**, 1744–1750.

Bennett, J. L. (1980). *J. Parasitol.* **66**, 742–747.

Biagi, G. L., Barbaro, A. M., Guerra, M. C., Babbini, M., Gaiardi, M., Bartoletti, M., and Borea, P. A. (1980). *Med. Chem.* **23**, 193–201.

Biggio, G., Corda, M. G., Lamberti, C., and Gessa, G. L. (1979). *Eur. J. Pharmacol.* **58**, 215–216.

Biggio, G., Corda, M. G., De Montis, G., and Gessa, G. L. (1980a). *In* "Receptors for Neurotransmitters and Peptide Hormones" (G. Pepeu, M. J. Kuhar, and S. J. Enna, eds.), pp. 265–270. Raven, New York.

Biggio, G., Corda, M. G., De Montis, G., Stefanini, E., and Gessa, G. L. (1980b). *Brain Res.* **193**, 589–593.

Biggio, G., Guarneri, P., and Corda, M. G. (1981a). *Brain Res.* **216**, 210–214.

Biggio, G., Corda, M. G., Concas, A., and Gessa, G. L. (1981b). *Brain Res.* **220**, 344–349.

Biggio, G., Guarneri, P., Corda, M. G., Concas, A., Salis, M., Calderini, G., and Toffano, G. (1983). *In* "Receptors as Supramolecular Entities" (G. Biggio, E. Costa, G. L. Gessa, and P. F. Spano, eds.), pp. 267–272. Pergamon, Oxford.

Biscoe, T. J., and Fry, J. P. (1984). *In* "Actions and Interactions of GABA and Benzodiazepines" (N. G. Bowery, ed.), pp. 217–237. Raven, New York.

Blair, T., and Webb, G. A. (1977). *J. Med. Chem.* **20**, 1206–1210.

Blanchard, J.-C., and Cotrel, C. (1983). *Actual Chim.* **November**, 37–46.

Blanchard, J.-C., and Julou, L. (1983). *J. Neurochem.* **40**, 601–607.

Blanchard, J.-C., Boireau, A., Garret, C., and Julou, L. (1979). *Life Sci.* **24**, 2417–2420.

Blanchard, J.-C., Boireau, A., and Julou, L. (1983). *Pharmacology* **27** (Suppl. 2), 59–69.

Blaschke, G., and Markgraf, H. (1980). *Chem. Ber.* **113**, 2031–2035.

Blount, J., Fryer, R. I., Gilman, N. W., and Todaro, L. J. (1983). *Mol. Pharmacol.* **24**, 425–428.

Blum, J. E., Haefely, W., Jalfre, M., Polc, P., and Schärer, K. (1973). *Arzneimittelforschung* **23**, 377–389.

Boast, C. A., Bernard, P. S., Barbaz, B. S., and Bergen, K. M. (1983). *Neuropharmacology* **22**, 1511–1521.

Bold, J. M., Gardener, C. R., and Walker, R. J. (1982). *Br. J. Pharmacol.* **76**, 241P.

Bonetti, E. P., Pieri, L., Cumin, R., Schaffner, R., Pieri, M., Gamzu, E. R., Müller, R. K. M., and Haefely, W. (1982). *Psychopharmacology* **78**, 8–18.

Bouetti, E. P., Polc, P., and Pieri, L. (1984). *Neuroscience Lett.* Suppl. **18**, § 267.

Borbe, H. O., Müller, W. E., and Wollert, U. (1980). *Brain Res.* **182**, 466–469.

Borea, P. A. (1981). *Boll. Soc. Ital. Biol. Sper.* **57**, 628–632.

Borea, P. A. (1983). *Arzneimittelforschung* **33**, 1086–1088.

Borea, P. A., and Bonora, A. (1983). *Biochem. Pharmacol.* **32**, 603–607.

Borea, P. A., Gilli, G., and Bertolasi, V. (1979). *Farmaco, Ed. Sci.* **34**, 1073–1082.

Borea, P. A., Gilli, G., Bertolasi, V., and Sacerdoti, M. (1982). *Biochem. Pharmacol.* **31**, 889–891.

Borea, P. A., Supavilai, P., and Karobath, M. (1983). *Brain Res.* **280**, 383–386.

Borer, R., Gerecke, M., and Kyburz, E. (1983). *Chem. Abstr.* **99**, 5633n.

Bosio, A., Lucchi, L., Spano, P. F., and Trabucchi, M. (1982). *Toxicol. Lett.* **13**, 99–104.

Bosmann, H. B., Case, K. R., and DiStefano, P. (1977). *FEBS Lett.* **82**, 368–372.

Bosmann, H. B., Penny, D. P., Case, K. R., and Averill, K. (1980). *Proc. Natl. Acad. Sci. U.S.A.* **77**, 1195–1198.

Boulenger, J.-P., Patel, J., and Marangos, P. J. (1982). *Neurosci. Lett.* **30**, 161–166.

Bourgeois, B. F. D., Dodson, W. E., and Ferendell, Z. A. (1983). *Epilepsia* **24**, 238–244.

Bowdler, J. M., and Green, R. (1982). *Br. J. Pharmacol.* **76**, 291–298.

Bowdler, J. M., Green, A. R., Minchin, M. C. W., and Nutt, D. J. (1983). *J. Neural Transm.* **65**, 3–12.

Bowery, N. G., Hill, D. R., and Hudson, A. L. (1983). *Br. J. Pharmacol.* **78**, 191–206.

Bowery, N. G., Hill, D. R., Hudson, A. L., Price, G. W., Turnbull, M. J., and Wilkin, G. P. (1984). *In* "Actions and Interactions of GABA and Benzodiazepines" (N. G. Bowery, ed.), pp. 81–108. Raven, New York.

Bowling, A. C., and DeLorenzo, R. J. (1982). *Science* **216**, 1247–1250.

Braestrup, C., and Nielsen, M. (1978). *Brain Res.* **147**, 170–173.

Braestrup, C., and Nielsen, M. (1980). *Trends Pharmacol. Sci.* **1**, 424–427.

Braestrup, C., and Nielsen, M. (1981a). *J. Neurochem.* **37**, 333–341.

Braestrup, C., and Nielsen, M. (1981b). *Nature (London)* **294**, 472–474.

Braestrup, C., and Nielsen, M. (1983). *Handb. Psychopharmacol.* **17**, 285–384.

Braestrup, C., and Squires, R. F. (1977). *Proc. Natl. Acad. Sci. U.S.A.* **74**, 3805–3809.

Braestrup, C., and Squires, R. F. (1978a). *Eur. J. Pharmacol.* **48**, 263–270.

Braestrup, C., and Squires, R. F. (1978b). *Br. J. Psychiat.* **133**, 249–260.

Braestrup, C., Albrechtsen, R., and Squires, R. F. (1977). *Nature (London)* **269**, 702–704.

Braestrup, C., Nissen, C., Squires, R. F., and Schousobe, A. (1978). *Neurosci. Lett.* **9**, 45–49.

Braestrup, C., Nielsen, M., Biggio, G., and Squires, R. F. (1979a). *Neurosci. Lett.* **13**, 219–224.

Braestrup, C., Nielsen, M., Krogsgaard-Larsen, P., and Falch, E. (1979b). *Nature (London)* **280**, 331–333.

Braestrup, C., Nielsen, M., Nielsen, E. B., and Lyon, M. (1979c). *Psychopharmacology* **65**, 273–277.

Braestrup, C., Nielsen, M., and Squires, R. F. (1979d). *Life Sci.* **24**, 347–350.

Braestrup, C., Nielsen, M., Krogsgaard-Larsen, P., and Falch, E. (1980a). *In* "Receptors for Neurotransmitters and Peptide Hormones" (G. Pepeu, J. H. Kuhar, and S. J. Enna, eds.), pp. 301–312. Raven, New York.

Braestrup, C., Nielsen, M., and Olsen, C. E. (1980b). *Proc. Natl. Acad. Sci. U.S.A.* **77**, 2288–2292.

Braestrup, C., Schmiechen, R., Neef, G., Nielsen, M., and Petersen, E. N. (1982). *Science* **216**, 1241–1243.

Braestrup, C., Nielsen, M., and Honoré, T. (1983a). *J. Neurochem.* **41**, 454–465.

Braestrup, C., Nielsen, M., and Honoré, T. (1983b). *In* "CNS-Receptors—From Molecular Pharmacology to Behaviour (P. Mandel and F. V. De Feudis, eds.), pp. 237–245. Raven, New York.

Brennan, M. J. W. (1982). *J. Neurochem.* **38**, 264–266.

Briley, M. S., and Langer, S. Z. (1978). *Eur. J. Pharmacol.* **52**, 129–132.

Brown, C. L., and Martin, I. L. (1982). *Br. J. Pharmacol.* **77**, 312P.

Brown, C. L., and Martin, I. L. (1983a). *Br. J. Pharmacol.* **79**, 288P.

Brown, C. L., and Martin, I. L. (1983b). *Neurosci. Lett.* **35**, 37–40.

Bruns, R. F., Katims, J. J., Annans, Z., Snyder, S. H., and Daly, J. W. (1983). *Neuropharmacology* **22**, 1523–1529.

Burch, T. P., and Ticku, M. K. (1980). *Eur. J. Pharmacol.* **67**, 325–326.

Burch, T. P., and Ticku, M. K. (1981). *Proc. Natl. Acad. Sci. U.S.A.* **78**, 3945–3949.

Burch, T. P., Thyagarajan, R., and Ticku, M. K. (1983). *Mol. Pharmacol.* **23**, 52–59.

Burnham, W. M., Niznik, H. B., Okazaki, M. M., and Kigh, S. J. (1983). *Brain Res.* **279**, 59–362.

Bymaster, F. P., Lacefield, W. B., and Wong, D. T. (1982). *Soc. Neurosci.* **8**, 579.

Cain, M., Weber, R. W., Guzman, F., Cook, J. M., Barker, J. A., Rice, K. C., Crawley, J. N., Paul, S. M., and Skolnick, P. (1982). *J. Med. Chem.* **25**, 1081–1091.

Calderini, G., Bonetti, A. C., Aldino, A., Savoini, G., Di Perri, B., Biggio, G., and Toffano, G. (1981). *Neurobiol. Aging* **2**, 309–313.

Camerman, A., and Camerman, N. (1970). *Science* **168**, 1457.

Camerman, A., and Camerman, N. (1972). *J. Am. Chem. Soc.* **94**, 268–272.

Camerman, A., and Camerman, N. (1983). *J. Neurochem.* **41**, 114.

Candy, J. M., and Martin, I. L. (1979a). *Nature (London)* **280**, 172–174.

Candy, J. M., and Martin, I. L. (1979b). *J. Neurochem.* **32**, 655–658.

Carlen, P. L., Gurevich, N., and Polc, P. (1983a). *Brain Res.* **271**, 115–119.

Carlen, P. L., Gurevich, N., and Polc, P. (1983b). *Brain Res.* **271**, 358–364.

Cepeda, C., Tanaka, T., Besselièvre, R., Potier, P., Naquet, R., and Rossier, J. (1981). *Neurosci. Lett.* **24**, 53–57.

Cerione, R. A., Strulovici, B., Benovic, J. L., Lefkowitz, R. J., and Caron, M. G. (1983). *Nature (London)* **306**, 562–566.

Chan, C. Y., Gibbs, T. T., Borden, L. A., and Farb, D. G. (1983). *Life Sci.* **33**, 2061–2069.

Chang, L.-R., and Barnard, E. A. (1982). *J. Neurochem.* **39**, 1507–1518.

Chang, L.-R., Barnard, E. A., Lo, M. M. S., and Dolly, J. O. (1981). *FEBS Lett.* **126**, 309–312.

Chang, R. S. L., and Snyder, S. H. (1978). *Eur. J. Pharmacol.* **48**, 213–218.

Chang, R. S. L., Tran, V. T., and Snyder, S. H. (1980). *Brain Res.* **190**, 95–110.

Chen, A., Gee, K. W., and Yamamura, H. T. (1983a). *Fed. Proc. Fed. Am. Soc. Exp. Biol.* **42**, 878.

Chen, A. D., Davis, T. P., and Yamamura, H. I. (1983b). *Proc. West. Pharmacol. Soc.* **26**, 225–230.

Chisholm, J., Kellogg, C., and Lippa, A. (1983). *Brain Res.* **267**, 388–391.

Chiu, T. H., and Rosenberg, H. C. (1978). *Life Sci.* **23**, 1153–1158.

Chiu, T. H., and Rosenberg, H. C. (1979). *Eur. J. Pharmacol.* **56**, 337–345.

Chiu, T. H., and Rosenberg, H. C. (1981). *J. Neurochem.* **36**, 336–338.

Chiu, T. H., and Rosenberg, H. C. (1982). *J. Neurochem.* **39**, 1716–1725.

Chiu, T. H., and Rosenberg, H. C. (1983a). *Trends Pharmacol. Sci.* **4**, 348–350.

Chiu, T. H., and Rosenberg, H. C. (1983b). *Mol. Pharmacol.* **23**, 289–294.
Chiu, T. H., Dryden, D. M., and Rosenberg, H. C. (1982). *Mol. Pharmacol.* **21**, 57–65.
Choi, D. W., Farb, D. H., and Fischbach, G. D. (1981a). *J. Neurophysiol.* **45**, 621–631.
Choi, D. W., Farb, D. H., and Fischbach, G. D. (1981b). *J. Neurophysiol.* **45**, 632–643.
Chweh, A. Y., Swinyard, E. A., and Wolf, H. H. (1983a). *J. Neurochem.* **41**, 830–833.
Chweh, A. Y., Swinyard, E. A., Wolf, H. H., and Kupferberg, H. J. (1983b). *Epilepsia* **24**, 668–677.
Clanachan, A. S., and Marshall, R. J. (1980). *Br. J. Pharmacol.* **71**, 459–466.
Clanachan, A. S., Hammond, J. R., and Paterson, A. R. P. (1981). *Br. J. Pharmacol.* **74**, 835P–836P.
Clow, A., Glover, V., Armando, I., and Sandler, M. (1983). *Life Sci.* **33**, 735–741.
Coen, E., Abbracchio, M. P., Balduini, W., Cagiano, R., Cuomo, V., Lombardelli, G., Peruzzi, G., Ragusa, M. C., and Cattabeni, F. (1983). *Psychopharmacology* **81**, 261–266.
Colello, G. D., Hockenbery, D. M., Bosmann, H. B., Fuchs, S., and Folkers, K. (1978). *Proc. Natl. Acad. Sci. U.S.A.* **75**, 6319–6323.
Comar, D., Mazière, M., Godot, J. M., Berger, G., and Soussaline, F. (1979). *Nature (London)* **280**, 329–331.
Comar, C., Mazière, M., Cepeda, C., Godot, J. M., Menini, C., and Naquet, R. (1981). *Eur. J. Pharmacol.* **75**, 21–26.
Concas, A., Salis, M., and Biggio, G. (1983). *Life Sci.* **32**, 1175–1182.
Conti-Tronconi, B. M., and Rafteri, M. A. A. (1982). *Rev. Biochem.* **51**, 491–530.
Cook, P. J., and James, I. M. (1982). *Clin. Sci.* **62**, 53P.
Corbella, A., Gariboldi, P., and Jommi, G. (1973). *J. Chem. Soc., Chem. Commun.* 721–722.
Corda, M. G., Concas, A., Rossetti, Z., Guarneri, P., Corongiu, F. P., and Biggio, G. (1981). *Brain Res.* **229**, 264–269.
Corda, M. G., Blaker, W. D., Mendelson, W. B., Guidotti, A., and Costa, E. (1983a). *Proc. Natl. Acad. Sci. U.S.A.* **80**, 2072–2076.
Corda, M. G., Costa, E., and Guidotti, A. (1983b). In "Benzodiazepine Recognition Site Ligands: Biochemistry and Pharmacology" (G. Biggio and E. Costa, eds.), pp. 121–127. Raven, New York.
Corradetti, R., Moroni, F., and Pepeu, G. (1980). *Pharmacol. Res. Commun.* **12**, 581–585.
Corsico, N., Barone, D., Diena, A., Landsberg, P., Pizzocheri, F., Quaglia, M. G., and Glässer, A. (1982). *Coll. Int. Neuropsychopharmacol., 13th, Jerusalem, June 20–25* p. 123 (Abstr.).
Costa, E. (1979). *Trends Pharmacol. Sci.* **1**, 41–44.
Costa, E. (1983a). In "Receptors as Supramolecular Entities" (G. Biggio, E. Costa, G. L. Gessa, and P. F. Spano, eds.), pp. 213–235. Pergamon, Oxford.
Costa, E. (1983b). In "Benzodiazepine Recognition Site Ligands: Biochemistry and Pharmacology" (G. Biggio and E. Costa, eds.), pp. 249–253. Raven, New York.
Costa, E., and Guidotti, A. (1982). In "Brain Peptides and Hormones" (R. Collu et al., eds.), pp. 107–114. Raven, New York.
Costa, E., Guidotti, A., and Mao, C. C. (1975). *Adv. Biochem. Pharmacol.* **14**, 113–130.
Costa, E., Guidotti, A., and Toffano, G. (1978). *Br. J. Psychiat.* **133**, 239–248.
Costa, E., Guidotti, A., Massotti, M., and Mazzari, S. (1980). In "Neurotransmitters and their Receptors" (U. Z. Littauer, Y. Dudai, I. Silman, V. I. Teichberg, and Z. Vogel, eds.), pp. 417–427. Wiley, New York.
Costa, E., Corda, M. G., Epstein, B., Forchetti, C., and Guidotti, A. (1983a). In "The Benzodiazepines: From Molecular Biology to Clinical Practice" (E. Costa, ed.), pp. 117–136. Raven, New York.
Costa, E., Forchetti, C. M., Guidotti, A., and Wise, B. C. (1983b). In "Dale's Principle of Communication between Neurons" (N. N. Osborne, ed.), pp. 161–177. Pergamon, Oxford.

Costa, E., Corda, M. G., and Guidotti, A. (1983c). *Neuropharmacol.* **22**, 1481–1492.
Costa, T., Rodbard, D., and Pert, C. B. (1979). *Nature (London)* **277**, 315–317.
Cowen, P. J., Green, A. R., Nutt, D. J., and Martin, I. L. (1981). *Nature (London)* **290**, 54–55.
Crawley, J. N., Marangos, P. J., Stivers, J., and Goodwin, F. K. (1982). *Neuropharmacology* **21**, 85–89.
Crippen, G. M. (1979). *J. Med. Chem.* **22**, 988–997.
Crippen, G. M. (1980). *J. Med. Chem.* **23**, 599–606.
Crippen, G. M. (1981). *J. Med. Chem.* **24**, 198–203.
Crippen, G. M. (1982). *Mol. Pharmacol.* **22**, 11–19.
Czernik, A. J., Tetrack, B., Kalinsky, H. J., Psychoyos, S., Cash, W. D., Tsai, C., Rinehart, R. K., Granat, F. R., Lovell, R. A., Brundish, D. E., and Wade, R. (1982). *Life Sci.* **30**, 363–372.
Czuczwar, S. J., Turski, L., and Kleinrok, Z. (1981). *Neuropharmacology* **20**, 675–679.
Damm, H. W., Müller, W. E., and Wollert, U. (1979). *Eur. J. Pharmac.* **55**, 331–333.
Darragh, A., Lambe, R., Kenny, M., Brick, I., Taaffe, W., and O'Boyle, C. (1982a). *Br. J. Clin. Pharmacol.* **14**, 677–682.
Darragh, A., Lambe, R., Brick, I., and O'Boyle, C. (1982b). *Br. J. Clin. Pharmacol.* **14**, 871–872.
Darragh, A., Lambe, R., Kenny, M., and Brick, I. (1983a). *Eur. J. Pharmacol.* **24**, 569–570.
Darragh, A., Lambe, R., O'Boyle, C., Kenny, M., and Brick, I. (1983b). *Psychopharmacology* **80**, 192–195.
Davies, L. P., and Hambley, J. W. (1983). *Gen. Pharmacol.* **14**, 307–309.
Davies, L. P., and Huston, V. (1981). *Eur. J. Pharmacol.* **73**, 209–211.
Davies, L. P., Cook, A. F., Poonian, M., and Taylor, K. M. (1980). *Life Sci.* **26**, 1089–1095.
Davies, L. P., Hambley, J. W., and Johnston, G. A. R. (1982). *Neurosci. Lett.* **29**, 57–61.
Davis, L. G., McIntosh, H., and Reker, D. (1981). *Pharmacol. Biochem. Behav.* **14**, 839–844.
Davis, W. C., and Ticku, M. K. (1981). *Neurosci. Lett.* **23**, 209–213.
Dawson, G. W., Jue, S. G., and Brogden, R. N. (1984). *Drugs* **27**, 132–147.
De Angelis, L., Predoninato, M., and Vertua, R. (1972). *Arzneimittelforschung* **22**, 1328–1333.
De Lorenzo, R. J., Brudette, S., and Holderness, J. (1981). *Science* **213**, 546–549.
Del Zompo, M., Bocchetta, A., Corsini, C. U., Tallman, J. F., and Gessa, G. L. (1983). *In* "Benzodiazepine Recognition Site Ligands: Biochemistry and Pharmacology" (G. Biggio and E. Costa, eds.), pp. 239–248. Raven, New York.
De Souza, E. B., Anholt, R. R. H., Murphy, K. M. M., Snyder, S. H., and Kuhar, M. J. (1984). Submitted.
DiStefano, P., Case, K. R., Colello, D., and Bosman, H. B. (1979). *Cell Biol. Int. Rep.* **3**, 163–167.
Doble, A. (1982). *Eur. J. Pharmacol.* **83**, 313–316.
Doble, A. (1983). *J. Neurochem.* **40**, 1605–1612.
Doble, A., and Iversen, L. L. (1982). *Nature (London)* **295**, 522–523.
Doble, A., Iversen, L. L., Bowery, N. G., Hill, D. R., and Hudson, A. L. (1981). *Neurosci. Lett.* **27**, 199–204.
Doble, A., Iversen, L. L., and Martin, I. L. (1982a). *Br. J. Pharmacol.* **75**, 42P.
Doble, A., Iversen, L. L., and Martin, I. L. (1982b). *Br. J. Pharmacol.* **76**, 238P.
Dorow, R. G., Seidler, J., and Schneider, H. H. (1982). *Br. J. Clin. Pharmacol.* **13**, 561–565.
Dorow, R., Horowski, R., Paschelke, G., Amin, M., and Braestrup, C. (1983). *Lancet* **1**, 98–99.
Dubnick, B., Lippa, A. S., Klepner, C. A., Coupet, J., Greenblatt, E. N., and Beer, B. (1983). *Pharmacol., Biochem. Behav.* **18**, 311–318.
Dudai, Y. (1979). *Brain Res.* **167**, 422–425.
Dudai, Y., Yavin, Z., and Yavin, E. (1979). *Brain Res.* **177**, 418–422.
Duka, T., Höllt, V., and Herz, A. (1979). *Brain Res.* **179**, 147–156.

Eberts, F. S., Philopoulos, Y., Reineke, L. M., Vlick, R. W., and Metzler, C. M. (1977). *Pharmacologist* **19**, 165 (Abstr. No. 221).

Eberts, F. S., Philopoulos, Y., Reineke, L. M., and Vlick, R. W. (1981). *Clin. Pharmacol. Ther.* **29**, 81–93.

Ehlert, F. J., Roeske, W. R., Braestrup, C., Yamamura, S. H., and Yamamura, H. I. (1981). *Eur. J. Pharmacol.* **70**, 593–596.

Ehlert, F. J., Ragan, P., Chen, A., Roeske, W. R., and Yamamura, H. I. (1982). *Eur. J. Pharmacol.* **78**, 249–253.

Ehlert, F. J., Roeske, W. R., Gee, K. W., and Yamamura, H. I. (1983a). *Biochem. Pharmacol.* **32**, 2375–2383.

Ehlert, F. J., Roeske, W. R., Yamamura, S. H., and Yamamura, H. I. (1983b). *In* "Molecular Pharmacology of Neurotransmitter Receptors" (T. Segawa *et al.*, eds.), pp. 209–220. Raven, New York.

Essman, E. J., and Valzelli, L. (1981). *Pharmacol. Res. Commun.* **13**, 665–671.

Everett, G. M., and Richards, R. K. (1944). *J. Pharmacol. Exp. Ther.* **81**, 402–407.

Fanelli, R. J., and McNamara, J. O. (1983). *J. Pharmacol. Exp. Ther.* **226**, 147–150.

Fehske, K. J., and Müller, W. E. (1982). *Brain Res.* **238**, 286–291.

Fehske, K. J., Müller, W. E., and Wollert, U. (1979). *Biochim. Biophys. Acta* **577**, 346–359.

Fehske, K. J., Zübe, I., Borbe, H. O., Wollert, U., and Müller, W. E. (1982). *Naunyn-Schmiedeberg's Arch. Pharmacol.* **319**, 172–177.

Feller, D. J., Schroeder, F., and Bylund, D. B. (1983). *Biochem. Pharmacol.* **32**, 2217–2223.

Ferendelli, J. A., and Daniels-McQueen, S. (1982). *J. Pharmacol. Exp. Ther.* **220**, 29–34.

File, S. E., and Lister, R. G. (1983). *Pharmacol., Biochem. Behav.* **18**, 185–188.

File, S. E., and Mabbut, P. S. (1983). *Br. J. Pharmacol.* **78**, 76P.

Fong, J. C., Okada, K., and Goldstein, M. (1982a). *Eur. J. Pharmacol.* **77**, 57–59.

Fong, J., Okada, K., Lew, J. Y., and Goldstein, M. (1982b). *Brain Res.* **266**, 152–154.

Freund, G. (1980). *Life Sci.* **27**, 987–992.

Fryer, R. I. (1983). *In* "Benzodiazepines. From Molecular Biology to Clinical Practice" (E. Costa, ed.), pp. 7–20. Raven, New York.

Fryer, R. I., Leimgruber, W., and Trybulski, E. J. (1982). *J. Med. Chem.* **25**, 1050–1055.

Fujimoto, M., and Okabayashi, T. (1981). *Life Sci.* **28**, 895–901.

Fujimoto, M., and Okabayashi, T. (1982). *Chem. Pharmacol. Bull.* **30**, 1014–1017.

Fujimoto, M., and Okabayshi, T. (1983). *Life Sci.* **32**, 2393–2400.

Fujimoto, M., Tsukinoki, Y., Hirose, K., Hirai, K., and Okabayashi, T. (1980a). *Chem. Pharm. Bull.* **28**, 1374–1377.

Fujimoto, M., Tsukinoki, Y., Hirose, K., Kazuok, K., Ryusei, K., and Okabayashi, T. (1980b). *Chem. Pharm. Bull.* **28**, 1378–1386.

Fujimoto, M., Hirai, K., and Okabayashi, T. (1982a). *Life Sci.* **30**, 51–57.

Fujimoto, M., Kawasaki, K., Matsushita, A., and Okabayashi, T. (1982b). *Eur. J. Pharmacol.* **80**, 259–262.

Fung, S.-C., and Fillenz, M. (1983). *Neurosci. Lett.* **42**, 61–66.

Gallager, D. W., and Mallorga, P. (1980). *Science* **208**, 64–66.

Gallager, D. W., and Wakeman, E. A. (1982). *Eur. J. Pharmacol.* **85**, 143–153.

Gallager, D. W., Thomas, J. W., and Tallman, J. F. (1978). *Biochem. Pharmacol.* **27**, 2745–2749.

Gallager, D. W., Mallorga, P., and Tallman, J. F. (1980a). *Brain Res.* **189**, 209–220.

Gallager, D. W., Mallorga, P., Thomas, J. W., and Tallman, J. F. (1980b). *Fed. Proc., Fed. Am. Soc. Exp. Biol.* **39**, 3043–3049.

Gallager, D. W., Mallorga, P., Oertel, W., Henneberry, R., and Tallman, J. (1981a). *J. Neurosci.* **1**, 218–225.

Gallager, D. W., Mallorga, P., Swaiman, K. F., Neale, E. A., and Nelson, P. G. (1981b). *Brain Res.* **218**, 319–330.

Garattini, S., Caccia, S., and Mennini, T. (1982). *J. Clin. Psychiat.* **43**, 19–22.

Gavish, M. (1983). *Life Sci.* **33**, 1479–1483.

Gavish, M., and Snyder, S. H. (1980a). *Nature (London)* **287**, 651–652.

Gavish, M., and Snyder, S. H. (1980b). *Life Sci.* **26**, 579–582.

Gavish, M., and Snyder, S. H. (1981). *Proc. Natl. Acad. Sci. U.S.A.* **78**, 1939–1942.

Gavish, M., Chang, S. L., and Snyder, S. H. (1979). *Life Sci.* **25**, 783–790.

Gee, K. W., and Yamamura, H. I. (1982a). *Life Sci.* **30**, 2245–2252.

Gee, K. W., and Yamamura, H. I. (1982b). *Life Sci.* **31**, 1939–1945.

Gee, K. W., and Yamamura, H. I. (1982c). *Eur. J. Pharmacol.* **82**, 239–241.

Gee, K. W., and Yamamura, H. I. (1983a). *J. Neurochem.* **41**, 1407–1413.

Gee, K. W., and Yamamura, H. I. (1983b). In "Benzodiazepine Recognition Site Ligands; Biochemistry and Pharmacology" (G. Biggio and E. Costa, eds.), pp. 1–9. Raven, New York.

Gee, K. W., Morelli, M., and Yamamura, H. I. (1982a). *Biochem. Biophys. Res. Commun.* **105**, 1532–1537.

Gee, K. W., Ehlert, F. J., and Yamamura, H. I. (1982b). *Biochem. Biophys. Res. Commun.* **106**, 1134–1140.

Gee, K. W., Horst, W. D., O'Brien, R., and Yamamura, H. I. (1982c). *Biochem. Biophys. Res. Commun.* **105**, 475–461.

Gee, K. W., Brinton, R. E., and Yamamura, H. I. (1983a). *Life Sci.* **32**, 1037–1040.

Gee, K. W., Brinton, R. E., and Yamamura, H. I. (1983b). *Brain Res.* **264**, 168–172.

Gee, K. W., Ehlert, F. J., and Yamamura, H. I. (1983c). *J. Pharmacol. Exp. Ther.* **225**, 132–137.

Gehlert, D. R., Yamamura, H. I., and Wamsley, J. K. (1983). *Eur. J. Pharmacol.* **95**, 329–330.

Gentsch, C., Lichtsteiner, M., and Feer, H. (1981). *Experientia* **37**, 1315–1316.

Graf, E., and El-Menshawy (1977). *Pharmazie in unserer Zeit* **6**, 171–178.

Grandison, L., Cavagnini, F., Schmid, R., Invitti, C., and Guidotti, A. (1982). *J. Clin. Endocrinol. Metab.* **54**, 597–601.

Guarneri, P., Corda, M. G., Concas, A., and Biggio, G. (1981). *Brain Res.* **209**, 216–220.

Guarneri, P., Corda, M. G., Concas, A., Salis, M., Calderini, G., Toffano, G., and Biggio, G. (1982). *Neurobiol. Aging* **3**, 227–231.

Guidotti, A. (1983). In "Pharmacologic and Biochemical Aspects of Neurotransmitter Receptors" (H. Yoshida and H. I. Yamamura, eds.), pp. 267–274. Wiley, New York.

Guidotti, A., Toffano, G., and Costa, E. (1978). *Nature (London)* **275**, 553–555.

Guidotti, A., Baraldi, M., Schwartz, J. P., and Costa, E. (1979). *Pharmacol., Biochem. Behav.* **10**, 803–807.

Guidotti, A., Konkel, D. R., Ebstein, B., Corda, M. G., Wise, B. C., Krutsch, H., Meek, J. L., and Costa, E. (1982). *Proc. Natl. Acad. Sci. U.S.A.* **79**, 6084–6088.

Guidotti, A., Corda, M. G., and Costa, E. (1983a). *Adv. Biochem. Pharmacol.* **38**, 95–103.

Guidotti, A., Forchetti, C. M., Corda, M. G., Konkel, D., Bennett, C. D., and Costa, E. (1983b). *Proc. Natl. Acad. Sci. U.S.A.* **80**, 3531–3535.

Guidotti, A., Saiani, L., Wise, B. C., and Costa, E. (1983c). *J. Neural Transm. Suppl.* **18**, 213–225.

Guidotti, A., Corda, M. G., Vaccarino, F. M., and Wise, B. C. (1984). In "Actions and Interactions of GABA and Benzodiazepines" (N. G. Bowery, ed.), pp. 191–202. Raven, New York.

Haefely, W. (1983a). *J. Psychoact. Drugs* **15**, 19–34.

Haefely, W. (1983b). In "Discoveries in Pharmacology" (M. J. Parnham and J. Bruinvals, eds.), Vol. 1, pp. 269–306. Elsevier, Amsterdam.

Haefely, W. (1983c). In "Benzodiazepine Recognition Site Ligands: Biochemistry and Pharmacology" (G. Biggio and E. Costa, eds.), pp. 73–93. Raven, New York.

Haefely, W. (1983d). L'Eucéphale **9**, 143B–150B.

Haefely, W. (1983e). *In* "Psychopharmacology 1" (D. G. Grahame-Smith and P. J. Cowen, eds.), Part 1: Preclinical Psychopharmacology, pp. 107–151. Excerpta Medica, Amsterdam.

Haefely, W. (1984a). *In* "Actions and Interactions of GABA and Benzodiazepines" (N. G. Bowery, ed.), pp. 263–285. Raven, New York.

Haefely, W. (1984b). *Neuroscience Lett.* **47**, 201–206.

Haefely W. (1984c). *Clin. Neuropharmacol.* **7**(Suppl. 1), 670–671.

Haefely, W. (1985). *In* "Psychopharmacology 2" (D. G. Grahame-Smith, ed.), Part 1: Preclinical Psychopharmacology. Excerpta Medica, Amsterdam (in press).

Haefely, W., and Polc, P. (1983). *In* "Anxiolytics: Neurochemical, Behavioral and Clinical Perspectives" (J. B. Malick, S. J. Enna, and H. I. Yamamura, eds.), pp. 113–145. Raven, New York.

Haefely, W., and Polc, P. (1985). *In* "Benzodiazepine–GABA Receptors and Chloride Channels: Structural and Functional Properties" (R. W. Olsen and J. C. Venter, eds.). Alan R. Liss, New York (in press).

Haefely, W., Kulcsár, A., Möhler, H., Pieri, L., Polc, P., and Schaffner, R. (1975). *Adv. Biochem. Psychopharmacol.* **14**, 131–151.

Haefely, W., Bandle, E. F., Burkard, W. P., Da Prada, M., Keller, H. H., Kettler, R., Möhler, H., and Richards, J. G. (1980). *In* "Etats déficitaires cérébraux liés à l'âge" (R. Tissot, ed.), pp. 329–353. Librairie de l'Université, Georg, Geneva.

Haefely, W., Pieri, L, Polc, P., and Schaffner, R. (1981a). *Handb. Exp. Pharmacol.* **55**, 13–262.

Haefely, W., Hunkeler, W., Kyburz, E., Möhler, H., Pieri, L., Polc, P., and Gerecke, M. (1981b). European Patent Application 27, 214, April 22, 1981, priority Oct. 4, 1979; *Chem. Abstr.* **95**, 115, 621g.

Haefely, W., Polc, P., Pieri, L., Schaffner, R., and Laurent, J.-P. (1983). *In* "The Benzodiazepines: From Molecular Biology to Clinical Practice" (E. Costa, ed.), pp. 21–66. Raven, New York.

Hamon, M., and Soubrié, P. (1983). *Neurochem. Int.* **5**, 663–672.

Hammond, J. R., Paterson, A. R. P., and Clanachan, A. S. (1981). *Life Sci.* **29**, 2207–2214.

Hammond, J. R., Jarvis, S. M., Paterson, A. R. P., and Clanachan, A. S. (1983). *Biochem. Pharmacol.* **32**, 1229–1235.

Hariton, C., Jadot, G., Mesdjian, E., Valli, M., Bonyard, P., and Mandel, P. (1983). *J. Pharmacol. (Paris)* **14**, 425–436.

Harrison, N. L., and Simmonds, M. A. (1983). *Eur. J. Pharmacol.* **87**, 155–158.

Hassal, C. H., Holmes, S. W., Johnson, W. H., Krohn, A., Smithen, C. E., and Thomas, W. A. (1977). *Experientia* **33**, 1492–1493.

Heizmann, P., Eckert, M., and Ziegler, W. H. (1983). *Br. J. Clin. Pharmacol.* **16**, 43S–49S.

Henn, F. (1980). *Brain Res. Bull.* **5** (Suppl. 2), 879–883.

Henn, F. A., and Henke, D. J. (1978). *Neuropharmacology* **17**, 985–988.

Hertz, L., and Mukerji, S. (1979). *Can. J. Physiol. Pharmacol.* **58**, 217–220.

Hester, J. B., Rudzik, A. D., and VonVoigtlander, P. F. (1980). *J. Med. Chem.* **23**, 392–402.

Hetmar, O., Nielsen, M., and Braestrup, C. (1983). *J. Neurochem.* **41**, 217–221.

Heusner, J. E., and Bosman, H. B. (1981). *Life Sci.* **29**, 971–974.

Hironaka, T., Fuchino, K., and Fujii, T. (1983). *Jpn. J. Pharmacol.* **33**, 95–102.

Hirose, K., Matsushita, A., Eigyo, M., Jyoyama, H., Fujita, A., Tsukinoki, Y., Shiomi, T., and Matsubara, K. (1981). *Arzneimittelforschung* **31**, 63–69.

Hirsch, J. D. (1981). *Exp. Neurol.* **72**, 91–98.

Hirsch, J. D. (1982). *Pharmacol., Biochem. Behav.* **16**, 245–248.

Hirsch, J. D., and Kochman, R. L. (1983). *Arch. Int. Pharmacodyn.* **265**, 211–218.

Hirsch, J. D., and Lydigsen, J. L. (1981). *Eur. J. Pharmacol.* **72**, 357–360.

Hirsch, J. D., Kochman, R. L., and Sumner, P. R. (1982). *Mol. Pharmacol.* **21**, 618–628.

Honoré, T., Nielsen, M., and Braestrup, C. (1983). *J. Neural Transm.* **58**, 83–98.

Horton, R. W., Prestwich, S. A., and Meldrum, B. S. (1982). *J. Neurochem.* **39**, 864–870.

Horton, R. W., Prestwich, S. A., and Sykes, C. C. (1983). *Br. J. Pharmacol.* **80**, 431P.

Howells, R. D., Hiller, J. M., and Simon, E. J. (1979). *Life Sci.* **25**, 2131–2136.

Huang, A., Barker, J. L., Paul, S. M., Moncada, V., and Skolnick, P. (1980). *Brain Res.* **190**, 485–491.

Hullihan, J. P., Spector, S., Taniguchi, T., and Wang, J. K. T. (1983). *Br. J. Pharmacol.* **78**, 321–327.

Hunkeler, W., Möhler, H., Pieri, L., Polc, P., Bonetti, E. P., Cumin, R., Schaffner, R., and Haefely, W. (1981). *Nature (London)* **290**, 514–516.

Hunt, W. A. (1983). *Neurosci. Biobehav. Rev.* **7**, 87–95.

Hunt, P., Husson, J.-M., and Raynaud, J.-P. (1979). *J. Pharm. Pharmacol.* **31**, 448–451.

Ishii, K., Kano, T., Akutagawa, M., Makino, M., Tanaka, T., and Ando, J. (1982). *Eur. J. Pharmacol.* **83**, 329–333.

Itil, T. M., Polvan, N., Egilmez, S., Saletu, B., and Marasa, J. (1973). *Curr. Ther. Res.* **15**, 603–615.

Ito, Y., and Kuriyama, K. (1982). *Brain Res.* **236**, 351–363.

Iwata, N., and Mikumi, N. (1980). *Psychopharmacology* **71**, 117–122.

Jaffé, E. H., and Cuello, A. C. (1981). *J. Neurochem.* **37**, 1457–1466.

Jelenc, P. C., Cantor, C. R., and Simon, S. R. (1978). *Proc. Natl. Acad. Sci. U.S.A.* **75**, 3564–3566.

Jensen, L. H., and Petersen, E. N. (1983). *J. Neural Transm.* **58**, 183–191.

Jensen, L. H., Petersen, E. N., and Braestrup, C. (1983). *Life Sci.* **33**, 393–399.

Jensen, M. S., and Lambert, J. D. (1983). *Neurosci. Lett.* **40**, 175–179.

Jochemsen, R., Wesselman, J. G. J., Hermans, J., van Boxtel, C. J., and Breimer, D. D. (1983a). *Br. J. Clin. Pharmacol.* **16**, 285S–290S.

Jochemsen, R., Wesselman, J. G. J., van Boxtel, C. J., Hermans, J., and Breimer, D. D. (1983b). *Br. J. Clin. Pharmacol.* **16**, 291S–297S.

Johnson, R. W., and Yamamura, H. I. (1979). *Life Sci.* **25**, 1613–1620.

Johnston, G. A. R., and Skerritt, J. H. (1984). *In* "Actions and Interactions of GABA and Benzodiazepines" (N. G. Bowery, ed.), pp. 179–189. Raven, New York.

Jones, B. J., and Oakley, N. R. (1981). *Br. J. Pharmacol.* **74**, 884P–885P.

Jones, B. J., and Oakley, N. R. (1982). *Br. J. Pharmacol.* **76**, 302P.

Julou, L., Bardone, M. C., Blanchard, J. C., Ganet, C., and Stutzman, J. M. (1983). *Pharmacology* **27**, (Suppl. 2), 46–58.

Kafka, M. S., Wirz-Justice, A., Naber, D., Marangos, P. J., O'Donohue, T. L., and Wehr, T. A. (1982). *Neuropsychobiology* **8**, 41–50.

Kaijima, M., Le Gal La Salle, G., and Rossier, J. (1983). *Eur. J. Pharmacol.* **93**, 113–115.

Kaplan, S. A., and Jack, M. C. (1981). *Handb. Exp. Pharmacol.* **55**, 321–358.

Karobath, M., and Lippitsch, M. (1979). *Eur. J. Pharmacol.* **58**, 485–488.

Karobath, M., and Sperk, G. (1979). *Proc. Natl. Acad. Sci. U.S.A.* **76**, 1004–1006.

Karobath, M., and Supavilai, P. (1982). *Neurosci. Lett.* **31**, 65–69.

Karobath, M., Sperk, G., and Schönbeck, G. (1978). *Eur. J. Pharmacol.* **49**, 323–326.

Karobath, M., Placheta, P., Lippitsch, M., and Krogsgaard-Larsen, P. (1979). *Nature (London)* **278**, 748–749.

Karobath, M., Rogers, J., and Bloom, F. E. (1980a). *Neuropharmacology* **19**, 125–128.

Karobath, M., Placheta, P., Lippitsch, M., and Krogsgaard-Larsen, P. (1980b). *In* "Receptors for Neurotransmitters and Peptide Hormones" (G. Pepeu, M. J. Kuhar, and S. J. Enna, eds.), pp. 313–320. Raven, New York.

Karobath, M., Supavilai, P., Placheta, P., and Sieghart, W. (1980c). *In* "Neurotransmitters and their Receptors" (U. Z. Littauer, Y. Dudai, I. Silman, V. I. Teichberg, and Z. Vogel, eds.), pp. 429–438. Wiley, New York.

Karobath, M., Drexler, G., and Supavilai, P. (1981). *Life Sci.* **28**, 307–313.

Kennessey, A., Cantor, E. H., Semenuk, G., and Spector, S. (1983). *Pharmacologist* **25**, 165.

Kennedy, B., and Leonard, B. E. (1980). *Biochem. Soc. Trans.* **8**, 59–60.

Kish, S. J., Sperk, G., and Hornykiewicz, O. (1983a). *Neuropharmacology* **22**, 1303–1309.

Kish, S. J., Shannak, K. S., Perry, T. L., and Hornykiewicz, O. (1983b). *J. Neurochem.* **41**, 1495–1497.

Klepner, C. A., Lippa, A. S., Benson, D. I., Sano, M. C., and Beer, B. (1979). *Pharmacol., Biochem. Behav.* **11**, 457–462.

Kley, H., Scheidemantel, U., Bering, B., and Müller, W. (1983). *Eur. J. Pharmacol.* **87**, 503–504.

Klotz, K. L., Bocchetta, A., Neale, J. H., Thomas, J. W., and Tallman, J. F. (1984). *Life Sci.* **34**, 293–299.

Kochman, R. L., and Hirsch, J. D. (1982). *Mol. Pharmacol.* **22**, 335–341.

Koe, B. K. (1983). *Drug Dev. Res.* **3**, 421–432.

Korneyev, A.YA. (1982). *Neuropharmacology* **21**, 1355–1358.

Korneyev, A.YA. (1983). *Eur. J. Pharmacol.* **90**, 227–230.

Korneyev, A.YA., and Factor, M. I. (1981). *Eur. J. Pharmacol.* **71**, 127–130.

Korneyev, A.YA., and Factor, M. I. (1983). *Mol. Pharmacol.* **23**, 310–314.

Kragh-Hansen, U. (1983). *Biochem. J.* **209**, 135–142.

Kraus, V. M. B., Dasheiff, R. M., Fanelli, R. J., and McNamara, J. O. (1983). *Brain Res.* **277**, 305–309.

Krogsgaard-Larsen, P., and Arnt, J. (1980). *Brain Res. Bull.* **5** (Suppl. 2), 867–872.

Krogsgaard-Larsen, P., Falch, E., and Jacobsen, P. (1984). *In* "Actions and Interactions of GABA and Benzodiazepines" (N. G. Bowery, ed.), pp. 109–132. Raven, New York.

Kuhn, W., Neuser, D., and Przuntek, H. (1981). *J. Neurochem.* **37**, 1045–1047.

Kuriyama, K., and Ito, Y. (1983). *In* "CNS Receptors—From Molecular Pharmacology to Behavior" (P. Mandel and F. V. De Feudis, eds.), pp. 59–70. Raven, New York.

Kuriyama, K., and Ueno, E. (1983). *In* "Molecular Pharmacology of Neurotransmitter Receptors" (T. Segawa *et al.*, eds.), pp. 221–231. Raven, New York.

Lakoski, J. M., Aghajanian, G. K., and Gallager, D. W. (1983). *Eur. J. Pharmacol.* **88**, 241–245.

Lal, H., Mann, P. A., Jr., Shearman, G. T., and Arnold, S. L. (1981). *Eur. J. Pharmacol.* **75**, 115–119.

Lal, H., Mann, P., Gianforcaro, R., and Naudy, K. (1982). *Substance Alcohol Act./Misuse* **3**, 191–196.

Lal, H., Gherezghiher, T., and Carney, J. (1983). *Drug Dev. Res.* **3**, 75–79.

Lane, J. D., Crenshaw, M. C., Guerin, G. F., Cherek, D. R., and Smith, J. E. (1982). *Eur. J. Pharmacol.* **83**, 183–190.

Lang, B., Barnard, E. A., Chang, L.-R., and Dolly, J. O. (1979). *FEBS Lett.* **104**, 149–153.

Lapierre, Y. D., and Oyewumi, K. L. (1983). *Prog. Neuro-Psychopharmacol. Biol. Psychiat.* **7**, 805–807.

Lapin, I. P. (1980). *Pharmacol., Biochem. Behav.* **13**, 337–341.

Lavé, D., Abrid, C., Gnerret, M., Kiechel, J. R., Lallemand, A., and Rullière, R. (1980). *Thérapie* **35**, 533–543.

Lázniček, M., Lamka, J., and Květina, J. (1982). *Biochem. Pharmacol.* **31**, 1455–1458.

Leeb-Lundberg, F., and Olsen, R. W. (1982). *Mol. Pharmacol.* **21**, 320–328.

Leeb-Lundberg, F., and Olsen, R. W. (1983). *Mol. Pharmacol.* **23**, 315–325.

Leeb-Lundberg, F., Snowman, A., and Olsen, R. W. (1980). *Proc. Natl. Acad. Sci. U.S.A.* **77**, 7468–7472.

Leeb-Lundberg, F., Snowman, A., and Olsen, R. W. (1981a). *J. Neurosci.* **1**, 471–477.

Leeb-Lundberg, F., Snowman, A., and Olsen, R. W. (1981b). *Eur. J. Pharmacol.* **72**, 125–129.

Leeb-Lundberg, F., Napias, C., and Olsen, R. W. (1981c). *Brain Res.* **216**, 399–408.

Le Fur, G. (1982). *Encéphale* **8**, 145–150.

Le Fur, G., Mizoule, J., Burgevin, M. C., Ferris, O., Heaulme, M., Gauthier, A., Guérémy, C., and Uzan, A. (1981). *Life Sci.* **28**, 1439–1448.

Le Fur, G., Perrier, M. L., Vaucher, N., Imbault, F., Flamier, A., Benavides, J., Uzan, A., Renault, C., Dubroeucq, M. C., and Guérémy, C. (1983a). *Life Sci.* **32**, 1839–1847.

Le Fur, G., Guilloux, F., Rufat, P., Benavides, J., Uzan, A., Renault, C., Dubroeucq, M. C., and Guérémy, C. (1983b). *Life Sci.* **32**, 1849–1856.

Le Fur, G., Vaucher, N., Perrier, M. L., Flamier, A., Benavides, J., Renault, C., Dubroeucq, M. C., Guérémy, C., and Uzan, A. (1983c). *Life Sci.* **33**, 449–457.

Lescovelli, M., Catellani, A., and Perbellini, D. (1976). *Arzneimittelforschung* **26**, 1623–1626.

Leslie, S. W., Friedman, M. B., and Coleman, R. R. (1980). *Biochem. Pharmacol.* **29**, 2439–2443.

Levine, A. S., and Morley, J. E. (1982). *Science* **217**, 77–79.

Linscheid, P., and Lehn, J.-M. (1967). *Bull. Soc. Chim. France* 992–997.

Lippa, A. S., Sano, M. C., Coupet, J., Klepner, C. A., and Beer, B. (1978a). *Life Sci.* **23**, 2213–2218.

Lippa, A. S., Klepner, C. A., Yunger, L., Sano, M. C., Smith, W. V., and Beer, B. (1978b). *Pharmacol., Biochem. Behav.* **9**, 853–856.

Lippa, A. S., Critchett, D., Sano, M. C., Klepner, C. A., Greenblatt, E. N., Coupet, J., and Beer, B. (1979a). *Pharmacol., Biochem. Behav.* **10**, 831–843.

Lippa, A. S., Coupet, J., Greenblatt, E. N., Klepner, C. A., and Beer, B. (1979b). *Pharmacol., Biochem. Behav.* **11**, 99–106.

Lippa, A. S., Klepner, C. A., Benson, D. I., Critchett, D. J., Sano, M. C., and Beer, B. (1980). *Brain Res.* **5**, 861–865.

Lippa, A. S., Beer, B., Sano, M. C., Vogel, R. A., and Meyerson, L. R. (1981). *Life Sci.* **28**, 2343–2347.

Lippa, A. S., Meyerson, L. R., and Beer, B. (1982a). *Life Sci.* **31**, 1409–1417.

Lippa, A. S., Jackson, D., Wennogle, L. P., Beer, B., and Meyerson, L. R. (1982b). *In* "Pharmacology of Benzodiazepines" (E. Usdin, P. Skolnick, J. F. Tallman, D. Greenblatt, and S. M. Paul, eds.), pp. 431–440. Macmillan, New York.

Lippke, K. P., Schunack, W. G., Wenning, W., and Müller, W. E. (1983). *J. Med. Chem.* **26**, 499–503.

Lister, R. G., File, S. E., and Greenblatt, D. J. (1983). *Life Sci.* **32**, 2033–2040.

Lloyd, H. G. E., Morgan, P. F., Perkins, M. N., and Stone, T. W. (1981). *Br. J. Pharmacol.* **74**, 886P–887P.

Lo, M. M. S., and Snyder, S. H. (1983). *J. Neurosci.* **3**, 2270–2279.

Lo, M. M. S., Strittmatter, S. M., and Snyder, S. H. (1982). *Proc. Natl. Acad. Sci. U.S.A.* **79**, 680–684.

Lo, M. M. S., Niehoff, D. L., Kuhar, M. J., and Snyder, S. H. (1983a). *Neurosci. Lett.* **39**, 37–44.

Lo, M. M. S., Niehoff, D. L., Kuhar, M. J., and Snyder, S. H. (1983b). *Nature (London)* **306**, 57–60.

Locock, R. A., Baker, G. B., Micetich, R. G., Coutts, R. T., and Benderly, A. (1982). *Prog. Neuro-Psychopharmacol. Biol. Psychiat.* **6**, 407–410.

Lowenstein, P. R., and Cardinali, D. P. (1983a). *Neuroendocrinology* **37**, 150–154.

Lowenstein, P. R., and Cardinali, D. P. (1983b). *Eur. J. Pharmacol.* **86**, 287–289.

McCarthy, K. D., and Harden, T. K. (1981). *J. Pharmacol. Exp. Ther.* **216**, 183–191.

MacDonald, R. L. (1978). *Nature (London)* **271**, 563–564.

MacDonald, R. L., and Barker, J. L. (1978). *Science* **200**, 775–777.

MacDonald, R. L., and Barker, J. L.(1979a). *Brain Res.* **167**, 323–336.

MacDonald, R. L., and Barker, J. L. (1979b). *Neurology* **29**, 432–447.

MacDonald, J. F., Barker, J. L., Paul, S. M., Marangos, P. J., and Skolnick, P. (1979). *Science* **205**, 715–717.

Mackerer, C. R., and Kochman, R. L. (1978). *Proc. Sco. Exp. Biol. Med.* **158**, 393–397.
Mackerer, C. R., Kochman, R. L., Bierschenk, B. A., and Bremner, S. S. (1978). *J. Pharmacol. Exp. Ther.* **206**, 405–413.
Maderdrut, J. L., Oppenheim, R. W., and Reitzel, J. L. (1983). *Brain Res.* **289**, 385–390.
Maggi, A., Satinover, J., Oberdorfer, M., Mann, E., and Enna, J. (1980). *Brain Res. Bull.* **5** (Suppl. 2), 167–171.
Mallorga, P., Ebel, C., and Roth-Schechter, B. F. (1983). *Neurosci. Lett.* **39**, 45–50.
Marangos, P. J., and Crawley, J. N. (1982). *Neuropharmacology* **21**, 81–84.
Marangos, P. J., Paul, S. M., Greenblatt, P., Goodwin, F. K., and Skolnick, P. (1978). *Life Sci.* **20**, 1893–1900.
Marangos, P. J., Clark, R., Martino, A. M., Paul, S. M., and Skolnick, P. (1979a). *Psychiat. Res.* **1**, 121–130.
Marangos, P. J., Paul, S. M., Parma, A. M., Goodwin, F. K., Syapin, P., and Skolnick, P. (1979b). *Life Sci.* **24**, 851–858.
Marangos, P. J., Paul, S. M., Parma, A. M., and Skolnick, P. (1981a). *Biochem. Pharmacol.* **30**, 2171–2174.
Marangos, P. J., Patel, J., Hirata, F., Sondhein, D., Paul, S. M., Skolnick, P., and Goodwin, F. K. (1981b). *Life Sci.* **29**, 259–267.
Marangos, P. J., Patel, J., Boulenger, J.-P., and Clark-Rosenberg, R. (1982). *Mol. Pharmacol.* **22**, 26–32.
Martin, I. L., and Brown, C. L. (1983). *In* "Benzodiazepine Recognition Site Ligands: Biochemistry and Pharmacology" (G. Biggio and E. Costa, eds.), pp. 65–72. Raven, New York.
Martin, I. L., and Candy, J. M. (1978). *Neuropharmacology* **17**, 993–998.
Martin, I. L., and Doble, A. (1983). *J. Neurochem.* **40**, 1613–1619.
Martin, I. L., Brown, C. L., Doble, A. (1983). *Life Sci.* **32**, 1925–1933.
Martin, I. L., Brown, C. L., and Doble, A. (1984). *In* "Actions and Interactions of GABA and Benzodiazepines" (N. G. Bowery, ed.), pp. 167–177. Raven, New York.
Martini, C., and Lucacchini, A. (1982). *J. Neurochem.* **38**, 1768–1770.
Martini, C., Lucacchini, A., and Ronca, G. (1981). *Prep. Biochem.* **11**, 487–499.
Martini, C., Lucacchini, A., Ronca, G., Hrelia, S., and Rossi, C. A. (1982). *J. Neurochem.* **38**, 15–19.
Martini, C., Giannaccini, G., and Lucacchini, A. (1983a). *Biochim. Biophys. Acta* **728**, 289–292.
Martini, C., Rigacci, T., and Lacacchini, A. (1983b). *J. Neurochem.* **41**, 1183–1185.
Massotti, M., and Guidotti, A. (1980). *Life Sci.* **27**, 847–854.
Massotti, M., Guidotti, A., and Costa, E. (1981). *J. Neurosci.* **1**, 409–418.
Matlib, M. A., and Schwartz, A. (1983). *Life Sci.* **32**, 2837–2842.
Matlib, M. A., Lee, S.-W., Depover, A., and Schwartz, A. (1983). *Eur. J. Pharmacol.* **89**, 327–328.
Matsumoto, K., and Fukuda, H. (1982a). *Life Sci.* **30**, 935–943.
Matsumato, K., and Fukuda, H. (1982b). *Neurosci. Lett.* **32**, 175–179.
Matthew, E., Laskin, J. D., Zimmerman, E. A., Weinstein, I. B., Hsu, K. C., and Engelhardt, D. L. (1981). *Proc. Natl. Acad. Sci. U.S.A.* **78**, 3935–3939.
Maurer, R. (1979). *Neurosci. Lett.* **12**, 65–68.
Mazière, M., Prenant, C., Sastre, J., Crouzel, M., Comar, D., Hautraye, P., Kaijima, M., Guibert, B., and Naquet, R. (1983a). *C. R. Acad. Sci. Paris* **296**, 871–876.
Mazière, M., Prenant, C., Sastre, J., Crouzel, M., Comar, D., Cepeda, C., Hautraye, P., Kaijima, M., Guibert, B., and Naquet, R. (1983b). *Encephale* **9**, 151B–160B.
Medina, J. H., and Novas, M. L. (1983). *Eur. J. Pharmacol.* **88**, 377–382.
Medina, J. H., Novas, M. L., Wolfman, C. N. V., Levi de Stein, M., and De Robertis, E. (1983a). *Neuroscience* **9**, 331–335.

Medina, J. H., Novas, M. L., and de Robertis, E. (1983b). *J. Neurochem.* **41**, 703–709.

Medina, J. H., Novas, M. L., and de Robertis, E. (1983c). *Eur. J. Pharmacol.* **90**, 125–128.

Meiners, B. A., and Salama, A. I. (1982). *Eur. J. Pharmacol.* **78**, 315–322.

Meldrum, B., and Braestrup, C. (1984). In "Actions and Interactions of GABA and Benzodiazepines" (N. G. Bowery, ed.), pp. 133–153. Raven, New York.

Meldrum, B. S., Evans, M. C., and Braestrup, C. (1983). *Eur. J. Pharmacol.* **91**, 255–259.

Mendelson, W. B., Davis, T., Paul, S. M., and Skolnick, P. (1983a). *Life Sci.* **32**, 2241–2246.

Mendelson, W. B., Cain, J. M., Cook, J. M., Paul, S. M., and Skolnick, P. (1983b). *Science* **219**, 414–416.

Mendelson, W. B., Cain, M., Cook, J. M., Paul, S. M., and Skolnick, P. (1983c). In "Sleep" (W. P. Koella, ed.), pp. 279–281. Karger, Basel.

Mennini, T., and Garattini, S. (1982). *Life Sci.* **31**, 2025–2035.

Mennini, T., and Garattini, S. (1983). In "Benzodiazepine Recognition Site Ligands: Biochemistry and Pharmacology" (G. Biggio and E. Costa, eds.), pp. 189–199. Raven, New York.

Mennini, T., Cotecchia, S., Caccia, S., and Garattini, S. (1982a). *J. Pharm. Pharmacol.* **34**, 394–395.

Mennini, T., Cotecchia, S., Caccia, S., and Garattini, S. (1982b). *Pharmacol., Biochem. Behav.* **16**, 529–532.

Mennini, T., Abbiati, A., Caccia, S., Cotecchia, S., Gomez, A., and Garattini, S. (1982c). *Naunyn-Schmiedeberg's Arch. Pharmacol.* **321**, 112–115.

Mereu, G., and Biggio, G. (1983). In "Benzodiazepine Recognition Site Ligands: Biochemistry and Pharmacology" (G. Biggio and E. Costa, eds.), pp. 201–209. Raven, New York.

Mernoff, S. T., Cherwinski, H. M., Becker, J. W., and de Blas, A. L. (1983). *J. Neurochem.* **41**, 752–758.

Miledi, R., and Sumikawa, K. (1982). *Biometr. Res.* **3**, 390–399.

Mimaki, T., Deshmukh, P. P., and Yamamura, H. I. (1980). *J. Neurochem.* **35**, 1473–1475.

Minchin, M. C. W., and Nutt, D. J. (1983). *J. Neurochem.* **41**, 1507–1512.

Mitchell, P. R., and Martin, I. L. (1978). *Neuropharmacology* **17**, 317–320.

Mitchell, R., and Wilson, L. E. (1983). *Neuropharmacology* **22**, 935–938.

Mizuno, S., Ogawa, N., and Mori, A. (1982). *Neurochem. Res.* **7**, 1487–1493.

Möhler, H. (1981). *Trends Pharmacol. Sci.* 116–118.

Möhler, H. (1982). *Eur. J. Pharmacol.* **80**, 435–436.

Möhler, H. (1983). In "Benzodiazepine Recognition Site Ligands: Biochemistry and Pharmacology" (G. Biggio and E. Costa, eds.), pp. 47–56. Raven, New York.

Möhler, H. (1984a). In "Highlights in Receptor Chemistry" (C. Melchiorre and M. Gianella, eds.), pp. 185–194. Elsevier, Amsterdam.

Möhler, H. (1984b). In "Actions and Interactions of GABA and Benzodiazepines" (N. G. Bowery, ed.), pp. 155–166. Raven, New York.

Möhler, H., and Okada, T. (1977a). *Science* **198**, 849–851.

Möhler, H., and Okada, T. (1977b). *Life Sci.* **20**, 2101–2110.

Möhler, H., and Okada, T. (1978). *Br. J. Psychiat.* **133**, 261–268.

Möhler, H., and Richards, J. G. (1981a). *Nature (London)* **294**, 763–765.

Möhler, H., and Richards, J. G. (1981b). *Br. J. Pharmacol.* **74**, 813P–814P.

Möhler, H., and Richards, J. G. (1983a). In "The Benzodiazepines: From Molecular Biology to Clinical Practice" (E. Costa, ed.), pp. 93–116. Raven, New York.

Möhler, H., and Richards, J. G. (1983b). In "Anxiolytics: Neurochemical, Behavioral, and Clinical Perspectives" (J. B. Malick, S. J. Enna, and H. I. Yamamura, eds.), pp. 15–40. Raven, New York.

Möhler, H., and Richards, J. G. (1983c). *Br. J. Pharmacol.* **79**, 280P.

Möhler, H., Okada, T., Heitz, P., and Ulrich, J. (1978a). *Life Sci.* **22**, 985–996.

Möhler, H., Okada, T., and Enna, S. J. (1978b). *Brain Res.* **156**, 391–395.

Möhler, H., Polc, P., Cumin, R., Pieri, L., and Kettler, R. (1979). *Nature (London)* **278**, 563–565.
Möhler, H., Battersby, M. K., and Richards, J. G. (1980). *Proc. Natl. Acad. Sci. U.S.A.* **77**, 1666–1670.
Möhler, H., Sieghart, W., Polc, P., Bonetti, E. P., and Hunkeler, W. (1981a). In "Pharmacology of Benzodiazepines" (E. Usdin, P. Skolnick, J. F. Tallman, H. D. Greenblatt, and S. M. Paul, eds.), pp. 63–70. Macmillan, New York.
Möhler, H., Richards, J. G., and Wu, J.-Y. (1981b). *Proc. Natl. Acad. Sci. U.S.A.* **78**, 1935–1938.
Möhler, H., Burkhard, W. P., Keller, H. H., Richards, J. G., and Haefely, W. (1981c). *J. Neurochem.* **37**, 714–722.
Möhler, H., Sieghart, W., Richards, R.-G., and Hunkeler, W. (1984). *Eur. J. Pharmacol.* **102**, 191–192.
Moingeon, P., Bidart, J. M., Alberici, G. F., and Bohnon, C. (1983). *Eur. J. Pharmacol.* **92**, 147–149.
Morelli, M., Gee, K. W., and Yamamura, H. I. (1982). *Life Sci.* **31**, 77–81.
Morgan, P. F., and Stone, T. W. (1982a). *J. Neurochem.* **39**, 1446–1451.
Morgan, P. F., and Stone, T. W. (1982b). *Neurosci. Lett.* **29**, 159–162.
Morgan, P. F., and Stone, T. W. (1983). *Br. J. Pharmacol.* **79**, 973–977.
Morgan, P. F., Lloyd, H. G. E., and Stone, T. W. (1983a). *Eur. J. Pharmacol.* **87**, 121–126.
Morgan, P. F., Lloyd, H. G. E., and Stone, T. W. (1983b). *Neurosci. Lett.* **41**, 183–188.
Morin, A. M., Tanaka, I. A., and Wasterlain, C. G. (1981). *Life Sci.* **28**, 2257–2263.
Mueser, T., Isaac, L., and Radulovacki, M. (1983). *Physiol. Behav.* **31**, 237–239.
Müller, W. E., and Stillbauer, A. E. (1983). *Pharmacol., Biochem. Behav.* **18**, 545–549.
Müller, W. E., and Wollert, U. (1979). *Pharmacology* **19**, 59–67.
Müller, W. E., Schläfer, U., and Wollert, U. (1978). *Neurosci. Lett.* **9**, 239–243.
Murata, H., Kougo, K., Yasumura, A., Nakajima, E., and Shindo, H. (1973). *Chem. Pharm. Bull.* **21**, 404–414.
Nagy, A., and Lijtha, A. (1983). *J. Neurochem.* **40**, 414–417.
Nagy, J., Kardos, J., Maksay, G., and Simonyi, M. (1981). *Neuropharmacology* **20**, 529–533.
Niehoff, D. L., and Kuhar, M. J. (1983). *J. Neurosci.* **3**, 2091–2097.
Niehoff, D. L., and Whitehouse, P. J. (1983). *Brain Res.* **276**, 237–245.
Niehoff, D. L., Mashal, R. D., Horst, W. D., O'Brien, R. A., Palacios, J. M., and Kuhar, M. J. (1982). *J. Pharmacol. Exp. Ther.* **221**, 670–675.
Niehoff, D. L., Mashal, R. D., and Kuhar, M. J. (1983). *Eur. J. Pharmacol.* **92**, 131–134.
Nielsen, M., and Braestrup, C. (1980). *Nature (London)* **286**, 606–607.
Nielsen, M., and Braestrup, C. (1983). *Eur. J. Pharmacol.* **96**, 321–322.
Nielsen, M., Gredal, O., and Braestrup, C. (1979). *Life Sci.* **25**, 679–686.
Nielsen, M., Schou, H., and Braestrup, C. (1981). *J. Neurochem.* **36**, 276–285.
Ninan, P. T., Insel, T. M., Cohen, R. M., Cook, J. M., Skolnick, P., and Paul, S. M. (1982). *Science* **218**, 1332–1334.
Nistri, A., and Berti, C. (1983). *Neurosci. Lett.* **39**, 199–204.
Nistri, A., and Constanti, A. (1978). *Neuropharmacology* **17**, 127–135.
Niznik, H. B., Kish, S. J., and Burnham, W. M. (1983). *Life Sci.* **33**, 425–430.
Norstrand, I. F., Debons, A. F., Libbin, R. M., and Slade, W. R., Jr. (1983). *Enzyme* **29**, 61–65.
Nutt, D. J. (1983). In "Benzodiazepine Recognition Site Ligands: Biochemistry and Pharmacology" (G. Biggio and E. Costa, eds.), pp. 153–157. Raven, New York.
Nutt, D. J., and Minchin, M. C. W. (1983). *J. Neurochem.* **41**, 1513–1517.
Oakley, N. R., and Jones, B. J. (1980). *Eur. J. Pharmacol.* **68**, 381–382.
Oakley, N. R., and Jones, B. J. (1982). *Neuropharmacology* **21**, 587–589.
Oakley, N. R., and Jones, B. J. (1983). *Eur. J. Pharmacol.* **87**, 499–500.
O'Boyle, C., Lambe, R., Darragh, A., Taffe, W., Brick, I., and Kenney, M. (1983). *Br. J. Anaesthesiol.* **55**, 349–356.

O'Brien, R. A., and Spirt, N. M. (1980). *Life Sci.* **26**, 1441–1445.

Oka, J.-I., Fukuda, H., and Kudo, Y. (1981). *Gen. Pharmacol.* **12**, 385–389.

Okazaki, M. M., Madras, B. K., Livingston, K. E., Spero, L., and Burnham, W. M. (1983). *Life Sci.* **33**, 409–414.

Olsen, R. W. (1981). *J. Neurochem.* **37**, 1–13.

Olsen, R. W. (1982). *Annu. Rev. Pharmacol. Toxicol.* **22**, 245–277.

Olsen, R. W., and Leeb-Lundberg, F. (1980). *Eur. J. Pharmacol.* **65**, 101–104.

Olsen, R. W., and Leeb-Lundberg, F. (1981). *In* "Neurotransmitters, Seizures, and Epilepsy" (P. L. Morselli, ed.), pp. 151–163. Raven, New York.

Ongini, E. (1983). *In* "Benzodiazepine Recognition Site Ligands: Biochemistry and Pharmacology" (G. Biggio and E. Costa, eds.), pp. 211–225. Raven, New York.

Ongini, E., Barzaghi, C., and Marzanatti, M. (1983). *Eur. J. Pharmacol.* **95**, 125–129.

Oriowo, M. A. (1983). *J. Pharm. Pharmacol.* **35**, 511–515.

Overstreet, D. H., and Yamamura, H. I. (1979). *Life Sci.* **25**, 1865–1878.

Owen, F., Poulter, M., Waddington, J. L., Mashall, R. D., and Crow, T. J. (1983). *Brain Res.* **278**, 373–375.

Palacios, J. M., and Kuhar, M. J. (1980). *Brain Res. Bull.* **5** (Suppl. 2), 145–148.

Palacios, J. M., and Kuhar, M. J. (1982). *Dev. Brain Res.* **1**, 531–539.

Palacios, J. M., Niehoff, D. L., and Kuhar, M. J. (1979). *Brain Res.* **179**, 390–395.

Palacios, J. M., Niehoff, D. L., and Kuhar, M. J. (1981a). *Neurosci. Lett.* **25**, 101–105.

Palacios, J. M., Wamsley, J. K., and Kuhar, M. J. (1981b). *Brain Res.* **214**, 155–162.

Patel, J. B., and Malick, J. B. (1982). *Eur. J. Pharmacol.* **78**, 323–333.

Patel, J., and Marangos, P. J. (1982). *Neurosci. Lett.* **30**, 157–160.

Patel, J., Marangos, P. J., and Goodwin, F. K. (1981). *Eur. J. Pharmacol.* **72**, 419–420.

Patel, J., Marangos, P. J., Skolnick, P., Paul, S. M., and Martino, A. M. (1982). *Neurosci. Lett.* **29**, 79–82.

Patel, J. B., Martin, C., and Malick, J. B. (1983). *Eur. J. Pharmacol.* **86**, 295–298.

Paterson, I. A., and Roberts, M. H. T. (1983). *Brain Res.* **278**, 274–278.

Paul, S. M., and Skolnick, P. (1978). *Science* **202**, 892–894.

Paul, S. M., Syapin, P. J., Paugh, B. A., Moncada, V., and Skolnick, P. (1979). *Nature (London)* **281**, 688–689.

Paul, S. M., Skolnick, P., and Zatz, M. (1980a). *Biochem. Biophys. Res. Commun.* **96**, 632–638.

Paul, S. M., Zatz, M., and Skolnick, P. (1980b). *Brain Res.* **187**, 243–246.

Paul, S. M., Luu, M. D., and Skolnick, P. (1982). *In* "Pharmacology of Benzodiazepines" (E. Usdin, P. Skolnick, J. F. Tallman, D. Greenblatt, and S. M. Paul, eds.), pp. 87–92. Macmillan, New York.

Pax, R., Bennett, J. L., and Fetterer, R. (1978). *Arch. Pharmacol.* **304**, 309–315.

Pedigo, N. W., Schoemaker, H., Morelli, M., McDougal, J. N., Malick, J. B., Burks, T. F., and Yamamura, H. I. (1981). *Neurobiol. Aging* **2**, 83–88.

Pérez, C., and Rubio, M. C. (1981). *Gen. Pharmacol.* **12**, 489–492.

Petersen, E. N. (1983). *Eur. J. Pharmacol.* **94**, 117–124.

Petersen, E. N., and Buus-Lassen, J. (1981). *Psychopharmacology* **75**, 236–239.

Petersen, E. N., Paschalke, G., Kehr, W., Nielsen, M., and Braestrup, C. (1982). *Eur. J. Pharmacol.* **82**, 217–221.

Petersen, E. N., Jensen, L. H., Honoré, T., and Braestrup, C. (1983). *In* "Benzodiazepine Recognition Site Ligands: Biochemistry and Pharmacology" (G. Biggio and E. Costa, eds.), pp. 57–64. Raven, New York.

Petkov, V. V., and Yanev, S. (1982). *Pharmacol. Res. Commun.* **14**, 739–744.

Petrack, B., Czernik, A. J., Cassidy, J. P., Bernard, P., and Yokoyama, N. (1983). *In* "Benzodiazepine Recognition Site Ligands: Biochemistry and Pharmacology" (G. Biggio and E. Costa, eds.), pp. 129–137. Raven, New York.

Phillis, J. W., and Wu, P. H. (1982). *Med. Hypotheses* **9**, 361–367.

Pieri, L., Schaffner, R., Scherschlicht, R., Polc, P., Sepinwall, J., Davidson, A., Möhler, H., Cumin, R., Da Prada, M., Burkard, W. P., Keller, H. H., Müller, R. K. M., Gerold, M., Pieri, M., Cook, L., and Haefely, W. (1981). *Drug Res.* **31**, 2180–2201.

Pieri, L., Polc, P., Bonetti, E. P., Burkard, W. P., Cumin, R., and Haefely, W. (1983). *Arch. Pharmacol.* **322**, R95.

Placheta, P., and Karobath, M. (1979). *Brain Res.* **178**, 580–583.

Poddar, M. K., Urquhart, D., and Sinha, A. K. (1980). *Brain Res.* **193**, 519–528.

Polc, P., Ropert, N., and Snyder, D. M. (1981a). *Brain Res.* **217**, 216–220.

Polc, P., Laurent, J.-P., Scherschlicht, R., and Haefely, W. (1981b). *Arch. Pharmacol.* **316**, 317–325.

Polc, P., Bonetti, E. P., Schaffner, R., and Haefely, W. (1982). *Arch. Pharmacol.* **321**, 260–264.

Pong, S.-S., Dehaven, R., and Wang, C. C. (1981). *Biochim. Biophys. Acta* **646**, 143–150.

Pong, S.-S., Dehaven, R., and Wang, C. C. (1982). *J. Neurosci.* **2**, 966–971.

Prado de Carvalho, L., Venault, P., Cavalheiro, E., Kaijima, M., Valin, A., Dodd, L. H., Potier, P., Rossier, J., and Chapouthier, G. (1983a). In "Benzodiazepine Recognition Site Ligands: Biochemistry and Pharmacology" (G. Biggio and E. Costa, eds.), pp. 175–187. Raven, New York.

Prado de Carvalho, L., Grecksch, G., Chapouthier, G., and Rossier, J. (1983b). *Nature (London)* **301**, 64–66.

Prezioso, P. J., and Neale, J. H. (1983). *Brain Res.* **288**, 354–358.

Prozialeck, W. C., and Weiss, B. (1982). *J. Pharmacol. Exp. Ther.* **222**, 509–516.

Quast, U., and Mählmann, H. (1982). *Biochem. Pharmacol.* **31**, 2761–2768.

Quast, U., Mählmann, H., and Vollmer, K.-O. (1982). *Mol. Pharmacol.* **22**, 20–25.

Ramanjaneyulu, R., and Ticku, M. K. (1984). *J. Neurochem.* **42**, 221–229.

Ramanujam, V. M. S., and Trieff, N. M. (1978). *J. Pharm. Pharmacol.* **30**, 542–546.

Rapold, H. J., Follath, F., Scollo-Lavizzari, G., Kehl, O., and Ritz, R. (1984). *Dtsch. Med. Wochenschr.* **109**, 340–344.

Reeves, P. M., and Schweizer, M. P. (1983). *Brain Res.* **270**, 376–379.

Regan, J. W., Yamamura, H. I., Yamada, S., and Roeske, W. R. (1981). *Life Sci.* **28**, 991–998.

Rehavi, M., Skolnick, P., and Paul, S. M. (1982). *Eur. J. Pharmacol.* **79**, 353–356.

Reisine, T. D., Wastek, G. J., Speth, R. C., Bird, E. D., and Yamamura, H. I. (1979). *Brain Res.* **165**, 183–187.

Reisine, T. D., Overstreet, D., Gale, K., Rossor, M., Iversen, L., and Yamamura, H. I. (1980). *Brain Res.* **199**, 79–88.

Ribak, C. E., Vaughn, J. E., Saito, K., Barber, R., and Roberts, E. (1977). *Brain Res.* **126**, 1–18.

Rice, K. C., Brossi, A., Tallman, J., Paul, S. M., and Skolnick, P. (1979). *Nature (London)* **278**, 854–855.

Richards, J. G., and Möhler, H. (1984). *Neuropharmacology* **23**, 233–242.

Richards, J. G., Möhler, H., Schoch, P., Häring, P., Takács, B., and Stähli, C. (1984). *J. Receptor Res.* **4**, 657–669.

Richards, J. G., Möhler, H., and Haefely, W. (1985). In "Mechanisms of Drug Action" (G. N. Woodruff, ed.), Macmillan, London (in press).

Richards, J. G., Möhler, H., and Haefely, W. (1982). *Trends Pharmacol. Sci.* **3**, 233–235.

Richter, J. A., and Holtman, J. R. (1982). *Prog. Neurobiol.* **18**, 275–319.

Robertson, H. A. (1979). *Eur. J. Pharmacol.* **56**, 163–166.

Robertson, H. A. (1980). *Eur. J. Pharmacol.* **66**, 249–252.

Robertson, H. A. (1983). *Prog. Neuro-Psychopharmacol. Biol. Psychiat.* **7**, 637–640.

Robertson, H. A., Martin, I. L., and Candy, J. M. (1978). *Eur. J. Pharmacol.* **50**, 455–457.

Robertson, H. A., Baker, G. B., Coutts, R. T., Benderly, A., Locock, R. A., and Martin, I. L. (1981). *Eur. J. Pharmacol.* **76**, 281–284.

Robertson, H. A., Riives, M., Black, D. A. S., and Peterson, M. R. (1984). *Brain Res.* **291**, 388–390.

Rodbard, D., Costa, T., and Pert, C. B. (1979). *Nature (London)* **280**, 173–174.

Rohde, B. H., and Harris, R. A. (1982). *Brain Res.* **253**, 133–141.

Römer, D., Büscher, H. H., Hill, R. C., Maurer, R., Petscher, I. J., Zeigner, H., Benson, W., Finner, E., Milkowski, W., and Thies, P. W. (1982a). *Life Sci.* **31**, 1217–1220.

Römer, D., Büscher, H. H., Hill, R. C., Maurer, R., Petscher, T. F., Zeugner, H., Benson, W., Finner, E., Milkowski, W., and Thies, P. W. (1982b). *Nature (London)* **298**, 759–760.

Rommelspacher, H., Nanz, C., Borbe, H. O., Fehske, K. J., Müller, W. E., and Wollert, U. (1980). *Naunyn-Schmiedeberg's Arch. Pharmacol.* **314**, 97–100.

Rommelspacher, H., Nanz, C., Borbe, H. O., Fehske, K. J., Müller, W. E., and Wollert, U. (1981). *Eur. J. Pharmacol.* **70**, 409–416.

Rosenberg, H. C., and Chiu, T. H. (1979a). *Neurosci. Lett.* **15**, 277–281.

Rosenberg, H. C., and Chiu, T. H. (1979b). *Life Sci.* **24**, 803–808.

Rosenberg, H. C., and Chiu, T. H. (1981a). *Neurosci. Lett.* **24**, 49–52.

Rosenberg, H. C., and Chiu, T. H. (1981b). *Eur. J. Pharmacol.* **70**, 453–460.

Rossier, J., Dodd, R., Felblum, S., Valin, A., Prado de Carvalho, L., Potier, P., and Naquet, R. (1983). *Lancet* **1**, 77–78.

Roth-Schechter, B. F., Ebel, C., and Mallorga, P. (1983). *Eur. J. Pharmacol.* **87**, 169–170.

Ruffolo, R. R. (1982). *J. Auton. Pharmacol.* **2**, 277–295.

Rudzik, A. D., Hester, J. B., Tang, A. H., Straw, R. N., and Friis, W. (1973). *In* "The Benzodiazepines" (S. Garrattini, E. Mussini, and L. O. Randall, eds.), pp. 285–297. Raven, New York.

Saano, V. (1982a). *Pharmacol. Res. Commun.* **14**, 745–757.

Saano, V. (1982b). *Pharmacol. Res. Commun.* **14**, 971–981.

Saano, V., and Airaksinen, M. M. (1982). *Acta Pharmacol. Toxicol.* **51**, 300–308.

Saano, V., and Urtti, A. (1982). *Pharmacol. Biochem. Behav.* **17**, 367–369.

Saano, V., Urtti, A., and Airaksinen, M. M. (1981). *Pharmacol. Res. Commun.* **13**, 75–85.

Sabato, U. C., Aguilar, J. S., and De Robertis, E. (1981a). *J. Recept. Res.* **2**, 119–133.

Sabato, U. C., Aguilar, J. S., Medina, J. H., and De Robertis, E. (1981b). *Neurosci. Lett.* **27**, 193–197.

Sabato, U. C., Novas, M. L., Lowenstein, P., Zieher, I. M., and De Robertis, E. (1981c). *Eur. J. Pharmacol.* **73**, 381–382.

Saito, K.-I., Goto, M., and Fukuda, H. (1983). *Jpn. J. Pharmacol.* **33**, 906–908.

Sakman, B., Hamill, O. P., and Bormann, J.(1983). *J. Neural Transm. Suppl.* **18**, 83–95.

Sandler, M. (1982). *Trends Pharmacol. Sci.* **3**, 471–472.

Schacht, U., and Baecker, G. (1982). *Drug Dev. Res. Suppl.* **1**, 83–93.

Schauzu, H. G., and Mager, P. P. (1983). *Pharmazie* **38**, 490.

Scharf, M. B., and Feil, P. (1983). *Life Sci.* **32**, 1771–1777.

Schliebs, R., Rothe, T., and Bigl, V. (1983). *Biomed. Biochim. Acta* **42**, 537–546.

Schlumpf, M., Richards, J. G., Lichtensteiger, W., and Möhler, H. (1983). *J. Neurosci.* **3**, 1478–1487.

Schmidt, R. F., Vogel, M. E., and Zimmerman, M. (1967). *Arch. Exp. Pathol. Pharmacol.* **253**, 69–82.

Schoch, P., and Möhler, H. (1983). *Eur. J. Pharmacol.* **95**, 323–324.

Schoch, P., Häring, P., Takács, B., Stähli, C., and Möhler, H. (1984). *J. Receptor Res.* **4**, 189–200.

Schoemaker, H., Morelli, M., Deshmukh, P., and Yamamura, H. I. (1982a). *Brain Res.* **248**, 396–401.

Schoemaker, H., Bliss, M., Yamamura, S. H., Horst, D., and Yamamura, H. I. (1982b). *In* "Brain Peptides and Hormones" (R. Collu *et al.*, eds.), pp. 115–123. Raven, New York.

Schoemaker, H., Smith, T. L., and Yamamura, H. I. (1983a). *Brain Res.* **258**, 347–350.
Schoemaker, H., Boles, R. G., Horst, W. D., and Yamamura, H. I. (1983b). *J. Pharmacol. Exp. Ther.* **225**, 61–69.
Scholl, H., Kloster, G., and Stöcklin, G. (1983). *J. Nucl. Med.* **24**, 417–422.
Schweri, M. M., Martin, J. V., Mendelson, W. B., Barrett, J. E., Paul, S. M., and Skolnick, P. (1983). *Life Sci.* **33**, 1505–1510.
Scollo-Lavizzari, G. (1983). *Eur. Neurol.* **22**, 7–11.
Seiler, P., and Zimmermann, I. (1983). *Drug Res.* **33**, 1519–1522.
Sellers, E. M., Naranjo, C. A., Khouw, V., and Greenblatt, D. J. (1982). In "Pharmacology of Benzodiazepines" (E. Usdin, P. Skolnick, J. F. Tallman, D. Greenblatt, and S. M. Paul), pp. 271–284. Macmillan, New York.
Serra, M., Concas, A., Salis, M., and Biggio, G. (1983). *Brain Res.* **273**, 347–351.
Sethy, V. H., and Harris, D. W. (1982). *Res. Commun. Chem. Pathol. Pharmacol.* **35**, 229–235.
Sethy, V. H., Daenzer, C. L., and Russell, R. R. (1983a). *J. Pharm. Pharmacol.* **35**, 194–195.
Sethy, V. H., Russell, R. R., and Daenzer, C. L. (1983b). *J. Pharm. Pharmacol.* **35**, 524–526.
Shah, D. S., Chambon, P., and Guidotti, A. (1981). *Neuropharmacology* **20**, 1115–1119.
Shannon, H. E., and Herling, S. (1983). *Eur. J. Pharmacol.* **92**, 155–157.
Shephard, R. A., Nielsen, E. B., and Broadhurst, P. L. (1982). *Eur. J. Pharmacol.* **77**, 327–330.
Sher, P. K. (1983). *Epilepsia* **24**, 313–320.
Sher, P. K., Schrier, B. K., and Van Putten, D. (1982). *Dev. Neurosci.* **5**, 271–277.
Sher, P., Study, R., Mazzetta, J., Barker, J. L., and Nelson, P. G. (1983). *Brain Res.* **268**, 171–176.
Sherman-Gold, R. (1983). *Neurochem. Int.* **5**, 171–174.
Sherman-Gold, R., and Dudai, Y. (1980). *Brain Res.* **198**, 485–490.
Sherman-Gold, R., and Dudai, Y. (1981). *FEBS Lett* **131**, 313–316.
Sherman-Gold, R., and Dudai, Y. (1983a). *Neurochem. Res.* **8**, 259–267.
Sherman-Gold, R., and Dudai, Y. (1983b). *Neurochem. Res.* **8**, 853–864.
Sherman-Gold, R., and Dudai, Y. (1983c). *J. Neurosci. Res.* **10**, 27–33.
Shibla, D. B., Gardell, M. A., and Neale, J. H. (1981). *Brain Res.* **210**, 471–474.
Sieghart, W. (1983). *Neurosci. Lett.* **38**, 73–78.
Sieghart, W., and Drexler, G. (1983). *J. Neurochem.* **41**, 47–55.
Sieghart, W., and Karobath, M. (1980). *Nature (London)* **286**, 285–287.
Sieghart, W., and Mayer, A. (1982a). *Eur. J. Pharmacol.* **31**, 71–74.
Sieghart, W., and Mayer, A. (1982b). *Neurosci. Lett.* **31**, 71–74.
Sieghart, W., and Möhler, H. (1982). *Eur. J. Pharmacol.* **81**, 171–173.
Sieghart, W., Supavilai, P., and Karobath, M. (1982). In "Pharmacology of Benzodiazepines" (E. Usdin, P. Skolnick, J. F. Tallman, D. Greenblatt, and S. M. Paul, eds.), pp. 141–148. Macmillan, New York.
Sieghart, W., Mayer, A., and Drexler, G. (1983). *Eur. J. Pharmacol.* **88**, 291–299.
Sigel, E., Mamalaki, C., and Barnard, E. A. (1982). *FEBS Lett.* **147**, 45–48.
Sigel, E., Stephenson, F. A., Mamalaki, C., and Barnard, E. A. (1983a). *J. Neurochem.* **41** (Suppl.), 113.
Sigel, E., Stephenson, A., Mamalaki, C., and Barnard, E. A. (1983b). *J. Biol. Chem.* **258**, 6965–6971.
Simmonds, M. A. (1983). *Trends Neurosci.* **6**, 279–281.
Simmonds, M. A. (1984). In "Actions and Interactions of GABA and Benzodiazepines" (N. G. Bowery, ed.), pp. 27–41. Raven, New York.
Sivam, S. P., and Ho, I. K. (1982). *Eur. J. Pharmacol.* **79**, 335–336.
Skerritt, J. H., and Johnston, G. A. R. (1983a). *Neurochem. Res.* **8**, 1351–1362.
Skerritt, J. H., and Johnston, G. A. R. (1983b). *Neurosci. Lett.* **38**, 315–320.
Skerritt, J. H., and Johnston, G. A. R. (1983c). *Eur. J. Pharmacol.* **89**, 193–198.

318 WILLY HAEFELY et al.

Skerritt, J. H., Trisdikoon, P., and Johnston, G. A. R. (1981). *Brain Res.* **215**, 398–403.
Skerritt, J. H., Willow, M., and Johnston, G. A. R. (1982a). *Neurosci. Lett.* **29**, 63–66.
Skerritt, J. H., Davis, L. P., Chow, S. C., and Johnston, G. A. R. (1982b). *Neurosci. Lett.* **32**, 169–174.
Skerritt, J. H., Chow, S. C., and Johnston, G. A. R. (1982c). *Neurosci. Lett.* **33**, 173–178.
Skerritt, J. H., Chow, S. C., Johnston, G. A. R., and Davis, L. P. (1982d). *Neurosci. Lett.* **34**, 63–68.
Skerritt, J. H., Johnston, G. A. R., and Braestrup, C. (1983a). *Eur. J. Pharmacol.* **86**, 299–301.
Skerritt, J. H., Johnston, G. A. R., Katiskas, T., Tabar, J., Nicholson, G. M., and Andrews, P. R. (1983b). *Neurochem. Res.* **8**, 1337–1350.
Skolnick, P., and Paul, S. M. (1982). *Int. Rev. Neurobiol.* **23**, 103–140.
Skolnick, P., and Paul, S. M. (1982). *J. Clin. Psychiat.* **44**, 12–19.
Skolnick, P., Marangos, P. J., Goodwin, F. K., Edwards, M., and Paul, S. (1978). *Life Sci.* **23**, 1473–1480.
Skolnick, P., Syapin, P. J., Paugh, B. A., Moncada, V., Marangos, P. J., and Paul, S. M. (1979). *Proc. Natl. Acad. Sci. U.S.A.* **76**, 1515–1518.
Skolnick, P., Paul, S. M., and Barker, J. L. (1980a). *Eur. J. Pharmacol.* **65**, 125–127.
Skolnick, P., Paul, S., Zatz, M., and Eskay, R. (1980b). *Eur. J. Pharmacol.* **66**, 133–136.
Skolnick, P., Lock, K.-L., and Paul, S. M. (1980c). *Eur. J. Pharmacol.* **67**, 179–186.
Skolnick, P., Paul, S. M., and Marangos, P. J. (1980d). *Fed. Proc., Fed. Am. Soc. Exp. Biol.* **39**, 3050–3055.
Skolnick, P., Lock, K.-L., Paugh, B., Marangos, P., Windsor, R., and Paul, S. (1980e). *Pharmacol., Biochem. Behav.* **12**, 685–689.
Skolnick, P., Moncada, V., Barker, J. L., and Paul, S. M. (1981). *Science* **211**, 1448–1450.
Skolnick, P., Hommer, D., and Paul, S. M. (1982a). *In* "Pharmacology of Benzodiazepines" (E. Usdin, P. Skolnick, J. F. Tallman, D. Greenblatt, and S. M. Paul, eds.), pp. 441–454. Macmillan, New York.
Skolnick, P., Rice, K. C., Barker, J. L., and Paul, S. M. (1982b). *Brain Res.* **233**, 143–156.
Skolnick, P., Schweri, M. M., Williams, E. F., Moncada, V. Y., and Paul, S. M. (1982c). *Eur. J. Pharmacol.* **78**, 133–136.
Skolnick, P., Schweri, M., Kutter, E., Williams, E., and Paul, S. (1982d). *J. Neurochem.* **39**, 1142–1146.
Skolnick, P., Marangos, P. J., and Paul, S. M. (1983a). *Adv. Neurol.* **34**, 359–364.
Skolnick, P., Paul, S., Crawley, J., Lewin, E., Lippa, A., Clody, D., Irmscher, K., Saiko, O., and Minck, K.-O. (1983b). *Eur. J. Pharmacol.* **88**, 319–327.
Skolnick, P., Schweri, M. M., Paul, S. M., Martin, J. V., Wagner, R. L., and Mendelson, W. B. (1983c). *Life Sci.* **32**, 2439–2445.
Slater, P., and Longman, D. A. (1979). *Life Sci.* **25**, 1963–1967.
Slater, P., and Bennett, M. W. R. (1981). *J. Pharm. Pharmcol.* **34**, 42–44.
Smart, T. G., Constanti, A., Bilbe, G., Brown, D. A., and Barnard, E. A. (1983). *Neurosci. Lett.* **40**, 55–59.
Smith, C. C., Lewis, M. E., and Tallman, J. F. (1982). *Pharmacol. Biochem. Behav.* **16**, 29–33.
Smokcum, R. W. J. (1983). *Eur. J. Pharmacol.* **86**, 259–264.
Sollenne, N. P., and Means, G. E. (1979). *Mol. Pharmacol.* **15**, 754.
Sonawane, B. R., Yaffe, S. J., and Shapiro, B. H. (1980). *Life Sci.* **27**, 1335–1338.
Soubrié, P., Thiébot, M. H., Jobert, A., Montastine, J. L., Hery, F., and Hamon, M. (1980). *Brain Res.* **189**, 505–517.
Spencer, D. G., and Lal, H. (1983). *Drug Dev. Res.* **3**, 365–370.
Sperk, G., and Schlögl, E. (1979). *Brain Res.* **170**, 563–567.
Speth, R. C., and Yamamura, H. I. (1979). *Eur. J. Pharmacol.* **54**, 397–399.

Speth, R. C., Wastek, G. J., Johnson, P. C., and Yamamura, H. I. (1978). *Life Sci.* **22**, 859–866.
Speth, R. C., Bresolin, N., and Yamamura, H. I. (1979a). *Eur. J. Pharmacol.* **59**, 159–160.
Speth, R. C., Wastek, G. J., and Yamamura, H. I. (1979b). *Life Sci.* **24**, 351–358.
Speth, R. C., Wastek, G. J., Reisine, T. D., and Yamamura, H. I. (1979c). *Neurosci. Lett.* **13**, 243–247.
Squires, R. F. (1981). *In* "GABA and Benzodiazepine Receptors" (E. Costa, G. Di Chiara, and G. L. Gessa, eds.), pp. 129–138. Raven, New York.
Squires, R. F. (1982). *In* "Brain Peptides and Hormones" (R. Collu *et al.*, eds.), pp. 93–106. Raven, New York.
Squires, R. F., and Braestrup, C. (1977). *Nature (London)* **266**, 732–734.
Squires, R. F., and Saederup, E. (1982). *Mol. Pharmacol.* **22**, 327–334.
Squires, R. F., Benson, D. I., Braestrup, C., Coupet, J., Klepner, C. A. Myers, V., and Beer, B. (1979). *Pharmacol., Biochem. Behav.* **10**, 825–830.
Squires, R. F., Klepner, C. A., and Benson, D. I. (1980). *In* "Receptors for Neurotransmitters and Peptide Hormones" (G. Pepeu, M. J. Kuhar, and S. J. Enna, eds.), pp. 285–293. Raven, New York.
Stapleton, S., Prestwich, S. A., and Horton, R. W. (1982). *Eur. J. Pharmacol.* **84**, 221–224.
Stephenson, F. A., and Olsen, R. W. (1982). *J. Neurochem.* **39**, 1579–1586.
Stephenson, F. A., and Olsen, R. W. (1983). *In* "CNS-Receptors—From Molecular Pharmacology to Behavior" (P. Mandel and F. V. De Feudis, eds.), pp. 71–80. Raven, New York.
Stephenson, F. A., Watkins, A. E., and Olsen, R. W. (1982). *Eur. J. Biochem.* **123**, 291–298.
Sternbach, L. H. (1973). *In* "The Benzodiazepines" (S. Garattini, E. Mussini, and L. O. Randall, eds.), pp. 1–26. Raven, New York.
Sternbach, L. H. (1978). *Prog. Drug Res.* **22**, 229–266.
Sternbach, L. H., Randall, L. O., and Gustavson, S. R. (1964). *Psychopharmacol. Agents* **1**, 137–224.
Sternbach, L. H., Randall, L. O., Banziger, R., and Lehr, H. (1968). *In* "Drugs Affecting the Nervous System" (A. Burger, ed.), pp. 237–264. Dekker, New York.
Stohler, H. R. (1978). *Curr. Chemother.* 147–148.
Strittmatter, W. J., Hirata, F., Axelrod, J., Mallorga, P., Tallman, J. F., and Henneberry, R. C. (1979). *Nature (London)* 282, 857–859.
Study, R. E., and Barker, J. L. (1981). *Proc. Natl. Acad. Sci. U.S.A.* **78**, 7180–7184.
Sunjić, V., Lisini, A., Sega, A., Kovač, T., Kajfež, F., and Ruščić, B. (1979). *J. Heterocyc. Chem.* **16**, 757–761.
Sung, S.-C., and Saneyoshi, N. (1982). *Eur. J. Pharmacol.* **81**, 505–508.
Supavilai, P., and Karobath, M. (1979). *Eur. J. Pharmacol.* **60**, 111–113.
Supavilai, P., and Karobath, M. (1980a). *Eur. J. Pharmacol.* **64**, 91–93.
Supavilai, P., and Karobath, M. (1980b). *Neurosci. Lett.* **19**, 337–341.
Supavilai, P., and Karobath, M. (1981a). *J. Neurochem.* **36**, 798–803.
Supavilai, P., and Karobath, M. (1981b). *Eur. J. Pharmacol.* **70**, 183–193.
Supavilai, P., and Karobath, M. (1983). *Eur. J. Pharmacol.* **91**, 145–146.
Supavilai, P., Mannonen, A. M., and Karobath, M. (1982a). *Neurochem. Int.* **4**, 259–268.
Supavilai, P., Mannonen, A., Collins, J. F., and Karobath, M. (1982b). *Eur. J. Pharmacol.* **81**, 687–691.
Syapin, P. J., and Rickman, D. W. (1981). *Eur. J. Pharmacol.* **72**, 117–120.
Syapin, P. J., and Skolnick, P. (1979). *J. Neurochem.* **32**, 1047–1051.
Tallman, J. F. (1980). *Brain Res. Bull.* **5** (Suppl. 2), 829–832.
Tallman, J. F., and Gall-ger, D. W. (1979). *Pharmacol. Biochem. Behav.* **10**, 809–813.
Tallman, J. F., Thomas, J. W., and Gallager, D. W. (1978). *Nature (London)* **274**, 383–385.
Tallman, J. F., Thomas, J. W., and Gallager, D. W. (1979). *Life Sci.* **24**, 873–880.

Taniguchi, T., Wang, J. K. T., and Spector, S. (1980). *Life Sci.* **27**, 171–178.
Taniguchi, T., Wang, J. K. T., and Spector, S. (1981). *Eur. J. Pharmacol.* **70**, 587–588.
Taniguchi, T., Wang, J. K. T., and Spector, S. (1982). *Biochem. Pharmacol.* **31**, 589–590.
Tardy, M., Costa, M. F., Rolland, B., Fages, C., and Gonnard, P. (1981). *J. Neurochem.* **36**, 1587–1589.
Thampy, K. G., and Barnes, E. M. (1984). *J. Biol. Chem.* **259**, 1753–1757.
Thiébot, M.-H., Doare, L., Puech, A. J., and Simon, P. (1982). *Eur. J. Pharmacol.* **84**, 103–106.
Thomas, J. W., and Tallman, J. F. (1983). *J. Neurosci.* **3**, 433–440.
Thyagarajau, R., Ramanjaneyulu, R., and Ticku, M. K. (1983). *J. Neurochem.* **41**, 578–585.
Ticku, M. K. (1981). *Biochem. Pharmacol.* **30**, 1573–1579.
Ticku, M. K. (1983). *Neuropharmacology* **22**, 1459–1470.
Ticku, M. K., and Burch, T. (1980). *Biochem. Pharmacol.* **29**, 1217–1220.
Ticku, M. K., and Davis, W. C. (1981). *Eur. J. Pharmacol.* **71**, 521–522.
Ticku, M. K., and Davis, W. C. (1982). *J. Neurochem.* **38**, 1180–1182.
Ticku, M. K., and Maksay, G. (1983). *Life Sci.* **33**, 2363–2375.
Ticku, M. K., Burch, T. P., Thyagarajan, R., and Ramanjaneyulu, R. (1983). *In* "CNS Receptors—From Molecular Pharmacology to Behavior" (P. Mandel and F. V. De Feudis, eds.), pp. 81–91. Raven, New York.
Toffano, G. (1983). *In* "Neural Transmission, Learning and Memory" (R. Caputto and C. A. Marsan, eds.), pp. 97–104. Raven, New York.
Toffano, G., Leon, A., Massotti, M., Guidotti, A., and Costa, E. (1980). *In* "Receptors for Neurotransmitters and Peptide Hormones" (G. Pepeu, M. J. Kuhar, and S. J. Enna, eds.), pp. 133–142. Raven, New York.
Trybulski, E. J., Benjamin, L., Vitone, S., Walser, A., and Fryer, R. I. (1983a). *J. Med. Chem.* **26**, 367–372.
Trybulski, E. J., Benjamin, L. E., Earley, J. V., Fryer, R. I., Gilman, N. W., Reeder, E., Walser, A., Davidson, A. B., Horst, W. D., Sepinwall, J., O'Brien, R. A., and Dairman, W. (1983b). *J. Med. Chem.* **26**, 1589–1596.
Tsang, C. C., Speeg, K. V., Jr., and Wilkinson, G. R. (1981). *Life Sci.* **30**, 343–346.
Tuff, L. P., Racine, R. J., and Mishra, R. K. (1983). *Brain Res.* **277**, 91–98.
Tunnicliff, G., Smith, J. A., and Ngo, T. T. (1979). *Biochem. Biophys. Res. Commun.* **91**, 1018–1024.
Turski, L., Czuczwar, S. J., Turski, W., Sieklucka-Dziuba, M., and Kleinrok, Z. (1982). *Psychopharmacology* **76**, 198–200.
Ueno, E., and Kuriyama, K. (1981). *Neuropharmacology* **20**, 1169–1176.
Unnerstall, J. R., Kuhar, M. J., Niehoff, D. L., and Palacios, J. M. (1981). *J. Pharmacol. Exp. Ther.* **218**, 797–804.
Unnerstall, J. R., Niehoff, D. L., Kuhar, M. J., and Palacios, J. M. (1982). *J. Neurosci. Methods* **6**, 59–73.
Vaccarino, F. M., Ghetti, B., Wade, S. E., Rea, M. A., and Aprison, M. H. (1983). *J. Neurosci. Res.* **9**, 311–323.
Valdes, F., Fanelli, R. J., and McNamara, J. O. (1981). *Life Sci.* **29**, 1895–1900.
Valdes, F., Dasheiff, R. M., Birmingham, F., Crutcher, K. A., and McNamara, J. O. (1982). *Proc. Natl. Acad. Sci. U.S.A.* **79**, 193–197.
Valin, A., Dodd, R. H., Liston, D. R., Potier, P., and Rossier, J. (1982). *Eur. J. Pharmacol.* **85**, 93–97.
Villiger, J. W., Taylor, K. M., and Gluckman, P. D. (1982).*Pharmacol., Biochem. Behav.* **16**, 373–375.
Volicer, L., and Biagioni, T. M. (1982a). *J. Neurochem.* **38**, 591–593.
Volicer, L., and Biagioni, T. M. (1982b). *Neuropharmacology* **21**, 283–286.

Waddington, J. L., and Owen, F. (1978). *Neuropharmacology* **17**, 215–216.

Walker, C. R., and Peacock, J. H. (1981). *Dev. Brain Res.* **1**, 565–578.

Wamsley, J. K., and Palacios, J. M. (1983). *Curr. Methods Cell. Neurobiol.* **1**, 241–268.

Wamsley, J. K., Palacios, J. M., Young, W. S., III, and Kuhar, M. J. (1981). *J. Histochem. Cytochem.* **29**, 125–135.

Wamsley, J. K., Gee, K. W., and Yamamura, H. I. (1983). *Life Sci.* **33**, 2321–2329.

Wang, J. K. T., Taniguchi, T., and Spector, S. (1980). *Life Sci.* **27**, 1881–1888.

Wang, J. K. T., Taniguchi, T., Sugiura, M., and Spector, S. (1981). *Pharmacologist* **23**, 160.

Wastek, G. J., Speth, R. C., Reisine, T. D., and Yamamura, H. I. (1978). *Eur. J. Pharmacol.* **50**, 445–447.

Weissman, B. A., Cott, J., Paul, S. M., and Skolnick, P. (1983a). *Eur. J. Pharmacol.* **90**, 149–150.

Weissman, B. A., Cott, J., Hommer, D., Quirion, R., Paul, S., and Skolnick, P. (1983b). *In* "Benzodiazepine Recognition Site Ligands: Biochemistry and Pharmacology" (G. Biggio and E. Costa, eds.), pp. 139–151. Raven, New York.

White, W. F., Dichter, M. A., and Snodgrass, S. R. (1981). *Brain Res.* **215**, 162–176.

Wilkinson, M., Grovestine, D., and Hamilton, J. T. (1982). *Can. J. Physiol. Pharmacol.* **60**, 1003–1005.

Wilkinson, M., Wilkinson, D. A., Khan, I., and Crim, L. W. (1983a). *Brain Res. Bull.* **10**, 301–303.

Wilkinson, M., Bhanot, R., Wilkinson, A., and Brawer, J. R. (1983b). *Brain Res. Bull.* **11**, 279–281.

Williams, E. F., Rice, K. C., Paul, S. M., and Skolnick, P. (1980). *J. Neurochem.* **35**, 591–597.

Williams, E. F., Rice, K. C., Mattson, M., Paul, S. M., and Skolnick, P. (1981). *Pharmacol., Biochem. Behav.* **14**, 487–491.

Williams, M., and Risley, E. A. (1979). *Life Sci.* **24**, 833–842.

Williams, M., and Risley, E. A. (1982a). *Eur. J. Pharmacol.* **77**, 307–312.

Williams, M., and Risley, E. A. (1982b). *Arch. Int. Pharmacodyn.* **260**, 50–53.

Williams, M., and Yarbrough, G. G. (1979). *Eur. J. Pharmacol.* **56**, 273–276.

Williams, M., Risley, E. A., and Huff, J. R. (1981). *Can. J. Physiol. Pharmacol.* **59**, 897–900.

Williamson, M. J., Paul, S. M., and Skolnick, P. (1978a). *Life Sci.* **23**, 1935–1940.

Williamson, M. J., Paul, S. M., and Skolnick, P. (1978b). *Nature (London)* **275**, 551–553.

Willow, M., and Johnston, G. A. R. (1980). *Neurosci. Lett.* **18**, 323–327.

Willow, M., and Johnston, G. A. R. (1981). *J. Neurochem.* **37**, 1291–1294.

Willow, M., and Morgan, I. G. (1980). *Neurosci. Lett.* **20**, 147–152.

Wise, B. C., Guidotti, A., and Costa, E. (1983). *Proc. Natl. Acad. Sci. U.S.A.* **80**, 866–890.

Wong, D. T., and Bymaster, F. P. (1983). *Drug Dev. Res.* **3**, 67–73.

Wong, D. T., Bymaster, F. P., and Lane, P. T. (1980). *Brain Res. Bull.* **5**, 853–856.

Wong, D. T., Bymaster, F. P., and Lacefield, W. B. (1983a). *Drug Dev. Res.* **3**, 433–442.

Wong, D. T., Rathbun, R. C., Bymaster, F. P., and Lacefield, W. B. (1983b). *Life Sci.* **33**, 917–923.

Wong, G. B., and Sellers, E. M. (1979). *Biochem. Pharmacol.* **28**, 3265–3270.

Woolf, J. H., and Nixon, J. C. (1981). *Biochemistry* **20**, 4263–4296.

Wright, W. B., Brabander, H. J., Greenblatt, E. N., Day, I. P., and Hardy, R. A., Jr. (1978). *J. Med. Chem.* **21**, 1087–1089.

Yamamura, H. I., Mimaki, T., Yamamura, S. H., Horst, W. D., Morelli, M., Bautz, G., and O'Brien, R. A. (1982). *Eur. J. Pharmacol.* **77**, 351–354.

Yokoi, I., Rose, S. E., and Yanagita, T. (1981). *Life Sci.* **28**, 1591–1595.

Yokoyama, N., Ritter, B., and Neubert, A. D. (1982). *J. Med. Chem.* **25**, 337–339.

York, M. J., and Davies, L. P. (1982). *Can. J. Physiol. Pharmacol.* **60**, 302–307.

Young, W. S., and Kuhar, M. J. (1979a). *Nature (London)* **280**, 393–395.

Young, W. S., and Kuhar, M. J. (1979b). *Brain Res.* **179**, 255–270.
Young, W. S., and Kuhar, M. J. (1980). *J. Pharmacol. Exp. Ther.* **212**, 337–436.
Young, W. S., Niehoff, D., Kuhar, M. J., Beer, B., and Lippa, A. S. (1981). *J. Pharmacol. Exp. Ther.* **216** (2), 425–430.
Yousufi, M. A. K., Thomas, J. W., and Tallman, J. F. (1979). *Life Sci.* **25**, 463–470.
Ziegler, W. H., and Schalch, E. (1983). *In* "Sleep 1982" (W. P. Koella, ed.), pp. 427–429. Karger, Basel.
Zimmerman, T. W. (1983). *Gastroenterology* **84**, 1359.

SUBJECT INDEX

A

Acceptor sites, 180
Acetaminophen, 20
Acetylcholine, 172, 286
N-Acetyl-5-methoxykynurenamine, 173, 278
Acetylsalicylic acid, 151, 156–158, 160–162
Adenosine, 170
Adenosine deaminase, 277
Adenosine receptors, 185
Adenosine uptake, 294, 296
S-Adenosyl-L-methionine, 105, 270, 295
Adenylate cyclase, 105, 180
Adinazolam, 210, 211, 213, 214
Adrenaline, 71
β-Adrenergic agents, 71–74
Adrenergic pharmacophore, 72, 73
β-Adrenoceptors, 180
Agglutinin, 195
D-Ala-D-Ala terminal residues, 75–78
β-Alanine, 176
Alclofenac, 109
Alcohol dehydrogenase, 4
Aldehyde dehydrogenase, 4
Alkyl halides, 13
Alkyl sulfonates, 13
Allosteric modulators, 182
Alprazolam, 168, 210, 211, 214, 249, 256
Alprenolol, 71
AMBER, 49
Aminoindans, 96
Aminopyrine, 7
Aminotetralins, 96
Amitriptyline, 122, 125, 126
Amphetamines, 27, 28
2-d_1-Amphetamine, 27, 28
Angiotensin-converting enzyme, 117, 118
Anisatin, 270
Anisole, 20
Antibodies, 150
Anticonvulsants, 91–93, 265, 266
Antidepressants, 122–127
    tricyclic, 122, 123
    nontricyclic, 122–127

Antigens, 150
Antiinflammatory drugs, 147–162
Antiinflammatory steroids, 152, 153
Antioxidants, 32, 159, 161, 162
Antipsychotics, 93–101, 118–122
Antipyrine, 6
Apomorphine, 95, 98, 99, 101–104, 118, 119
Arachidonic acid, 107, 108, 110, 152–158,
    160
Artificial intelligence, 63
Arylpropionic acids, 109–111, 155
Atomic orbitals, 67
Atomic polarizabilities, 67
Autacoids, 152
Autoreceptors, 176
Avermectin $B_{1\alpha}$, 173, 267, 282
Azabicycloalkanes, 87

B

Baclofen, 262, 286
Barbiturates, 10, 93, 172, 231, 235, 246, 257,
    264–266, 268, 282, 286, 291
Barbiturate receptor, 175, 182, 188
Basophils, 149
Benperidol, 97
1-Benzazepines, 214, 215, 219
2-Benzazepines, 214, 216, 219
Benzodiazepine binding sites,
    low-affinity, 187, 292, 293
    nonneuronal, 187, 289–292
Benzodiazepine receptor agonists, 171, 175,
    177–179, 181–183, 194–219, 225,
    227, 228, 236, 241–243, 250, 266,
    289, 298, 299
Benzodiazepine receptor antagonists, 171, 175,
    178, 179, 181–183, 186, 194, 219–
    229, 232, 236, 241–243, 266, 289,
    297–299
Benzodiazepine receptor inverse agonists, 171,
    175, 178, 179, 181–183, 186, 194,
    219–228, 229, 232, 236, 241, 243,
    289, 298, 299

CUMULATIVE INDEX OF AUTHORS

CUMULATIVE INDEX OF TITLES